**Prentice Hall**

# WRITING and GRAMMAR

*Communication in Action*

## Bronze Level

# Grammar Exercise Workbook

## TEACHER'S EDITION

Prentice
Hall

Upper Saddle River, New Jersey
Glenview, Illinois
Needham, Massachusetts

Teacher's Edition

ISBN 0-13-043479-5

8 9 10

# Contents

**Note:** This workbook supports Chapters 14–29, (Part 2: Grammar, Usage, and Mechanics) of Prentice Hall *Writing and Grammar*.

**Chapter 14: Nouns and Pronouns**

14.1   Nouns
    Practice 1 . . . . . . . . . . . . . . . . . . . . . . . . . . . . . . . . . . . . . 1
    Practice 2 . . . . . . . . . . . . . . . . . . . . . . . . . . . . . . . . . . . . . 2
14.1   Collective and Compound Nouns
    Practice 1 . . . . . . . . . . . . . . . . . . . . . . . . . . . . . . . . . . . . . 3
    Practice 2 . . . . . . . . . . . . . . . . . . . . . . . . . . . . . . . . . . . . . 4
14.1   Common and Proper Nouns
    Practice 1 . . . . . . . . . . . . . . . . . . . . . . . . . . . . . . . . . . . . . 5
    Practice 2 . . . . . . . . . . . . . . . . . . . . . . . . . . . . . . . . . . . . . 6
14.2   Pronouns and Antecedents
    Practice 1 . . . . . . . . . . . . . . . . . . . . . . . . . . . . . . . . . . . . . 7
    Practice 2 . . . . . . . . . . . . . . . . . . . . . . . . . . . . . . . . . . . . . 8
14.2   Demonstrative and Interrogative Pronouns
    Practice 1 . . . . . . . . . . . . . . . . . . . . . . . . . . . . . . . . . . . . . 9
    Practice 2 . . . . . . . . . . . . . . . . . . . . . . . . . . . . . . . . . . . . . 10
14.2   Indefinite Pronouns
    Practice 1 . . . . . . . . . . . . . . . . . . . . . . . . . . . . . . . . . . . . . 11
    Practice 2 . . . . . . . . . . . . . . . . . . . . . . . . . . . . . . . . . . . . . 12

**Chapter 15: Verbs**

15.1   Action Verbs
    Practice 1 . . . . . . . . . . . . . . . . . . . . . . . . . . . . . . . . . . . . . 13
    Practice 2 . . . . . . . . . . . . . . . . . . . . . . . . . . . . . . . . . . . . . 14
15.2   Linking Verbs
    Practice 1 . . . . . . . . . . . . . . . . . . . . . . . . . . . . . . . . . . . . . 15
    Practice 2 . . . . . . . . . . . . . . . . . . . . . . . . . . . . . . . . . . . . . 16
15.2   Linking Verbs
    Practice 1 . . . . . . . . . . . . . . . . . . . . . . . . . . . . . . . . . . . . . 17
    Practice 2 . . . . . . . . . . . . . . . . . . . . . . . . . . . . . . . . . . . . . 18
15.3   Helping Verbs
    Practice 1 . . . . . . . . . . . . . . . . . . . . . . . . . . . . . . . . . . . . . 19
    Practice 2 . . . . . . . . . . . . . . . . . . . . . . . . . . . . . . . . . . . . . 20

**Chapter 16: Adjectives and Adverbs**

16.1   Adjectives
    Practice 1 . . . . . . . . . . . . . . . . . . . . . . . . . . . . . . . . . . . . . 21
    Practice 2 . . . . . . . . . . . . . . . . . . . . . . . . . . . . . . . . . . . . . 22
16.1   Articles; Nouns Used as Adjectives
    Practice 1 . . . . . . . . . . . . . . . . . . . . . . . . . . . . . . . . . . . . . 23
    Practice 2 . . . . . . . . . . . . . . . . . . . . . . . . . . . . . . . . . . . . . 24
16.1   Proper Adjectives and Compound Adjectives
    Practice 1 . . . . . . . . . . . . . . . . . . . . . . . . . . . . . . . . . . . . . 25
    Practice 2 . . . . . . . . . . . . . . . . . . . . . . . . . . . . . . . . . . . . . 26
16.1   Possessive Adjectives
    Practice 1 . . . . . . . . . . . . . . . . . . . . . . . . . . . . . . . . . . . . . 27
    Practice 2 . . . . . . . . . . . . . . . . . . . . . . . . . . . . . . . . . . . . . 28
16.1   Demonstrative and Interrogative Adjectives
    Practice 1 . . . . . . . . . . . . . . . . . . . . . . . . . . . . . . . . . . . . . 29
    Practice 2 . . . . . . . . . . . . . . . . . . . . . . . . . . . . . . . . . . . . . 30
16.2   Adverbs
    Practice 1 . . . . . . . . . . . . . . . . . . . . . . . . . . . . . . . . . . . . . 31
    Practice 2 . . . . . . . . . . . . . . . . . . . . . . . . . . . . . . . . . . . . . 32
16.2   Adverbs
    Practice 1 . . . . . . . . . . . . . . . . . . . . . . . . . . . . . . . . . . . . . 33
    Practice 2 . . . . . . . . . . . . . . . . . . . . . . . . . . . . . . . . . . . . . 34
16.2   Adverbs Used in Sentences
    Practice 1 . . . . . . . . . . . . . . . . . . . . . . . . . . . . . . . . . . . . . 35
    Practice 2 . . . . . . . . . . . . . . . . . . . . . . . . . . . . . . . . . . . . . 36

## Chapter 17: Prepositions

17.1  Prepositions
    Practice 1 . . . . . . . . . . . . . . . . . . . . . . . . . . . . 37
    Practice 2 . . . . . . . . . . . . . . . . . . . . . . . . . . . . 38
17.2  Prepositions Used in Sentences
    Practice 1 . . . . . . . . . . . . . . . . . . . . . . . . . . . . 39
    Practice 2 . . . . . . . . . . . . . . . . . . . . . . . . . . . . 40

## Chapter 18: Conjunctions and Interjections

18.1  Conjunctions
    Practice 1 . . . . . . . . . . . . . . . . . . . . . . . . . . . . 41
    Practice 2 . . . . . . . . . . . . . . . . . . . . . . . . . . . . 42
18.2  Interjections
    Practice 1 . . . . . . . . . . . . . . . . . . . . . . . . . . . . 43
    Practice 2 . . . . . . . . . . . . . . . . . . . . . . . . . . . . 44

## Chapter 19: Basic Sentence Parts and Patterns

19.1  The Basic Sentence
    Practice 1 . . . . . . . . . . . . . . . . . . . . . . . . . . . . 45
    Practice 2 . . . . . . . . . . . . . . . . . . . . . . . . . . . . 46
19.2  Complete Subjects and Predicates
    Practice 1 . . . . . . . . . . . . . . . . . . . . . . . . . . . . 47
    Practice 2 . . . . . . . . . . . . . . . . . . . . . . . . . . . . 48
19.3  Compound Subjects and Compound Verbs
    Practice 1 . . . . . . . . . . . . . . . . . . . . . . . . . . . . 49
    Practice 2 . . . . . . . . . . . . . . . . . . . . . . . . . . . . 50
19.4  Hard-to-Find Subjects
    Practice 1 . . . . . . . . . . . . . . . . . . . . . . . . . . . . 51
    Practice 2 . . . . . . . . . . . . . . . . . . . . . . . . . . . . 52
19.4  Sentences Beginning with *There* or *Here*
    Practice 1 . . . . . . . . . . . . . . . . . . . . . . . . . . . . 53
    Practice 2 . . . . . . . . . . . . . . . . . . . . . . . . . . . . 54
19.5  Direct Objects
    Practice 1 . . . . . . . . . . . . . . . . . . . . . . . . . . . . 55
    Practice 2 . . . . . . . . . . . . . . . . . . . . . . . . . . . . 56
19.5  Distinguishing Direct Objects
    Practice 1 . . . . . . . . . . . . . . . . . . . . . . . . . . . . 57
    Practice 2 . . . . . . . . . . . . . . . . . . . . . . . . . . . . 58
19.5  Direct Objects in Questions
    Practice 1 . . . . . . . . . . . . . . . . . . . . . . . . . . . . 59
    Practice 2 . . . . . . . . . . . . . . . . . . . . . . . . . . . . 60
19.5  Indirect Objects
    Practice 1 . . . . . . . . . . . . . . . . . . . . . . . . . . . . 61
    Practice 2 . . . . . . . . . . . . . . . . . . . . . . . . . . . . 62
19.5  Distinguishing Indirect Objects
    Practice 1 . . . . . . . . . . . . . . . . . . . . . . . . . . . . 63
    Practice 2 . . . . . . . . . . . . . . . . . . . . . . . . . . . . 64
19.5  Subject Complements
    Practice 1 . . . . . . . . . . . . . . . . . . . . . . . . . . . . 65
    Practice 2 . . . . . . . . . . . . . . . . . . . . . . . . . . . . 66
19.5  Compound Subject Complements
    Practice 1 . . . . . . . . . . . . . . . . . . . . . . . . . . . . 67
    Practice 2 . . . . . . . . . . . . . . . . . . . . . . . . . . . . 68

## Chapter 20: Phrases and Clauses

20.1  Prepositional Phrases (Adjective)
    Practice 1 . . . . . . . . . . . . . . . . . . . . . . . . . . . . 69
    Practice 2 . . . . . . . . . . . . . . . . . . . . . . . . . . . . 70
20.1  Prepositional Phrases (Adverb)
    Practice 1 . . . . . . . . . . . . . . . . . . . . . . . . . . . . 71
    Practice 2 . . . . . . . . . . . . . . . . . . . . . . . . . . . . 72
20.1  Appositives in Phrases
    Practice 1 . . . . . . . . . . . . . . . . . . . . . . . . . . . . 73
    Practice 2 . . . . . . . . . . . . . . . . . . . . . . . . . . . . 74
20.1  Participles
    Practice 1 . . . . . . . . . . . . . . . . . . . . . . . . . . . . 75
    Practice 2 . . . . . . . . . . . . . . . . . . . . . . . . . . . . 76

20.1   Participles in Phrases
    Practice 1 . . . . . . . . . . . . . . . . . . . . . . . . . . . . . 77
    Practice 2 . . . . . . . . . . . . . . . . . . . . . . . . . . . . . 78
20.2   Adjective Clauses
    Practice 1 . . . . . . . . . . . . . . . . . . . . . . . . . . . . . 79
    Practice 2 . . . . . . . . . . . . . . . . . . . . . . . . . . . . . 80
20.2   Adverb Clauses
    Practice 1 . . . . . . . . . . . . . . . . . . . . . . . . . . . . . 81
    Practice 2 . . . . . . . . . . . . . . . . . . . . . . . . . . . . . 82
20.2   Classifying Sentences by Structure
    Practice 1 . . . . . . . . . . . . . . . . . . . . . . . . . . . . . 83
    Practice 2 . . . . . . . . . . . . . . . . . . . . . . . . . . . . . 84
20.2   Classifying Sentences by Structure
    Practice 1 . . . . . . . . . . . . . . . . . . . . . . . . . . . . . 85
    Practice 2 . . . . . . . . . . . . . . . . . . . . . . . . . . . . . 86

**Chapter 21: Effective Sentences**

21.1   The Four Functions of Sentences
    Practice 1 . . . . . . . . . . . . . . . . . . . . . . . . . . . . . 87
    Practice 2 . . . . . . . . . . . . . . . . . . . . . . . . . . . . . 88
21.2   Shortening Sentences That Are Too Long
    Practice 1 . . . . . . . . . . . . . . . . . . . . . . . . . . . . . 89
    Practice 2 . . . . . . . . . . . . . . . . . . . . . . . . . . . . . 90
21.3   Using Different Sentence Openers
    Practice 1 . . . . . . . . . . . . . . . . . . . . . . . . . . . . . 91
    Practice 2 . . . . . . . . . . . . . . . . . . . . . . . . . . . . . 92
21.3   Improving Short Sentences
    Practice 1 . . . . . . . . . . . . . . . . . . . . . . . . . . . . . 93
    Practice 2 . . . . . . . . . . . . . . . . . . . . . . . . . . . . . 94
21.4   Correcting Sentence Fragments
    Practice 1 . . . . . . . . . . . . . . . . . . . . . . . . . . . . . 95
    Practice 2 . . . . . . . . . . . . . . . . . . . . . . . . . . . . . 96
21.4   Correcting Fragments (Phrases, Clauses)
    Practice 1 . . . . . . . . . . . . . . . . . . . . . . . . . . . . . 97
    Practice 2 . . . . . . . . . . . . . . . . . . . . . . . . . . . . . 98
21.4   Correcting Run-ons
    Practice 1 . . . . . . . . . . . . . . . . . . . . . . . . . . . . . 99
    Practice 2 . . . . . . . . . . . . . . . . . . . . . . . . . . . . .100
21.4   Correcting Run-ons
    Practice 1 . . . . . . . . . . . . . . . . . . . . . . . . . . . . .101
    Practice 2 . . . . . . . . . . . . . . . . . . . . . . . . . . . . .102
21.4   Recognizing Misplaced Modifiers
    Practice 1 . . . . . . . . . . . . . . . . . . . . . . . . . . . . .103
    Practice 2 . . . . . . . . . . . . . . . . . . . . . . . . . . . . .104
21.4   Correcting Misplaced Modifiers
    Practice 1 . . . . . . . . . . . . . . . . . . . . . . . . . . . . .105
    Practice 2 . . . . . . . . . . . . . . . . . . . . . . . . . . . . .106
21.4   Double Negatives
    Practice 1 . . . . . . . . . . . . . . . . . . . . . . . . . . . . .107
    Practice 2 . . . . . . . . . . . . . . . . . . . . . . . . . . . . .108
21.4   Common Usage Problems
    Practice 1 . . . . . . . . . . . . . . . . . . . . . . . . . . . . .109
    Practice 2 . . . . . . . . . . . . . . . . . . . . . . . . . . . . .110

**Chapter 22: Using Verbs**

22.1   The Four Principal Parts of Verbs (Regular)
    Practice 1 . . . . . . . . . . . . . . . . . . . . . . . . . . . . .111
    Practice 2 . . . . . . . . . . . . . . . . . . . . . . . . . . . . .112
22.1   The Four Principal Parts of Verbs (Irregular)
    Practice 1 . . . . . . . . . . . . . . . . . . . . . . . . . . . . .113
    Practice 2 . . . . . . . . . . . . . . . . . . . . . . . . . . . . .114
22.2   The Six Tenses of Verbs
    Practice 1 . . . . . . . . . . . . . . . . . . . . . . . . . . . . .115
    Practice 2 . . . . . . . . . . . . . . . . . . . . . . . . . . . . .116
22.2   The Six Progressive Forms of Verbs
    Practice 1 . . . . . . . . . . . . . . . . . . . . . . . . . . . . .117
    Practice 2 . . . . . . . . . . . . . . . . . . . . . . . . . . . . .118

22.3   Glossary of Troublesome Verbs
      Practice 1 . . . . . . . . . . . . . . . . . . . . . . . . . . . . . . . . . . . . .119
      Practice 2 . . . . . . . . . . . . . . . . . . . . . . . . . . . . . . . . . . . . .120

**Chapter 23: Using Pronouns**

23   The Three Cases of Personal Pronouns
      Practice 1 . . . . . . . . . . . . . . . . . . . . . . . . . . . . . . . . . . . . .121
      Practice 2 . . . . . . . . . . . . . . . . . . . . . . . . . . . . . . . . . . . . .122
23   Cases of Personal Pronouns (Nominative, Objective)
      Practice 1 . . . . . . . . . . . . . . . . . . . . . . . . . . . . . . . . . . . . .123
      Practice 2 . . . . . . . . . . . . . . . . . . . . . . . . . . . . . . . . . . . . .124
23   Cases of Personal Pronouns (Possessive)
      Practice 1 . . . . . . . . . . . . . . . . . . . . . . . . . . . . . . . . . . . . .125
      Practice 2 . . . . . . . . . . . . . . . . . . . . . . . . . . . . . . . . . . . . .126

**Chapter 24: Making Words Agree**

24.1   Agreement Between Subjects and Verbs
      Practice 1 . . . . . . . . . . . . . . . . . . . . . . . . . . . . . . . . . . . . .127
      Practice 2 . . . . . . . . . . . . . . . . . . . . . . . . . . . . . . . . . . . . .128
24.1   Agreement Between Subjects and Verbs
      Practice 1 . . . . . . . . . . . . . . . . . . . . . . . . . . . . . . . . . . . . .129
      Practice 2 . . . . . . . . . . . . . . . . . . . . . . . . . . . . . . . . . . . . .130
24.1   Agreement with Compound Subjects
      Practice 1 . . . . . . . . . . . . . . . . . . . . . . . . . . . . . . . . . . . . .131
      Practice 2 . . . . . . . . . . . . . . . . . . . . . . . . . . . . . . . . . . . . .132
24.1   Special Problems with Subject-Verb Agreement
      Practice 1 . . . . . . . . . . . . . . . . . . . . . . . . . . . . . . . . . . . . .133
      Practice 2 . . . . . . . . . . . . . . . . . . . . . . . . . . . . . . . . . . . . .134
24.2   Agreement Between Pronouns and Antecedents
      Practice 1 . . . . . . . . . . . . . . . . . . . . . . . . . . . . . . . . . . . . .135
      Practice 2 . . . . . . . . . . . . . . . . . . . . . . . . . . . . . . . . . . . . .136

**Chapter 25: Using Modifiers**

25.1   Comparison of Regular Adjectives and Adverbs
      Practice 1 . . . . . . . . . . . . . . . . . . . . . . . . . . . . . . . . . . . . .137
      Practice 2 . . . . . . . . . . . . . . . . . . . . . . . . . . . . . . . . . . . . .138
25.1   Comparison of Irregular Adjectives and Adverbs
      Practice 1 . . . . . . . . . . . . . . . . . . . . . . . . . . . . . . . . . . . . .139
      Practice 2 . . . . . . . . . . . . . . . . . . . . . . . . . . . . . . . . . . . . .140
25.1   Using the Comparative and Superlative Degrees
      Practice 1 . . . . . . . . . . . . . . . . . . . . . . . . . . . . . . . . . . . . .141
      Practice 2 . . . . . . . . . . . . . . . . . . . . . . . . . . . . . . . . . . . . .142
25.2   Glossary of Troublesome Adjectives and Adverbs
      Practice 1 . . . . . . . . . . . . . . . . . . . . . . . . . . . . . . . . . . . . .143
      Practice 2 . . . . . . . . . . . . . . . . . . . . . . . . . . . . . . . . . . . . .144

**Chapter 26: Punctuation**

26.1   End Marks
      Practice 1 . . . . . . . . . . . . . . . . . . . . . . . . . . . . . . . . . . . . .145
      Practice 2 . . . . . . . . . . . . . . . . . . . . . . . . . . . . . . . . . . . . .146
26.1   End Marks
      Practice 1 . . . . . . . . . . . . . . . . . . . . . . . . . . . . . . . . . . . . .147
      Practice 2 . . . . . . . . . . . . . . . . . . . . . . . . . . . . . . . . . . . . .148
26.2   Commas in Compound Sentences
      Practice 1 . . . . . . . . . . . . . . . . . . . . . . . . . . . . . . . . . . . . .149
      Practice 2 . . . . . . . . . . . . . . . . . . . . . . . . . . . . . . . . . . . . .150
26.2   Commas in a Series, Between Adjectives
      Practice 1 . . . . . . . . . . . . . . . . . . . . . . . . . . . . . . . . . . . . .151
      Practice 2 . . . . . . . . . . . . . . . . . . . . . . . . . . . . . . . . . . . . .152
26.2   Commas That Set Off Added Elements
      Practice 1 . . . . . . . . . . . . . . . . . . . . . . . . . . . . . . . . . . . . .153
      Practice 2 . . . . . . . . . . . . . . . . . . . . . . . . . . . . . . . . . . . . .154
26.2   Commas That Set Off Nonessential Elements
      Practice 1 . . . . . . . . . . . . . . . . . . . . . . . . . . . . . . . . . . . . .155
      Practice 2 . . . . . . . . . . . . . . . . . . . . . . . . . . . . . . . . . . . . .156

26.2  Special Uses of the Comma
       Practice 1 . . . . . . . . . . . . . . . . . . . . . . . . . . . . . . . .157
       Practice 2 . . . . . . . . . . . . . . . . . . . . . . . . . . . . . . . .158
26.3  Semicolons
       Practice 1 . . . . . . . . . . . . . . . . . . . . . . . . . . . . . . . .159
       Practice 2 . . . . . . . . . . . . . . . . . . . . . . . . . . . . . . . .160
26.3  Colons
       Practice 1 . . . . . . . . . . . . . . . . . . . . . . . . . . . . . . . .161
       Practice 2 . . . . . . . . . . . . . . . . . . . . . . . . . . . . . . . .162
26.4  Quotation Marks with Direct Quotations
       Practice 1 . . . . . . . . . . . . . . . . . . . . . . . . . . . . . . . .163
       Practice 2 . . . . . . . . . . . . . . . . . . . . . . . . . . . . . . . .164
26.4  Quotation Marks with Other Punctuation
       Practice 1 . . . . . . . . . . . . . . . . . . . . . . . . . . . . . . . .165
       Practice 2 . . . . . . . . . . . . . . . . . . . . . . . . . . . . . . . .166
26.4  Quotation Marks or Underlining
       Practice 1 . . . . . . . . . . . . . . . . . . . . . . . . . . . . . . . .167
       Practice 2 . . . . . . . . . . . . . . . . . . . . . . . . . . . . . . . .168
26.5  Hyphens
       Practice 1 . . . . . . . . . . . . . . . . . . . . . . . . . . . . . . . .169
       Practice 2 . . . . . . . . . . . . . . . . . . . . . . . . . . . . . . . .170
26.5  Apostrophes (Nouns and Pronouns)
       Practice 1 . . . . . . . . . . . . . . . . . . . . . . . . . . . . . . . .171
       Practice 2 . . . . . . . . . . . . . . . . . . . . . . . . . . . . . . . .172
26.5  Apostrophes (Contractions)
       Practice 1 . . . . . . . . . . . . . . . . . . . . . . . . . . . . . . . .173
       Practice 2 . . . . . . . . . . . . . . . . . . . . . . . . . . . . . . . .174

**Chapter 27: Capitalization**

27  Capitals for Sentences and the Word *I*
       Practice 1 . . . . . . . . . . . . . . . . . . . . . . . . . . . . . . . .175
       Practice 2 . . . . . . . . . . . . . . . . . . . . . . . . . . . . . . . .176
27  Capitals for Proper Nouns (Names, Places)
       Practice 1 . . . . . . . . . . . . . . . . . . . . . . . . . . . . . . . .177
       Practice 2 . . . . . . . . . . . . . . . . . . . . . . . . . . . . . . . .178
27  Capitals for Other Proper Nouns
       Practice 1 . . . . . . . . . . . . . . . . . . . . . . . . . . . . . . . .179
       Practice 2 . . . . . . . . . . . . . . . . . . . . . . . . . . . . . . . .180
27  Capitals for Proper Adjectives
       Practice 1 . . . . . . . . . . . . . . . . . . . . . . . . . . . . . . . .181
       Practice 2 . . . . . . . . . . . . . . . . . . . . . . . . . . . . . . . .182
27  Capitals for Titles of People
       Practice 1 . . . . . . . . . . . . . . . . . . . . . . . . . . . . . . . .183
       Practice 2 . . . . . . . . . . . . . . . . . . . . . . . . . . . . . . . .184
27  Capitals for Titles of Things
       Practice 1 . . . . . . . . . . . . . . . . . . . . . . . . . . . . . . . .185
       Practice 2 . . . . . . . . . . . . . . . . . . . . . . . . . . . . . . . .186
27  Capitals in Letters
       Practice 1 . . . . . . . . . . . . . . . . . . . . . . . . . . . . . . . .187
       Practice 2 . . . . . . . . . . . . . . . . . . . . . . . . . . . . . . . .188

**Diagraming** . . . . . . . . . . . . . . . . . . . . . . . . . . . . . . . . .**189**

Diagraming Basic Sentence Parts (Subject and Verb)
       Practice 1 . . . . . . . . . . . . . . . . . . . . . . . . . . . . . . . .189
       Practice 2 . . . . . . . . . . . . . . . . . . . . . . . . . . . . . . . .190
Diagraming Basic Sentence Parts (Compound Subjects and Verbs)
       Practice 1 . . . . . . . . . . . . . . . . . . . . . . . . . . . . . . . .191
       Practice 2 . . . . . . . . . . . . . . . . . . . . . . . . . . . . . . . .192
Diagraming Basic Sentence Parts (Complements)
       Practice 1 . . . . . . . . . . . . . . . . . . . . . . . . . . . . . . . .193
       Practice 2 . . . . . . . . . . . . . . . . . . . . . . . . . . . . . . . .194
Diagraming Prepositional Phrases and Appositives
       Practice 1 . . . . . . . . . . . . . . . . . . . . . . . . . . . . . . . .195
       Practice 2 . . . . . . . . . . . . . . . . . . . . . . . . . . . . . . . .196

Diagraming Clauses
    Practice 1 . . . . . . . . . . . . . . . . . . . . . . . . . . . . . . . . . .197
    Practice 2 . . . . . . . . . . . . . . . . . . . . . . . . . . . . . . . . . .198
    Practice 3 . . . . . . . . . . . . . . . . . . . . . . . . . . . . . . . . . .199

**ANSWERS**

**Chapter 14: Nouns and Pronouns**

14.1   Nouns . . . . . . . . . . . . . . . . . . . . . . . . . . . . . . . . . . .201
14.1   Collective and Compound Nouns . . . . . . . . . . . . . . . . . . . .201
14.1   Common and Proper Nouns. . . . . . . . . . . . . . . . . . . . . . . .201
14.2   Pronouns and Antecedents . . . . . . . . . . . . . . . . . . . . . . . .202
14.2   Demonstrative and Interrogative Pronouns . . . . . . . . . . . . . . .202
14.2   Indefinite Pronouns . . . . . . . . . . . . . . . . . . . . . . . . . . . .203

**Chapter 15: Verbs**

15.1   Action Verbs . . . . . . . . . . . . . . . . . . . . . . . . . . . . . . .203
15.2   Linking Verbs . . . . . . . . . . . . . . . . . . . . . . . . . . . . . . .204
15.2   Linking Verbs . . . . . . . . . . . . . . . . . . . . . . . . . . . . . . .204
15.3   Helping Verbs . . . . . . . . . . . . . . . . . . . . . . . . . . . . . . .205

**Chapter 16: Adjectives and Adverbs**

16.1   Adjectives . . . . . . . . . . . . . . . . . . . . . . . . . . . . . . . . .205
16.1   Articles; Nouns Used as Adjectives . . . . . . . . . . . . . . . . . . .206
16.1   Proper Adjectives and Compound Adjectives . . . . . . . . . . . . . .206
16.1   Possessive Adjectives . . . . . . . . . . . . . . . . . . . . . . . . . . .207
16.1   Demonstrative and Interrogative Adjectives . . . . . . . . . . . . . . .207
16.2   Adverbs . . . . . . . . . . . . . . . . . . . . . . . . . . . . . . . . . .208
16.2   Adverbs . . . . . . . . . . . . . . . . . . . . . . . . . . . . . . . . . .208
16.2   Adverbs Used in Sentences . . . . . . . . . . . . . . . . . . . . . . . .209

**Chapter 17: Prepositions**

17.1   Prepositions. . . . . . . . . . . . . . . . . . . . . . . . . . . . . . . .210
17.2   Prepositions Used in Sentences . . . . . . . . . . . . . . . . . . . . .210

**Chapter 18: Conjunctions and Interjections**

18.1   Conjunctions . . . . . . . . . . . . . . . . . . . . . . . . . . . . . . .211
18.2   Interjections. . . . . . . . . . . . . . . . . . . . . . . . . . . . . . . .211

**Chapter 19: Basic Sentence Parts and Patterns**

19.1   The Basic Sentence . . . . . . . . . . . . . . . . . . . . . . . . . . . .212
19.2   Complete Subjects and Predicates . . . . . . . . . . . . . . . . . . . .213
19.3   Compound Subjects and Compound Verbs . . . . . . . . . . . . . . .213
19.4   Hard-to-Find Subjects . . . . . . . . . . . . . . . . . . . . . . . . . .213
19.4   Sentences Beginning with *There* or *Here* . . . . . . . . . . . . . . .214
19.5   Direct Objects. . . . . . . . . . . . . . . . . . . . . . . . . . . . . . .214
19.5   Distinguishing Direct Objects . . . . . . . . . . . . . . . . . . . . . .215
19.5   Direct Objects in Questions . . . . . . . . . . . . . . . . . . . . . . .215
19.5   Indirect Objects . . . . . . . . . . . . . . . . . . . . . . . . . . . . . .216
19.5   Distinguishing Indirect Objects . . . . . . . . . . . . . . . . . . . . .216
19.5   Subject Complements . . . . . . . . . . . . . . . . . . . . . . . . . . .217
19.5   Compound Subject Complements. . . . . . . . . . . . . . . . . . . . .217

**Chapter 20: Phrases and Clauses**

20.1   Prepositional Phrases (Adjective) . . . . . . . . . . . . . . . . . . . .218
20.1   Prepositional Phrases (Adverb) . . . . . . . . . . . . . . . . . . . . .218
20.1   Appositives in Phrases . . . . . . . . . . . . . . . . . . . . . . . . . .219
20.1   Participles. . . . . . . . . . . . . . . . . . . . . . . . . . . . . . . . .220
20.1   Participles in Phrases . . . . . . . . . . . . . . . . . . . . . . . . . .221
20.2   Adjective Clauses . . . . . . . . . . . . . . . . . . . . . . . . . . . . .221
20.2   Adverb Clauses . . . . . . . . . . . . . . . . . . . . . . . . . . . . . .222
20.2   Classifying Sentences by Structure . . . . . . . . . . . . . . . . . . .223
20.2   Classifying Sentences by Structure . . . . . . . . . . . . . . . . . . .223

**Chapter 21: Effective Sentences**

21.1   The Four Functions of Sentences . . . . . . . . . . . . . . . . . . . .224
21.2   Shortening Sentences That Are Too Long . . . . . . . . . . . . . . . .224
21.3   Using Different Sentence Openers . . . . . . . . . . . . . . . . . . . .225

21.3 Improving Short Sentences . . . . . . . . . . . . . . .225
21.4 Correcting Sentence Fragments . . . . . . . . . . . . . .225
21.4 Correcting Fragments (Phrases, Clauses) . . . . . . . . . . .226
21.4 Correcting Run-ons . . . . . . . . . . . . . . . . . .226
21.4 Correcting Run-ons . . . . . . . . . . . . . . . . . .227
21.4 Recognizing Misplaced Modifiers . . . . . . . . . . . . .227
21.4 Correcting Misplaced Modifiers . . . . . . . . . . . . .228
21.4 Double Negatives . . . . . . . . . . . . . . . . . . .228
21.4 Common Usage Problems . . . . . . . . . . . . . . . .229

## Chapter 22: Using Verbs

22.1 The Four Principal Parts of Verbs (Regular) . . . . . . . . .229
22.1 The Four Principal Parts of Verbs (Irregular) . . . . . . . . .229
22.2 The Six Tenses of Verbs . . . . . . . . . . . . . . . .230
22.2 The Six Progressive Forms of Verbs . . . . . . . . . . . .230
22.3 Glossary of Troublesome Verbs . . . . . . . . . . . . .231

## Chapter 23: Using Pronouns

23 The Three Cases of Personal Pronouns . . . . . . . . . . .232
23 Cases of Personal Pronouns (Nominative, Objective) . . . . . .232
23 Cases of Personal Pronouns (Possessive) . . . . . . . . . .232

## Chapter 24: Making Words Agree

24.1 Agreement Between Subjects and Verbs . . . . . . . . . .233
24.1 Agreement Between Subjects and Verbs . . . . . . . . . .233
24.1 Agreement with Compound Subjects . . . . . . . . . . .234
24.1 Special Problems with Subject-Verb Agreement . . . . . . . .234
24.2 Agreement Between Pronouns and Antecedents . . . . . . . .234

## Chapter 25: Using Modifiers

25.1 Comparison of Adjectives and Adverbs (Regular) . . . . . . .235
25.1 Comparison of Adjectives and Adverbs (Irregular) . . . . . . .235
25.1 Using the Comparative and Superlative Degrees . . . . . . . .236
25.2 Glossary of Troublesome Adjectives and Adverbs . . . . . . .236

## Chapter 26: Using Punctuation Marks

26.1 End Marks . . . . . . . . . . . . . . . . . . . . . .237
26.1 End Marks . . . . . . . . . . . . . . . . . . . . . .237
26.2 Commas (Compound Sentences) . . . . . . . . . . . . .238
26.2 Commas (Series, Between Adjectives) . . . . . . . . . . .238
26.2 Commas (Added Elements) . . . . . . . . . . . . . . .239
26.2 Commas (Nonessential Elements) . . . . . . . . . . . . .239
26.2 Commas (Dates, Places, Other Uses) . . . . . . . . . . . .239
26.3 Semicolons . . . . . . . . . . . . . . . . . . . . . .240
26.3 Colons . . . . . . . . . . . . . . . . . . . . . . . .240
26.4 Quotation Marks with Direct Quotations . . . . . . . . . .241
26.4 Quotation Marks with Other Punctuation . . . . . . . . . .241
26.4 Quotation Marks or Underlining . . . . . . . . . . . . .241
26.5 Hyphens . . . . . . . . . . . . . . . . . . . . . . .242
26.5 Apostrophes (Nouns and Pronouns) . . . . . . . . . . . .242
26.5 Apostrophes (Contractions) . . . . . . . . . . . . . . .243

## Chapter 27: Following Capitalization Rules

27 Capitals for Sentences and the Word *I* . . . . . . . . . . .243
27 Capitals for Proper Nouns . . . . . . . . . . . . . . . .243
27 Capitals for Proper Nouns . . . . . . . . . . . . . . . .244
27 Capitals for Proper Adjectives . . . . . . . . . . . . . .244
27 Capitals for Titles of People . . . . . . . . . . . . . . .244
27 Capitals for Titles of Things . . . . . . . . . . . . . . .245
27 Capitals in Letters . . . . . . . . . . . . . . . . . . .245

**Diagraming**Diagraming Basic Sentence Parts (Subject and Verb) . . . . . . . . .246
Diagraming Basic Sentence Parts (Compound Subjects and Verbs) . . . . . . .246
Diagraming Basic Sentence Parts (Complements) . . . . . . . . . . . . .247
Diagraming Prepositional Phrases and Appositives . . . . . . . . . . . .248
Diagraming Clauses . . . . . . . . . . . . . . . . . . . . . . . .249

## 14.1 Nouns • Practice 1

**People, Places, and Things.** A noun is the name of a person, place, or thing. Some of the things named by nouns can be seen. Some cannot.

| People | Places | Things |
|--------|--------|--------|
| mother | classroom | honesty |
| teacher | home | animal |
| Mrs. Brown | theater | automobile |
| sister | Lake Erie | patience |
| leader | store | notebook |
| doctor | beach | heart |

▶ **Exercise 1** **Identifying Nouns.** Underline the two nouns in each sentence.

**EXAMPLE:** Carol walked to the store.

1. In the summer we go to the lake.
2. Last month was my birthday.
3. Many birds fly south in winter.
4. My brother gave the best speech.
5. Her dog had four puppies.
6. At the park there were many ducks.
7. A light was shining in the window.
8. The teacher entered the classroom.
9. A large cat slept in front of the fireplace.
10. The man was known for his honesty.

▶ **Exercise 2** **Using Nouns in Sentences.** Fill in each blank with a noun.

**EXAMPLE:** ___Bill___ bought some new ___clothes___ .

1. The _____ has grown a foot since last year.
2. The trip to _____ will take two _____ .
3. My teacher, _____ , has redecorated her _____ .
4. Bob rode to school on a _____ .
5. I gave my _____ a _____ for a birthday present.
6. Many _____ grow in our _____ .
7. Tonight we are going to the _____ .
8. This homework assignment requires plenty of _____ .
9. We'll see _____ at the _____ .
10. I think the _____ will improve next _____ .

## (14.1) Nouns • Practice 2

▶ **Exercise 1** **Classifying Nouns.** The words in the following list are all nouns. Place each word in the correct column.

**EXAMPLE:** window

| People | Places | Things |
|--------|--------|--------|
|        |        | window |

1. pillow
2. happiness
3. teacher
4. lungs
5. tulip
6. beauty
7. string bean
8. map
9. giraffe
10. sister
11. sadness
12. bald eagle
13. growth
14. theater
15. magazine
16. carelessness
17. hotel
18. success
19. beach
20. couselor

| People | Places | Things |
|--------|--------|--------|
| _____ | _____ | _____ |
| _____ | _____ | _____ |
| _____ | _____ | _____ |
| _____ | _____ | _____ |
| _____ | _____ | _____ |
| _____ | _____ | _____ |
| _____ | _____ | _____ |

▶ **Writing Application** **Writing Sentences with Nouns.** Use the following instructions to write five sentences of your own. Underline the nouns you use.

**EXAMPLE:** Write a sentence using a noun that names an idea you cannot usually see.

*We have always admired your courage.*

1. Write a sentence using two nouns that name family members.

_____

_____

2. Write a sentence using a noun that names a living thing that you can see.

_____

_____

3. Write a sentence using a noun that names an idea you cannot usually see.

_____

_____

4. Write a sentence using a noun that names a nonliving thing that you can see.

_____

_____

5. Write a sentence using nouns that name two or more cities or states you would like to visit.

_____

_____

#  Collective and Compound Nouns • Practice 1

**Collective Nouns**   A collective noun names a group of individual people or things.

| COLLECTIVE NOUNS | | |
| --- | --- | --- |
| class | navy | crowd |
| flock | team | club |
| family | crew | band |

**Compound Nouns**   A compound noun is made up of two or more words. The chart shows the three ways that compound nouns can be written.

| COMPOUND NOUNS | | |
| --- | --- | --- |
| **Separate Words** | **Hyphenated Words** | **Combined Words** |
| high school | mother-in-law | baseball |
| post office | rock-climbing | typewriter |
| double play | left-hander | doghouse |

▶ **Exercise 1**   **Identifying Collective Nouns.**   Write the collective noun in each sentence in the blank at the right.

**EXAMPLE:** Our team lost the game. ____team____

1.  A large crowd stood on the platform. _____
2.  On Thursday the army marched six miles. _____
3.  The club held a meeting at my house. _____
4.  Our family owns a house in the country. _____
5.  A herd of sheep grazed on the hillside. _____
6.  The orchestra tuned up before the concert. _____
7.  Mr. Ferguson spoke to our class. _____
8.  Gretchen is the president of our committee. _____
9.  The navy sailed three ships into the harbor. _____
10. A large group went swimming at the lake. _____

▶ **Exercise 2**   **Identifying Compound Nouns.**   Underline the compound noun in each sentence.

**EXAMPLE:** We play basketball every Saturday.

1.  Large tomatoes are growing in our backyard.
2.  My great-grandfather is living with us.
3.  A new high school was built last year.
4.  Suddenly the doorknob began to turn slowly.
5.  The racehorse ran like the wind.
6.  I left angry, but I exercised self-control.
7.  There are three lifeguards at the beach this summer.
8.  The stars lie many light-years away.
9.  Two astronauts were flying in the landing-craft.
10. My bedroom is located at the end of the hall.

# 14.1 Collective and Compound Nouns • Practice 2

▶ **Exercise 1** **Recognizing Collective Nouns.** Each of the following groups of words contains one collective noun. Write each collective noun in the space provided.

**EXAMPLE:** noise   crowd   flower _____*crowd*_____

1. vegetable   radio      family      _____

2. jury         sailboat   happiness   _____

3. freedom      squad      plant       _____

4. crew         skyscraper  elephant    _____

5. finger       assembly   newspaper   _____

▶ **Exercise 2** **Identifying Compound Nouns.** Each of the following sentences has one or more compound nouns. Underline each compound noun.

**EXAMPLE:** The scouts hoisted their pennant up the flagpole.

1. In a desert, both people and animals search for water holes.

2. The dining room in our hotel is quite near the swimming pool.

3. This new typewriter belongs to my father-in-law.

4. She has pictures of a wolf spider, a horned beetle, and a praying mantis.

5. Our teams excel in football and basketball.

▶ **Exercise 3** **Finding the Correct Form of Compound Nouns.** Use a dictionary to find the correct spelling of each of the following compound nouns. Write the correct form in the space provided.

**EXAMPLE:** fire-drill   fire drill   firedrill _____*fire drill*_____

1. postmaster   post-master   post master   _____

2. side-line     side line     sideline      _____

3. son in law    soninlaw      son-in-law    _____

4. base ball     baseball      base-ball     _____

5. fire place     fire-place    fireplace     _____

# 14.1 Common and Proper Nouns • Practice 1

**Common and Proper Nouns** A common noun names one of a class of people, places, or things. A proper noun names a specific person, place, or thing. Proper nouns are always capitalized.

| Common Nouns | Proper Nouns |
|---|---|
| leader | George Washington |
| city | Los Angeles |
| river | Missouri River |
| state | Florida |
| writer | Mark Twain |

**▶ Exercise 1** **Identifying Common and Proper Nouns.** Underline the common nouns in the sentences below. Circle the proper nouns.

**EXAMPLE:** (Dave) hit a single.

1. I've just read a play by Shakespeare.

2. The Drama Club elected a new president.

3. Soon our family plans to visit Miami.

4. A new house is being built on Elm Street.

5. My father has been transferred to Colorado.

6. She named her new dog Max.

7. Have you ever seen the Statue of Liberty?

8. My favorite holiday is Thanksgiving.

9. My brother went climbing in the Rocky Mountains.

10. I have pictures of Niagara Falls.

**▶ Exercise 2** **Using Proper Nouns in Sentences.** Fill in each blank with a proper noun. Remember to capitalize each proper noun.

**EXAMPLE:** There is no coastline in ____Kansas____.

1. Her best friend in school was _____.

2. I enjoy _____ more than any other singer.

3. Bill has an autograph from _____.

4. Her family was moving to _____.

5. _____ is the most beautiful street in our community.

6. Have you ever visited _____?

7. The capital of our state is _____.

8. In my opinion, _____ was a very courageous leader.

9. Let's do some shopping at _____.

10. I think we should select _____ as our captain.

## 14.1 Common and Proper Nouns • Practice 2

▶**Exercise 1**  **Identifying Common and Proper Nouns.**  Place a *C* after each common noun and a *P* after each proper noun. Then for each common noun, write a corresponding proper noun. For each proper noun, write a corresponding common noun.

**EXAMPLE:** city ____*C*____ *Seattle* ____

1. street _____
2. Chevette _____
3. Los Angeles _____
4. general _____
5. Jane Austen _____
6. Lassie _____
7. song _____
8. mayor _____
9. Hank Aaron _____
10. river _____

▶**Writing Application**  **Writing Sentences with Different Types of Nouns.**  Write five sentences of your own, each using the kind of noun that fits the description given in the following list. Underline these nouns.

**EXAMPLE:** collective noun

_A *flock* of noisy geese flew overhead making sounds similar to dogs barking._

1. collective noun

_____

_____

2. compound noun that is hyphenated

_____

_____

3. three common nouns and two proper nouns

_____

_____

4. compound noun that is two separate words

_____

_____

5. compound noun that is a combined word

_____

_____

# 14.2 Pronouns and Antecedents • Practice 1

**Antecedents of Pronouns**   A pronoun takes the place of a noun or group of words acting as a noun. An antecedent is the noun (or group of words acting as a noun) for which a pronoun stands.

| PRONOUNS AND ANTECEDENTS |
| --- |
| ANTECEDENT      PRONOUN<br>      Bill made his way through the forest. |
| ANTECEDENT        PRONOUN<br>The duck couldn't fly because its wing was broken. |

**Personal Pronouns**   Personal pronouns refer to (1) the person speaking, (2) the person spoken to, or (3) the person, place, or thing spoken about.

| PERSONAL PRONUNS | | |
| --- | --- | --- |
| | **Singular** | **Plural** |
| First Person | I, me, my, mine | we, us, our, ours |
| Second Person | you, your, yours | you, your, yours |
| Third Person | he, him, his,<br>she, her, hers,<br>it, its | they, them, their,<br>theirs |

▶ **Exercise 1**   **Identifying Pronouns and Antecedents.**   Underline the personal pronoun in each sentence. Then, circle its antecedent.

**EXAMPLE:** (Betsy) has just written her first book.

1. The explorers sailed their ship across the Pacific.

2. Bill left his homework on the bus.

3. Where are you going, Bob?

4. The champion skater always performed on his newest skates.

5. The woman washed her car every week.

6. The actors practiced their parts at rehearsal.

7. Two deer led their young to the river.

8. The bicycle is yours, Martha.

9. When the astronaut landed his spaceship, the sun had already set.

10. A large sheepdog buries its bones behind the barn.

▶ **Exercise 2**   **Using Personal Pronouns.**   Fill in each blank with a personal pronoun.

**EXAMPLE:** Richard is late for _____*his*_____ appointment.

1. Albert Einstein devoted _____ life to science.

2. "Where are _____ gloves?" I asked myself.

3. Carol came forward to receive _____ award.

4. The Mississippi empties _____ waters into the Gulf of Mexico.

5. Since _____ canoe was the fastest, they won the race.

# 14.2 Pronouns and Antecedents • Practice 2

**Exercise 1** **Recognizing Antecedents.** Find the antecedent for each underlined pronoun in the following sentences and circle it.

**EXAMPLE:** (Martha) explained how <u>she</u> won the contest.

1. Ted tried to explain why <u>he</u> didn't phone.

2. Will the treasurer give <u>her</u> report?

3. Although the apples were red, <u>they</u> tasted sour.

4. If <u>they</u> arrive in time, the boys will do the work.

5. Baking cookies for the party is not a good idea. <u>It</u> takes too much time.

6. The rattlesnake kills <u>its</u> victims with venom.

7. Maria agreed that <u>she</u> was wrong.

8. Have the boys brought <u>their</u> swimsuits?

9. As the steamboat rounded the bend, black smoke poured from <u>its</u> smokestack.

10. The policeman gave <u>his</u> version of the accident.

**Exercise 2** **Identifying Personal Pronouns.** In the space provided, identify the underlined pronoun in each of the following sentences as *first person, second person,* or *third person.*

**EXAMPLE:** The teacher asked <u>him</u> a difficult question.

　　　　　*him　　　third person*

1. <u>We</u> tried to reach the police all morning.

   _____

2. The judge of the contest said that <u>your</u> dance was the best.

   _____

3. The jaguar struck the rock and injured <u>its</u> front paw.

   _____

4. The first two sketches of steamboats are <u>mine</u>.

   _____

5. My aunt said that <u>she</u> wallpapered the entire room in less than a day.

   _____

6. Alexander didn't follow the directions given to <u>him</u>.

   _____

7. A herd of bighorn sheep appeared, but <u>they</u> were frightened away by the airplane.

   _____

8. The doctor said that <u>I</u> can expect the hand to hurt for several days.

   _____

9. After some discussion the explorers chose <u>their</u> route through the mountains.

   _____

10. The violinist said <u>he</u> practices seven days a week.

   _____

**14.2** # Demonstrative and Interrogative Pronouns • Practice 1

**Demonstrative Pronouns**   A demonstrative pronoun points out a specific person, place, or thing.

| DEMONSTRATIVE PRONOUNS | |
| --- | --- |
| **Singular** | **Plural** |
| this    that | these    those |

**Interrogative Pronouns**   An interrogative pronoun is used to begin a question.

| INTERROGATIVE PRONOUNS |
| --- |
| what    which    who    whom    whose |

▷ **Exercise 1**   **Distinguishing Between Demonstrative and Interrogative Pronouns.**   Write whether each underlined word is a demonstrative or interrogative pronoun.

**EXAMPLE:** <u>Whom</u> did you see in the park?  _____interrogative_____

1. <u>What</u> are we eating for dinner? _____

2. <u>This</u> is the present I gave my mother. _____

3. Of all my courses, <u>that</u> is my best. _____

4. <u>What</u> is your name? _____

5. <u>Which</u> is your house? _____

6. <u>These</u> belong to the band. _____

7. Of all the flowers, <u>which</u> bloom earliest in spring? _____

8. <u>Whose</u> is that bicycle in the driveway? _____

9. <u>Those</u> were painted by Monet. _____

10. He said <u>these</u> are the world's smallest birds. _____

▷ **Exercise 2**   **Adding Demonstrative and Interrogative Pronouns to Sentences.**   Fill in each blank with a demonstrative or an interrogative pronoun.

**EXAMPLE:** _____Which_____ is the hardest event?

1. _____ did the Pilgrims do in 1620?

2. _____ have you purchased at the supermarket?

3. I saw _____ on television last week.

4. Are _____ the clothes you wanted me to wash?

5. _____ are you reading in class this week?

6. _____ were the skates that you left here after school on Wednesday.

7. _____ is the answer to the fifth question.

8. With _____ did you dance at the party last night?

9. Isn't _____ your brother over there?

10. _____ is your favorite game?

# 14.2 Demonstrative and Interrogative Pronouns • Practice 2

**Exercise 1** **Recognizing Demonstrative Pronouns.** Each of the following sentences contains a demonstrative pronoun. Write each demonstrative pronoun in the space after each sentence.

**EXAMPLE:** These are the highest grades I have ever received. ___*These*___

1. This is the computer I hope to get for my birthday. _____
2. My uncle plays the bassoon. This is a very difficult instrument to play. _____
3. That seems to be the shortest route to the village. _____
4. Of all his excuses, these are the poorest. _____
5. This has been the happiest day of my life. _____
6. Yes, these are the oldest tombstones in Lexington's cemetery. _____
7. She said those are the most interesting fossils. _____
8. Ronald likes to display his models built from toothpicks. These are his pride and joy. _____
9. Isn't that a poster of one of Georgia O'Keeffe's paintings? _____
10. Before leaving for college, my sister gave me her jade necklace and silver pin. Those had always been her favorites. _____

**Exercise 2** **Recognizing Interrogative Pronouns.** Each of the following items contains an interrogative pronoun. In the space provided, write each interrogative pronoun.

**EXAMPLE:** What happened to the cookies I baked? ___*What*___

1. To whom did you send the package? _____
2. That is beautiful. Whose is it? _____
3. She has two calculators. Which would you prefer to borrow? _____
4. Who is the actor with the high-pitched voice? _____
5. What is her occupation? _____
6. Who is coming to the party? _____
7. What should I say when I meet the Senator for the first time? _____
8. Which of the states has the largest deposits of coal? _____
9. With whom did you leave your telephone number and address? _____
10. Samantha has four albums by the Beatles. Which is the best? _____

## 14.2 Indefinite Pronouns • Practice 1

**Indefinite Pronouns**   Indefinite pronouns refer to people, places, or things, often without specifying which ones.

| INDEFINITE PRONOUNS | | | |
|---|---|---|---|
| **Singular** | | **Plural** | **Singular or Plural** |
| another | much | both | all |
| anybody | neither | few | any |
| anyone | nobody | many | more |
| anything | no one | others | most |
| each | nothing | several | none |
| either | one | | some |
| everybody | other | | |
| everyone | somebody | | |
| everything | someone | | |
| little | something | | |

▶ **Exercise 1**   **Identifying Indefinite Pronouns.**   Underline each indefinite pronoun in the sentences below.

**EXAMPLE:** <u>Both</u> of us are going to the zoo.

1. We want everybody to have fun at the party.
2. Neither of the trails looks difficult to climb.
3. He knew none of the answers on the test.
4. Somebody left a window open, and rain came in during the storm.
5. Karen gave each of the kittens a dish of food.
6. Several of these homes were built centuries ago.
7. Something tells me that we are going to have a problem.
8. Most of the team members have already boarded the bus.
9. We can accomplish little unless we work together.
10. Nothing succeeds like success.

▶ **Exercise 2**   **Using Pronouns in Sentences.**   Fill in each blank with an appropriate indefinite pronoun.

**EXAMPLE:** ___*Many*___ of these problems have two solutions.

1. _____ of those explorers have reached the summit of Mt. Everest.
2. By Saturday afternoon, _____ had been prepared for the dance.
3. _____ of the horses were grazing in the pasture.
4. I felt that _____ of the boys had an equal chance to win.
5. Will _____ be at the station to meet the train when it arrives?
6. Tulips and daffodils are growing in the garden. _____ are beautiful spring flowers.
7. During the play, _____ of the actors forgot their lines.
8. There is _____ we can do about it now.
9. She had finished _____ of her packing for the trip.
10. _____ of the quarterbacks threw any touchdown passes in the game.

## 14.2 Indefinite Pronouns • Practice 2

▶ **Exercise 1**    **Recognizing Indefinite Pronouns.**   Each of the following sentences contains at least one indefinite pronoun. In the space provided, write each indefinite pronoun.

**EXAMPLE:** Each refused to speak to the other.   _Each, other_

1.  Few in the class knew which nation colonized Angola. _____
2.  Has everyone already had lunch? _____
3.  Many of these insects burrow into the soil. _____
4.  Neither cared for the concert, but both complimented the bandleader. _____
5.  His excuse is that everyone arrived late. _____
6.  In the field grew poison ivy and poison sumac; both are plants that can cause rashes. _____
7.  Most can learn to use parallel bars after practicing for a while. _____
8.  Our family knew none of their guests. _____
9.  Most of the people I know would like to play the piano. _____
10. All of the poodles have been carefully trained. _____

▶ **Writing Application**    **Writing Sentences with Pronouns.**   Write a short sentence or pair of sentences using a pronoun that fits each of the descriptions given in the following list. Underline the pronoun that you use.

**EXAMPLE:** demonstrative pronoun that comes after its antecedent

  *I picked out some library books. These seemed the most interesting to me.*

1.  demonstrative pronoun at the beginning of the sentence

    _____

    _____

2.  demonstrative pronoun that comes after its antecedent

    _____

    _____

3.  interrogative pronoun with an antecedent

    _____

    _____

4.  interrogative pronoun without an antecedent

    _____

    _____

5.  indefinite pronoun with an antecedent

    _____

    _____

#  15.1 Action Verbs • Practice 1

**Visible and Mental Action**   An action verb tells what action someone or something is performing. Some actions are easy to see. Some are not, and they are called mental actions.

| Visible Action | | Mental Action | |
|---|---|---|---|
| run | swim | remember | decide |
| bring | hit | understand | believe |
| fly | eat | expect | hope |
| tell | smile | think | wonder |

▶ **Exercise 1**   **Recognizing Visible and Mental Actions.**   Underline each verb that shows visible action. Circle each verb that shows mental action.

**EXAMPLE:**   We rode our bicycles to school. Alice (believed) the untrue story.

1. We expect rain on Thursday afternoon.

2. They decided on a menu for dinner.

3. Bill carried the large flowerpot to the second floor.

4. The team scored its third touchdown in the fourth quarter.

5. She walked two miles to the grocery store.

6. I remembered the directions to your office.

7. The dog barked at strangers passing the house.

8. Many people worry about their jobs.

9. The airplane flew from Dallas to Chicago.

10. Alison wrote that story three years ago.

▶ **Exercise 2**   **Adding Action Verbs to Sentences.**   Fill in each blank with an appropriate action verb.

**EXAMPLE:**   She ____paddled____ her canoe across the lake.

1. Large herds of buffalo _____ on the prairies.

2. All of us _____ the homework assignment, Mrs. Pope.

3. A white rabbit _____ across the road and into the bushes.

4. In his recital, Karl _____ two difficult pieces on the piano.

5. We _____ a large Thanksgiving dinner for the entire family.

6. After all of this work is over, I _____ we can take a short rest.

7. I _____ why everyone is late for the party.

8. Following the large snowstorm, we _____ a huge snow fort.

9. We went outdoors and _____ in the park after the rain had ended.

10. The two men _____ along the trail until sunset.

## 15.1 Action Verbs • Practice 2

**▶ Exercise 1**    **Identifying Kinds of Action Verbs.**   On the line provided, write *visible* or *mental* to identify the kind of action that the underlined verb shows. Note that six are visible and four are mental.

**EXAMPLE:** Marcia <u>picked</u> a bushel of apples from the tree.    *visible*

1. My best friend <u>chews</u> her food thoroughly. _____
2. I <u>wonder</u> about my future all the time. _____
3. The fullback <u>dropped</u> the football in the end zone. _____
4. Four of us <u>crowded</u> into the back seat of the car. _____
5. We <u>expect</u> many people at the crafts fair. _____
6. The beetle <u>scurried</u> into a corner of the tent. _____
7. Like a great bird, the Concorde <u>landed</u> gracefully. _____
8. The hedgehog, a small mammal, <u>eats</u> insects. _____
9. I often <u>worry</u> about overpopulation. _____
10. I <u>remember</u> the day of the blackout very well. _____

**▶ Exercise 2**    **Recognizing Action Verbs.**   Underline the action verb in each sentence.

**EXAMPLE:** The plane from Madrid <u>arrived</u> three hours late.

1. The musician placed the piccolo in its case.
2. Bill sprinkled garlic onto the steaming bread.
3. This camera takes excellent pictures.
4. Years ago my grandmother baked her own pies for holidays.
5. My little brother waved the cowboy hat above his head.
6. The mayor cut the ribbon with a huge pair of scissors.
7. The ship struck the dock.
8. The fishermen occupied several villages near the river.
9. Darlene bought three albums this morning.
10. Flora plugged the leak in the water pipe with an old towel.

**▶ Writing Application**    **Writing Sentences with Action Verbs..**   Write ten original sentences, each using one of the following action verbs. Underline the verb in each sentence you write.

**EXAMPLE:** grow    *She <u>grows</u> snap beans in the garden.*

1. sing _____
2. ride _____
3. plant _____
4. tell _____
5. touch _____
6. watch _____
7. swim _____
8. read _____
9. drive _____
10. ask _____

**15.2** | # Linking Verbs • Practice 1

**The Most Common Linking Verb**  A linking verb connects a noun or pronoun at or near the beginning of a sentence with a word at or near the end. In English the most common linking verb is *be*.

| THE FORMS OF *BE* | | | | | |
|---|---|---|---|---|---|
| am | am being | can be | should be | have been | must have been |
| are | are being | could be | will be | has been | shall have been |
| is | is being | may be | would be | had been | will have been |
| was | was being | might be | | could have been | would have been |
| were | were being | must be | | might have been | |
| | | shall be | | | |

**Other Linking Verbs**  *Be* is the most commonly used linking verb, but there are some other important linking verbs. These are often used in the same way as *be* to link two parts of a sentence.

| OTHER LINKING VERBS | | | | | |
|---|---|---|---|---|---|
| appear | feel | look | seem | sound | taste |
| become | grow | remain | smell | stay | turn |

▶ **Exercise 1**  **Identifying Forms of the Linking Verb *Be*.**  Circle the form of *be* in each sentence below. Then underline the words in the sentence that are linked by the verb.

**EXAMPLE:** Gail (is) the captain of our team.

1. Those golden flowers must have been sunflowers.

2. I am president of our class.

3. Thursday is Kathy's thirteenth birthday.

4. Tennis must be difficult.

5. My favorite painting in the show was "The Starry Night."

6. You should have been happy with your grade on the test.

7. Her worst problem may have been her shyness.

8. A woman will be the next governor.

9. Steve will be a pirate at the costume party.

10. A pink shirt might be perfect for you.

▶ **Exercise 2**  **Recognizing Other Linking Verbs.**  Circle the linking verb in each sentence. Then underline the words that the verb links.

**EXAMPLE:** I (feel) good now.

1. This answer appears incorrect.

2. The three sisters always remained friends.

3. The pudding tastes sweet.

4. The lettuce stayed fresh in the refrigerator.

5. You look very handsome in that suit.

## 15.2 Linking Verbs • Practice 2

**Exercise 1** **Recognizing Forms of the Linking Verb *Be*.** Underline the form of *be* in each of the following sentences. Then circle the words that are linked by the verb.

**EXAMPLE:** That (dog) <u>is</u> a (collie) .

1. Your next book will be *When the Legends Die.*

2. That purple jewel is an amethyst.

3. The keys have been rusty for some time now.

4. Her favorite colors are turquoise and tan.

5. Judy was the star of the show.

6. Carlos Cruz might be our next mayor.

7. The best play was *You're a Good Man, Charlie Brown.*

8. She should have been happy after winning.

9. Most snowflakes are delicately shaped hexagons.

10. I am always very hungry by lunch time.

**Exercise 2** **Identifying Other Linking Verbs.** Underline the linking verb in each of the following sentences. Then circle the words that are linked by the verb.

**EXAMPLE:** With the storm, the (road) quickly <u>turned</u> (muddy) .

1. David appears hungry and tired.

2. His answer seemed wrong to me.

3. The two comics remained partners for thirty years.

4. The white, sandy beach looks inviting.

5. On this old record, the voices sound shrill and scratchy.

6. The apple pie smells delicious.

7. That quartz looks almost colorless.

8. Mary Ann became a fine lawyer.

9. For two years the house stayed empty.

10. This fabric feels rough to the touch.

# 15.2 Linking Verbs • Practice 1

**Action Verb or Linking Verb?**  To test whether a verb is a linking verb or an action verb, substitute *am*, *is*, or *are* for the verb. If the sentence still makes sense, then the original verb is a linking verb.

| Linking | Action |
|---|---|
| Carol *grew* weak. | Carol *grew* lettuce. |
| (Carol *is* weak?) | (Carol *is* lettuce?) |
| Yes, it's a linking verb. | No, it's an action verb. |

**Exercise 1**  **Distinguishing Between Linking Verbs and Action Verbs.**  Circle the verbs in the sentences below. On the lines at the right, write *AV* for each action verb, or *LV* for each linking verb.

**EXAMPLE:** The cat (looks) sick. ____LV____

1. I felt scared in the dark tunnel. _____

2. I felt the coarse mane on the horse's neck. _____

3. Roger turns fifteen next week. _____

4. She tasted the rich, red tomato soup. _____

5. We looked through the dusty window into the living room. _____

6. After the party, the room looked very messy. _____

7. We sounded the fire alarm at the gym. _____

8. The milk smells sour to me. _____

9. You grow taller every year. _____

10. That answer sounds incorrect. _____

**Exercise 2**  **Using Verbs in Sentences.**  Fill in each blank within the sentence with an appropriate verb. On the line after each sentence write *AV* for each action verb or *LV* for each linking verb.

**EXAMPLE:** A ghost ____appeared____ on the porch. ____AV____

1. Anne _____ secretary-treasurer of the student council. _____

2. Dad _____ into the driveway and drove up to the house. _____

3. The apples in that barrel _____ rotten. _____

4. With the proper fertilizer, plants _____ very strong. _____

5. After finishing college, she _____ a writer. _____

6. We _____ until the play ended. _____

7. The instruments in the orchestra _____ out of tune. _____

8. The large melons _____ ripe today. _____

9. That ice-cream cone certainly _____ delicious. _____

10. After practice, the players _____ very tired. _____

# 15.2 Linking Verbs • Practice 2

**Exercise 1** **Distinguishing Between Action Verbs and Linking Verbs.** Underline the verb in each of the following sentences. After each action verb write *AV* and after each linking verb write *LV*.

**EXAMPLE:** Suddenly a bright light <u>appeared</u> in the sky. ____*AV*____

1. The inspector sounded the alarm as a test. _____
2. During the drought the grass turned brown. _____
3. The room seems smaller now. _____
4. My brother grows tomatoes and scallions. _____
5. That robin appears at our bird feeder often. _____
6. The chocolate fudge tastes too sweet. _____
7. She stayed in Texas for two weeks. _____
8. Two years later my uncle became a judge. _____
9. The garage now looks clean. _____
10. Influenced by the bad weather, the animals turned skittish. _____

**Writing Application** **Writing Sentences with Linking Verbs.** Write ten sentences of your own, each using one of the following linking verbs. Underline the verbs and draw double-headed arrows connecting the words they link.

**EXAMPLE:** seem

The lost children <u>seem</u> frightened.

1. became _____
2. was _____
3. remain _____
4. sound _____
5. look _____
6. appear _____
7. felt _____
8. grew _____
9. smell _____
10. turned _____

**15.3** # Helping Verbs • Practice 1

**Recognizing Helping Verbs**   Helping verbs are added before the key part of the verb to make a verb phrase. The various forms of *be* are often used as helping verbs. Some other common verbs are also used as helping verbs.

| SOME FORMS OF *BE* USED AS HELPING VERBS | |
| --- | --- |
| **Helping Verbs** | **Key Verbs** |
| *am* | walking |
| *has been* | warned |
| *was being* | given |
| *could have been* | reminded |
| *will have been* | taking |

| OTHER HELPING VERBS | | | | |
| --- | --- | --- | --- | --- |
| do | have | shall | can | may |
| does | has | should | could | might |
| did | had | will | | must |
| | | would | | |

**Helping Verbs in Sentences**   Words in a verb phrase can be separated by other words.

| VERB PHRASES SEPARATED |
| --- |
| We *have* seldom *heard* from our cousins. |
| She *did* not *give* me a gift this year. |

▶ **Exercise 1**   **Identifying Helping Verbs.**   In the sentences below, underline each helping verb and circle the key verb in each verb phrase.

**EXAMPLE:** I <u>will</u> not (give) you any money.

1.  We should certainly leave soon.

2.  Will you be attending this school next year?

3.  Why is Carol laughing?

4.  The birds did not eat the seeds.

5.  I do not remember her name.

6.  Will you be coming to graduation?

7.  The river has seldom risen so high.

8.  We are certainly not competing in this race.

9.  Have you heard any new jokes?

10.  He may not arrive until this evening.

▶ **Exercise 2**   **Adding Helping Verbs to Sentences.**   Fill in each blank with a helping verb.

**EXAMPLE:** I ____*am*____ coming to your house for the weekend.

1.  We _____ _____ started our trip earlier in the morning.

2.  They _____ not _____ any flour to make the cake.

3.  That play _____ written by William Shakespeare.

4.  I _____ _____ expected her to give a better speech.

5.  Who _____ _____ expected such a large snowstorm?

# 15.3 Helping Verbs • Practice 2

> **Exercise 1** **Supplying Helping Verbs.** Each of the following sentences contains one or more blanks. Fill in each blank with a helping verb that makes sense in the sentence.

**EXAMPLE:** Lars ____should____ ____have____ followed the path.

1. Pasquale _____ win an important science award at graduation.
2. Judy _____ _____ taking medicine for her infection.
3. The team _____ _____ left for Boston by this time tomorrow.
4. He _____ ruined everything.
5. They _____ _____ taken better care of their tools.
6. My sister _____ read all of the Nancy Drew and Hardy Boys books.
7. I guess they thought we _____ not come anymore.
8. How _____ they travel to Mexico?
9. The city _____ planted a row of Norway maples along our street.
10. Our European visitors _____ _____ arrived this morning.

> **Exercise 2** **Finding Helping Verbs.** Underline the complete verb phrase from each of the following sentences. Include all the helping verbs, but do *not* include any of the words that may separate the parts of the verb phrase.

**EXAMPLE:** Have you walked the dogs yet?

1. Government officials were quickly sent to the flood area.
2. Have they planted the vegetables in straight rows?
3. The new pupils should have been taken to meet the principal.
4. Who has been doing research on early polar flights?
5. We should have really taken more food along on the picnic.
6. The girls have not yet chosen a captain.
7. Have you remembered the famous campaign slogan about Tippecanoe?
8. They had not planned on a complete power failure.
9. Your mother could have certainly reached them by phone.
10. Does anyone in the room remember Patrick's last name?

#  16.1 Adjectives • Practice 1

**Adjectives as Modifiers**  An adjective describes a noun or a pronoun. Adjectives usually answer one of these four questions about the nouns and pronouns they modify: *What kind? Which one? How many? How much?*

| ADJECTIVE QUESTIONS | | |
|---|---|---|
| **What Kind?** | *blue* house | *small* dog |
| **Which One?** | *this* bicycle | *each* state |
| **How Many?** | *two* balloons | *few* boys |
| **How Much?** | *no* snow | *enough* money |

▶ **Exercise 1**  **Recognizing Adjectives and the Words They Modify.**  Underline the two adjectives in each sentence below. Circle the words they modify. Do not underline *a, an,* or *the.*

**EXAMPLE:** The <u>vast, flat</u> (desert) stretched before him.

1. The sleek gray horse galloped across the pasture.

2. This fine novel was written by a friend of mine.

3. The long, narrow column of soldiers marched through the pass.

4. Every qualified person can enter the contest.

5. Bob loaded the plate with four large sandwiches.

6. Make one special wish and blow out the candles.

7. The car was a powerful and efficient vehicle.

8. During the winter, we had little snow and no temperatures that fell below zero.

9. I am proud and happy to receive the award.

10. Great flocks of large birds migrate here in the spring.

▶ **Exercise 2**  **Using Adjectives in Sentences.**  Fill in each blank with an adjective.

**EXAMPLE:** We took ____*beautiful*____ photographs of the sunset.

1. The _____ balloon carried the _____ men high above the city.

2. They sailed their _____ boat across the _____ lake.

3. We could see herds of _____ buffalo on the _____ plains.

4. She was wearing a _____ dress and a _____ hat.

5. We enjoy our _____ vacation.

6. Where are the _____ bowls and the _____ plates that you brought?

7. I have _____ new CD's for the party.

8. Give me your _____ sweater so I can stay warm.

9. We saw _____ games at the _____ stadium this fall.

10. She cooked a _____ Chinese dinner last night.

# 16.1 Adjectives • Practice 2

▶ **Exercise 1** **Recognizing Adjectives and the Words They Modify.** Draw an arrow pointing from each underlined adjective to the noun or pronoun it modifies.

**EXAMPLE:** He has not been well for several months.

1. A loud, shrill whistle pierced the air.
2. She is beautiful and graceful.
3. The desert, smooth and white, spread for miles before us.
4. We drove into the noisy, crowded intersection.
5. Tall and slim, he was the picture of health.
6. They are unhappy over the results of the poll.
7. We saw a small, round, hairy animal at the zoo.
8. I have some change, but we will need more money to get home.
9. In her third and fourth years, she broke the swimming records.
10. That man has several tickets to the game.

▶ **Exercise 2** **Recognizing Adjectives.** Underline all of the adjectives in the following paragraph. Do not underline *a, an,* or *the.*

For a brief moment, the bright sun peeked through the dark clouds. Shivering and uncomfortable, Terence looked up. "Could this cruel winter be coming to an end?" he wondered. As the icy wind blew, Terence held his old green coat closed tightly around his thin body.

▶ **Exercise 3** **Adding Adjectives to Sentences.** Fill in the blanks in each sentence with appropriate adjectives.

**EXAMPLE:** Maureen was surprised and delighted by the generous gift.

1. Brad was _____ and _____ after the _____ game.
2. The _____ ball was hit by the _____ batter.
3. The _____ child had a _____ cold.
4. _____ and _____, the _____ apples were ready to be picked.
5. The _____ dog played with the _____ child.
6. The _____ geese flew over the _____ house.
7. The _____ _____ barn needed some _____ _____ paint.
8. Carla, _____ and _____, pulled the _____ weeds.
9. Janet wanted a _____ dress for the _____ party.
10. Duncan helped the _____ girl get onto the _____ horse.

**16.1**

# Articles; Nouns Used as Adjectives
## • Practice 1

**Articles**   *The, a,* and *an* are known as *articles.* Articles stand in front of nouns and answer the question *Which one? The,* the definite article, refers to a specific person, place, or thing. *A* and *an,* the indefinite articles, refer to any single member in a group of people, places, or things. *A* is used before consonant sounds. *An* is used before vowel sounds.

| USING *A* AND *AN* | |
| --- | --- |
| **Consonant Sounds** | **Vowel Sounds** |
| a *b* right day | an *o* wl |
| a *h* ard test (*h* sound) | an *h* onest man (no *h* sound) |
| a *o* ne-of-a-kind (*w* sound) | an *o* pen window (*o* sound) |
| a *u* nion (*y* sound) | an *u* ncle (*u* sound) |

**Nouns Used as Adjectives**   A noun used as an adjective usually comes directly before another noun and answers the question *What kind?* or *Which one?*

| Nouns | Used as Adjectives |
| --- | --- |
| paper | a *paper* plate (*What kind* of plate?) |
| soccer | the *soccer* ball (*Which ball?*) |

**▶Exercise 1**   **Distinguishing Between Definite and Indefinite Articles.**   Fill in each blank with the kind of article described in the parentheses.

**EXAMPLE:**   _____*the*_____   large tiger (definite)

1. _____ honorable person (indefinite)
2. _____ new novel (definite)
3. _____ elderly man (indefinite)
4. _____ impossible undertaking (indefinite)
5. _____ uniform with gold braid (indefinite)
6. _____ old, stone castle (indefinite)
7. _____ one-sided game (indefinite)
8. _____ small, green parakeet (definite)
9. _____ unwritten essay (indefinite)
10. _____ road to success (definite)

**▶Exercise 2**   **Recognizing Nouns Used as Adjectives.**   In each sentence, underline the noun used as an adjective. Circle the noun modified by this adjective.

**EXAMPLE:** I am wearing a <u>cotton</u> (shirt).

1. My neighbor is the tax collector in town.
2. During the summer, I like to walk along the golf course.
3. I would not enjoy working as a dog warden.
4. Our police department has four new cars.
5. We are planning to build a town hall next year.

# 16.1 Articles; Nouns Used as Adjectives
## • Practice 2

▶ **Exercise 1**   **Distinguishing Between Definite and Indefinite Articles.**   Write the article that will correctly complete each of the following sentences. The word in parentheses tells you which kind of article to use.

**EXAMPLE:**   ___The___ ambulance raced up ___a___ one-way street. (definite; indefinite)

1.  Have you purchased _____ birthday cake yet? (definite)

2.  _____ older man stopped us in the street. (indefinite)

3.  Our captain hit both _____ single and _____ home run. (indefinite; indefinite)

4.  _____ oldest stamp in her collection is dated 1857. (definite)

5.  He always takes either_____ apple or _____ banana to school. (indefinite; indefinite)

6.  The piano has _____ ivory keyboard. (indefinite)

7.  _____ President addressed _____ joint session of Congress. (definite; indefinite)

8.  _____ audition notice for the show was posted by _____ director. (indefinite; definite)

9.  Where are _____ camera and _____ film? (definite; definite)

10. Tomorrow she will open _____ account at _____ bank. (indefinite; definite)

▶ **Exercise 2**   **Identifying Nouns Used as Adjectives.**   Underline the noun used as an adjective in the following sentences. Draw an arrow to the noun it modifies.

**EXAMPLE:**  A piano player entertained the guests.

1.  Did you speak to the newspaper reporter?

2.  My parents gave me a new tennis racket.

3.  Please change the light bulb in the den.

4.  The soldiers practiced under battle conditions.

5.  I have an appointment with the eye doctor.

6.  Were you able to repair the desk lamp?

7.  Many good hotels still provide room service.

8.  After dinner the whole family watched the television news.

9.  Building stone walls helps him relax.

10. What does that highway sign say?

# 16.1 Proper Adjectives and Compound Adjectives • Practice 1

**Proper Adjectives**   A proper adjective is a proper noun used as an adjective or an adjective formed from a proper noun. A proper noun used as an adjective does not change its form.

| Proper Nouns | Used as Proper Adjectives |
|---|---|
| Thanksgiving | *Thanksgiving* cards (*Which* cards?) |
| Mississippi | *Mississippi* mud (*What kind* of mud?) |

When an adjective is formed from a proper noun, the proper noun does change its form.

| Proper Nouns | Proper Adjectives Formed from Proper Nouns |
|---|---|
| Canada | *Canadian* people (*Which* people?) |
| Rome | *Roman* history (*What kind* of history?) |

**Compound Adjectives**   A compound adjective is made up of more than one word. Most compound adjectives are written as hyphenated words. Some are written as combined words.

| Hyphenated | Combined |
|---|---|
| a *big-league* player | a *billboard* sign |
| a *part-time* job | a *foolproof* plan |

▶ **Exercise 1**   **Identifying Proper Adjectives and Compound Adjectives.**   Write *proper* or *compound* in the blank to identify the underlined adjective in each sentence.

**EXAMPLE:** The French delegation entered the room. _____*proper*_____

1. The Maine coast is a beautiful vacation area. _____

2. He just concluded a whirlwind tour of the United States. _____

3. We needed a superhuman effort to reach the summit of the mountain. _____

4. Bob ordered a Greek salad from the menu. _____

5. Here is a short-term solution to the problem. _____

6. Your English class meets after lunch. _____

7. Following the basketball game, we went home for dinner. _____

8. In a topsy-turvy battle, we were finally declared the winners. _____

9. The Christmas celebration began early this year. _____

10. There are seventy-five students signed up for the course. _____

▶ **Exercise 2**   **Using Proper and Compound Adjectives in Sentences.**   Fill in each blank with a proper or compound adjective.

**EXAMPLE:** _____*Italian*_____ food is my favorite.

1. We took a tour of the magnificent _____ ruins.

2. They stopped at a _____ stand for lunch.

3. I expect to go out for the _____ team this fall.

4. The _____ language is difficult to learn.

5. Three people were _____ by the high temperature and smog.

## 16.1 Proper Adjectives and Compound Adjectives • Practice 2

▶ **Exercise 1** **Recognizing Proper Adjectives.** Underline the proper adjective in each of the following sentences. Then draw an arrow to the noun it modifies.

**EXAMPLE:** Do all Shakespearean sonnets have fourteen lines?

1. My sister played two Mozart symphonies.

2. The Austrian costumes at the fair were handmade.

3. The Easter holiday always reminds us of spring.

4. Has your Swiss watch been repaired?

5. A new Lincoln memorial has been dedicated in Springfield.

6. A well-known French fable was told.

7. Who would like to do a report on Elizabethan England?

8. Los Angeles smog affects the health of millions.

9. We read about the history of the American frontier.

10. I have pictures of the Mayan pyramids we visited last summer.

▶ **Exercise 2** **Recognizing Compound Adjectives.** Underline the compound adjective. Then draw an arrow to the noun it modifies.

**EXAMPLE:** After the accident, the oil-covered highway slowed traffic for hours.

1. They quickly chose the better-qualified candidate.

2. A farsighted person can usually read road signs.

3. Our hockey team scored two short-handed goals to win the game.

4. A huge hometown crowd turned out to welcome the hero.

5. Murphy likes to put on a know-it-all attitude.

6. Our teacher ordered thirty-five biology textbooks.

7. For her graduation party, my sister bought a bluish-green dress.

8. The volunteers smiled in spite of the heartbreaking news about the election.

9. The hit-and-run driver was given a heavy sentence.

10. A dark, shell-like covering protected the strange animal.

**16.1** # Possessive Adjectives • Practice 1

**Possessive Adjectives**   The following personal pronouns are often called *possessive adjectives: my, your, his, her, its, our,* and *their.* These pronouns are considered adjectives because they are used before nouns and answer the question *Which one?* They are also pronouns because they have antecedents.

| POSSESSIVE ADJECTIVES | | |
|---|---|---|
| ANTECEDENT<br>Bill took | POSSESSIVE<br>ADJECTIVE<br>*his* | NOUN<br>MODIFIED<br><u>uniform</u> to school. |
| ANTECEDENT<br>The men put | POSSESSIVE<br>ADJECTIVE<br>*their* | NOUN<br>MODIFIED<br><u>boat</u> on shore. |

▶ **Exercise 1**   **Identifying Possessive Adjectives.**   In each sentence below, underline the possessive adjective once and the noun it modifies twice. Circle the antecedent.

**EXAMPLE:** (I) am having <u>my</u> <u>tooth</u> filled tomorrow.

1. We are leaving our dog at the kennel.

2. The explorers pitched their tent in the woods.

3. On Monday, I am starting my training.

4. The crow protected its young from danger.

5. I took my parents to the play on opening night.

6. Sarah left her wallet in the car.

7. Yesterday, Bill became president of his class.

8. The general directed his men in battle.

9. They put on their costumes for Halloween.

10. You should give your suggestions to the principal.

▶ **Exercise 2**   **Using Possessive Adjectives in Sentences.**   Fill in each blank with a possessive adjective. Circle its antecedent.

**EXAMPLE:** (She) lost _____*her*_____ way in the forest.

1. Bill brought _____ parrot to class today.

2. The duck sat on _____ eggs to keep them warm.

3. We must finish _____ papers before tomorrow.

4. That old house is showing _____ age.

5. Carol took _____ sister shopping at the mall.

6. After _____ boat capsized, the boys were rescued by the Coast Guard.

7. When _____ trip to England had ended, George was sorry to leave.

8. You are responsible for keeping _____ room clean.

9. The wind was so strong that I lost _____ hat.

10. That dog is waiting for _____ dinner.

# 16.1 Possessive Adjectives • Practice 2

**Exercise 1** **Identifying Possessive Adjectives.** In each of the following sentences, a possessive adjective is underlined. Fill in the three columns below as shown in the example. Write the underlined word in the first column. Then write the noun it modifies in the second column and its antecedent in the third.

**EXAMPLE:** The puppy was chasing its tail.

| Possessive Adjective | Noun Modified | Antecedent |
|---|---|---|
| its | tail | puppy |

1. Leslie finally reached her father at work.
2. After throwing off his sunglasses, the lifeguard dived into the ocean.
3. Each year, our maple loses its leaves early in October.
4. The astronauts kept their appointment with the reporters.
5. Andrea must be ready to meet her responsibilities as a member of the family.
6. Les placed his backpack on the floor.
7. After petting her cat, Andrea took the dog for a walk.
8. Last summer, the Andersons spent two weeks at their cabin.
9. Homer cleaned his room in less than an hour.
10. The car is in good shape, but its tires need to be replaced.

| Possessive Adjective | Noun Modified | Antecedent |
|---|---|---|
| 1. _____ | _____ | _____ |
| 2. _____ | _____ | _____ |
| 3. _____ | _____ | _____ |
| 4. _____ | _____ | _____ |
| 5. _____ | _____ | _____ |
| 6. _____ | _____ | _____ |
| 7. _____ | _____ | _____ |
| 8. _____ | _____ | _____ |
| 9. _____ | _____ | _____ |
| 10. _____ | _____ | _____ |

**Exercise 2** **Using Possessive Adjectives.** Fill in the blank in each sentence with an appropriate possessive adjective.

**EXAMPLE:** Dina was learning how to tie her shoelaces.

1. Is this _____ favorite restaurant?
2. For _____ birthday, Jan wanted to go to an amusement park.
3. I thought _____ essay was very interesting.
4. The young ballerina's toes hurt after _____ ballet class.
5. Before giving _____ speech, Raymond was very nervous.

Name _____ Date _____

 **16.1** # Demonstrative and Interrogative
# Adjectives • Practice 1

**Demonstrative Adjectives**  The four demonstrative pronouns, *this, that, these,* and *those,* are often used as demonstrative adjectives.

| DEMONSTRATIVE ADJECTIVES | |
| --- | --- |
| *Pronoun:* We bought *that.* | *Pronoun:* He planted *those.* |
| *Adjective:* We bought *that* shirt. | *Adjective:* He planted *those* seeds. |

**Interrogative Adjectives**  *Which, what,* and *whose* can be used as adjectives.

| INTERROGATIVE ADJECTIVES | |
| --- | --- |
| *Pronoun:* *Which* will she want? | *Pronoun:* *Whose* is it? |
| *Adjective:* *Which* toy will she want? | *Adjective:* *Whose* book is it? |

▶ **Exercise 1**  **Recognizing Demonstrative Pronouns and Adjectives.**  Circle *this, that, these,* or *those* in each sentence. On each line at the right, tell whether the word is used as a *pronoun* or an *adjective.*

**EXAMPLE:**  Let's move (this) chair into your room. ____*adjective*____

1. These are the best ice skates I have ever owned. _____

2. Betsy chose this topic for her speech. _____

3. These trees must be one hundred years old. _____

4. This is going to be a beautiful day. _____

5. If we score this goal, we will win. _____

6. Winslow Homer painted these. _____

7. These designs were created by Leonardo da Vinci. _____

8. This year my birthday falls on Saturday. _____

9. I never thought of that. _____

10. That chair is too big for the room. _____

▶ **Exercise 2**  **Identifying Interrogative Pronouns and Adjectives.**  Circle the word *which, what,* or *whose* in each sentence. If it is used as a *pronoun,* write pronoun after it. If it is used as an *adjective,* write the noun it modifies after it.

**EXAMPLE:**  (Which) pen did you buy? ____*pen*____

1. Which way is it? _____

2. What kind of model did you build? _____

3. Whose hairdryer are you using? _____

4. Which novel did you enjoy best? _____

5. What have you planned for your vacation? _____

6. Which test was the hardest for you? _____

7. Whose play are you rehearsing? _____

8. What vegetable would you like for dinner? _____

9. Which of the children went to the party? _____

10. What happened in the world today? _____

## 16.1 Demonstrative and Interrogative Adjectives • Practice 2

▶ **Exercise 1**  **Recognizing Demonstrative Adjectives.**   Underline the word *this*, *that*, *these*, or *those* in the following sentences. If it is used as a pronoun, write *pronoun* after it. If it is used as an adjective, write the noun it modifies after it.

**EXAMPLE:** I read this last year. _____*pronoun*_____

1. Those bracelets are very expensive. _____
2. Can you imagine that? _____
3. I know this tunnel leads to daylight. _____
4. She found that novel hard to follow. _____
5. If you wish, you may have those. _____

▶ **Exercise 2**  **Recognizing Interrogative Adjectives.**   Underline the word *which*, *what*, or *whose* in each of the following sentences. If it is used as a pronoun, write *pronoun* after it. If it is used as an adjective, write the noun it modifies after it.

**EXAMPLE:** What do you want? _____*pronoun*_____

1. Which blouse did Connie finally buy? _____
2. What is his explanation for the mistake? _____
3. Whose mother will drive us to the game? _____
4. Which of us will pick up the speaker? _____
5. What kind of restaurant do you prefer? _____

▶ **Writing Application**  **Writing Sentences with Pronouns Used as Adjectives.**   Write ten sentences of your own, each using one of the following words to modify a noun. Draw an arrow pointing from each adjective to the word it modifies.

**EXAMPLE:** whose

Whose shoes are these on the steps? _____

1. what _____
2. her _____
3. that _____
4. our _____
5. these _____
6. which _____
7. their _____
8. this _____
9. his _____
10. my _____

# 16.2 Adverbs • Practice 1

**Adverbs That Modify Verbs**  An adverb modifies a verb, an adjective, or another adverb. An adverb that modifies a verb will answer one of these four questions: *Where? When? In what manner? To what extent?*

| ADVERBS THAT MODIFY VERBS | | |
|---|---|---|
| **Where?** | walked *away* | went *inside* |
| **When?** | went *today* | travels *seldom* |
| **In What Manner?** | works *carelessly* | runs *swiftly* |
| **To What Extent?** | *thoroughly* finished | *hardly* begun |

▶ **Exercise 1**  **Recognizing Adverbs That Modify Verbs.**  In each sentence, underline the adverb that modifies a verb. On each line at the right, write the question the adverb answers.

**EXAMPLE:** We never walk to school. ____*When?*____

1. She ran rapidly around the track. _____
2. I began my piano lessons reluctantly. _____
3. I had barely started eating when we had to leave. _____
4. The new building was completely destroyed by fire. _____
5. I have seldom heard such noise. _____
6. This summer we went to the shore frequently. _____
7. Slowly, he climbed the ladder. _____
8. They met outside. _____
9. The large dog climbed into its bed clumsily. _____
10. I was really surprised by the party you had arranged for me. _____

▶ **Exercise 2**  **Adding Adverbs to Modify Verbs.**  Fill in the blank in each sentence below with an appropriate adverb.

**EXAMPLE:** She ____*never*____ finishes her work on time.

1. The train rolled _____ down the track.
2. My uncle travels _____ to Europe.
3. Give me that pen _____.
4. The magazine arrives _____ at our house.
5. We had _____ finished painting the room by five o'clock.
6. Let's go _____ and talk about your ideas.
7. That quarterback _____ fumbles the ball.
8. The sun shone _____ on the painted desert.
9. The newspaper is printed _____ throughout the year.
10. They paddled their canoe _____ along the swollen stream.

## 16.2 Adverbs • Practice 2

**Exercise 1** **Identifying How Adverbs Modify Verbs.** Decide which question each of the underlined adverbs answers. Write each adverb in the appropriate column below.

**EXAMPLE:** Sally <u>carefully</u> wrapped the present.

| Where? | When? | In What Manner? | To What Extent? |
|--------|-------|-----------------|-----------------|
|        |       | carefully       |                 |

1. They went through the motions <u>mechanically</u>.
2. In the confusion, she <u>nearly</u> injured herself.
3. With much preparation, they <u>eventually</u> left.
4. The applause ended, and the star <u>finally</u> appeared.
5. Six volunteers worked <u>cautiously</u> to free the child.
6. My aunt arrived <u>yesterday</u> from Washington.
7. Another skyscraper is being erected <u>nearby</u>.
8. Everyone on the team <u>now</u> practices diving.
9. After his long trip, Father was <u>scarcely</u> tired.
10. At the wedding, people gathered <u>happily</u> around the bride.

| Where? | When? | In What Manner? | To What Extent? |
|--------|-------|-----------------|-----------------|
| _____ | _____ | _____ | _____ |
| _____ | _____ | _____ | _____ |
| _____ | _____ | _____ | _____ |
| _____ | _____ | _____ | _____ |

**Exercise 2** **Using Adverbs.** Fill in the blank in each sentence with an appropriate adverb that answers the given question in parentheses.

**EXAMPLE:** Dylan got to his appointment ____early____. (When?)

1. Camille treated _____ everyone she met. (In what manner?)
2. We waited for the train, which was _____ late. (To what extent?)
3. Stella is a _____ good basketball coach. (To what extent?)
4. Please stop talking _____. (When?)
5. It is against the rules to dance _____. (Where?)
6. We were _____ satisfied with the outcome of the game. (To what extent?)
7. The fans seemed _____ excited at that play. (To what extent?)
8. The detective looked _____ at the suspect. (In what manner?)
9. The dog barked _____ when he saw the cat. (In what manner?)
10. _____ we looked, we saw happy faces. (Where?)
11. Dianne will visit you _____, after the others have gone. (When?)
12. A new school is being built _____. (Where?)
13. The ice cream truck should be coming _____. (When?)
14. Bob spread the jam _____ on the toast. (In what manner?)
15. The game will start _____. (When?)

Name _____    Date _____

 **16.2** # Adverbs • Practice 1

**Adverbs That Modify Adjectives**   An adverb modifying an adjective answers only one question. *To what extent?*

| ADVERBS THAT MODIFY ADJECTIVES | |
|---|---|
| *very* happy | *completely* wrong |
| *too* close | *not* tired |

**Adverbs That Modify Other Adverbs**   An adverb modifying another adverb also answers just one question. *To what extent?*

| ADVERBS THAT MODIFY ADVERBS | |
|---|---|
| slept *very* soundly | spoke *quite* loudly |
| arrived *too* early | won *rather* easily |

▶ **Exercise 1**   **Recognizing the Words Adverbs Modify.**   Circle the word each underlined adverb modifies. On each blank write whether the circled word is an adjective or another adverb.

**EXAMPLE:** Rain fell very (heavily) for an hour. ____*adverb*____

1. His escape was too close for comfort. _____

2. I am very sorry about missing your party. _____

3. The tiger leaped extremely high. _____

4. The walls of the castle were so strong that no one could break through them. _____

5. The baby played rather quietly in her crib. _____

6. This engine seems rather noisy to me. _____

7. The cat crept very softly toward its prey. _____

8. We hardly ever eat lunch before 1:00 P.M. _____

9. I am playing tennis more often these days. _____

10. Carol seems less afraid of snakes now that she has read about them. _____

▶ **Exercise 2**   **Using Adverbs in Sentences.**   Fill in each blank with an appropriate adverb that answers the question *To what extent?*

**EXAMPLE:** I visit my uncle ___*very*___ frequently.

1. The town will start building the new park _____ soon.

2. Everyone seemed _____ upset by the coach's announcement.

3. You are spending _____ too much money on clothing.

4. _____ enough people have signed up for the baseball game.

5. They carried the priceless glass vase _____ carefully.

6. We arrived at the airport _____ late to catch our plane.

7. Gerald has a _____ good chance to win.

8. This year's play was _____ successful than last year's performance.

9. She skied _____ well for a beginner.

10. Will we arrive _____ soon?

## 16.2 Adverbs • Practice 2

▶ **Exercise 1** **Recognizing Adverbs That Modify Adjectives.** Underline the adverb in each of the following sentences. Then write the adjective the adverb modifies.

**EXAMPLE:** Sean was <u>almost</u> late for his dental appointment. _____*late*_____

1. The afternoon sun was unusually pleasant. _____
2. We heard a very loud knock on the back door. _____
3. He was too short for the role. _____
4. The author was extremely upset by the poor sales of her book. _____
5. The owner of the store has been seriously ill for some time. _____
6. This fruit salad is quite tart. _____
7. The defendant was absolutely still as the foreman of the jury rose. _____
8. She is thoroughly adept at walking the high wire. _____
9. In his prediction my father was almost right. _____
10. In spite of her defeat, she was not sad at all. _____

▶ **Exercise 2** **Recognizing Adverbs That Modify Other Adverbs.** In each of the following sentences, underline the adverb that modifies another adverb by answering the question *To what extent?* Then draw an arrow from the underlined adverb to the adverb it modifies.

**EXAMPLE:** The French visitors spoke <u>too</u> rapidly for me to understand them.

1. Time passed too slowly for the eager contestants.
2. Almost happily, the owner handed us the car keys.
3. The visitors were unusually well received by the mayor.
4. He was quite easily talked into changing his mind.
5. Debbie argued less loudly once she realized her error.
6. The movie ended rather suddenly.
7. The guest of honor arrived slightly late for the dinner.
8. This ring is entirely too expensive.
9. After receiving a ticket, my brother drove more slowly.
10. Do you promise to visit us relatively soon?

Name _____ Date _____

 **16.2** # Adverbs Used in Sentences • Practice 1

**Finding Adverbs in Sentences**  Some of the many possible locations of adverbs in sentences are shown in this chart.

| LOCATION OF ADVERBS IN SENTENCES |
|---|
| *At the Beginning of a Sentence:* Slowly, she walked away. |
| *At the End of a Sentence:* She walked away *slowly*. |
| *Before a Verb:* She *slowly* walked toward the door. |
| *After a Verb:* She walked *slowly* away. |
| *Before an Adjective:* I had a *very* slow start. |
| *Before another Adverb:* She walked *very* slowly. |

**Adverb or Adjective?**  Some words can be either adverbs or adjectives, depending on the word modified.

| ADVERB OR ADJECTIVE |
|---|
| *Adverb Modifying Verb:* He jumps *high*. |
| *Adjective Modifying Noun:* This is a *high* jump. |
| *Adverb Modifying Adjective:* It is *unusually* hot. |

▶ **Exercise 1**  **Distinguishing Between Adverbs and Adjectives.**  Write whether the underlined word in each sentence is an *adverb* or an *adjective*.

**EXAMPLE:** She appears <u>confused</u> by the instructions.  ___*adjective*___

1. This problem looks <u>easy</u> to me. _____

2. Karen completed the experiment <u>easily</u>. _____

3. I enjoy reading the <u>weekly</u> news magazine. _____

4. We were <u>hardly</u> surprised by the election results. _____

5. He dove <u>perfectly</u> off the board. _____

6. Mr. Henderson seems <u>uniquely</u> qualified for the job. _____

7. Carol always has a <u>friendly</u> smile for everyone. _____

8. The <u>second</u> act was the best part of the play. _____

9. I stooped <u>low</u> and picked up the napkin. _____

10. Bill has a very <u>low</u> opinion of himself. _____

▶ **Exercise 2**  **Using Adverbs and Adjectives in Sentences.**  Write an appropriate *adjective* or *adverb* in each blank.

**EXAMPLE:** The baby crawled ___*slowly*___ around its playpen.

1. Vincent performed _____ at his swim meet.

2. She won her _____ blue ribbon at the horse show.

3. Mom drove us _____ home from school.

4. We enjoyed a _____ ride in her motor boat.

5. The _____ scheduled train is not running today.

6. They _____ eat lunch at a fancy restaurant.

7. With _____ planning, we will succeed.

8. She dribbled the ball _____ past her opponents.

9. Who painted those _____ pictures?

10. This author _____ writes about modern America.

## 16.2 Adverbs Used in Sentences • Practice 2

**Exercise 1**  **Locating Adverbs in Sentences.**  Each of the following sentences contains one or two adverbs. Underline each adverb. Then draw arrows pointing from the adverbs to the words they modify.

**EXAMPLE:** She has never forgotten his consistently smiling face.

1. From 1831 to 1836, Charles Darwin sailed slowly from one part of the world to another.
2. The timid dog seldom approached strangers.
3. The chef had deliberately told us to let the soup cook.
4. On Tuesday, Marie was rather sad.
5. He rather vaguely explained his reasons for leaving.
6. Cautiously, the veterinarian edged toward the huge goat on the table.
7. She has almost completed the first act of her play.
8. In *Great Expectations*, Estella often teases Pip.
9. In anger, he totally stopped trying.
10. American farmers efficiently produce a variety of fruits and vegetables.

**Exercise 2**  **Distinguishing Between Adverbs and Adjectives.**  In the space provided, indicate whether the underlined word in each of the following sentences is an *adverb* or an *adjective*.

**EXAMPLE:** This is your last chance.  _____adjective_____

1. I am certain you have made a timely choice. _____
2. In folklore, a goblin is generally a homely character. _____
3. A new model was recently delivered. _____
4. Daily exercise is part of a good health program. _____
5. This was the actor's first appearance. _____
6. I finished early in the day. _____
7. After the play, she received a dozen lovely roses. _____
8. Most of all I remember his kindly way. _____
9. The leader feels she is only partly responsible for our getting lost. _____
10. Carlene runs in the park daily. _____

# 17.1 Prepositions • Practice 1

**Recognizing Prepositions**  A preposition relates the noun or pronoun following it to another word in the sentence. Prepositions of more than one word are compound prepositions.

| COMMON PREPOSITIONS | | | | |
|---|---|---|---|---|
| about | behind | during | in | to |
| above | below | except | of | under |
| across | beneath | for | over | up |
| after | beside | from | through | with |

| COMPOUND PREPOSITIONS | | |
|---|---|---|
| according to | by means of | instead of |
| ahead of | in addition to | next to |
| aside from | in back of | on account of |
| as of | in front of | on top of |
| because of | in place of | out of |

▶ **Exercise 1**  **Identifying Prepositions.**  Underline each preposition in these sentences.

**EXAMPLE:** He brought his lunch with him.

1. Above the blue sky is a dark universe.
2. "Can you take us across the river?" we asked.
3. Many animals live beneath the sea.
4. During our last visit, there was a hurricane.
5. We strung our hammock under the oak tree.
6. A large piano stood inside the music room.
7. The explorers knew their destination lay over the horizon.
8. Construction will begin within six months.
9. They arose and broke camp before dawn.
10. Underneath the ground was the chipmunk's burrow.

▶ **Exercise 2**  **Using Prepositions in Sentences.**  Fill in each blank with an appropriate preposition or compound preposition.

**EXAMPLE:** She ran _____out of_____ the room.

1. I would like corn _____ lima beans.
2. Bill poured the milk _____ the large pitcher.
3. Our trip is running _____ schedule.
4. _____ the house stands a huge maple tree.
5. Let's hold our meeting _____ lunch.
6. I will be waiting _____ the clock tower.
7. _____ the snowstorm, the game was canceled.
8. Anne left her coat _____ her locker.
9. _____ our solar system are billions of stars.
10. He passed the test _____ hard work.

## 17.1 Prepositions • Practice 2

> **Exercise 1**  **Recognizing Prepositions.**  Underline the preposition in each of the following sentences. Then rewrite the sentence using a different preposition.

**EXAMPLE:** My sister walked <u>near</u> the park. _____My sister walked into the park.____

1. The ticket holders waited patiently outside the theater.

   _____

2. A new dining room was built beside the old one.

   _____

3. The telephone book is under the table.

   _____

4. She placed the flower pots along the windowsill.

   _____

5. How did you get through the traffic jam?

   _____

6. The stamp show begins during winter vacation.

   _____

7. A housing development has been built across the river.

   _____

8. Let's pick the strawberries near the fence.

   _____

9. The doctor's office is around the corner.

   _____

10. Opposite the old statue, you will see the library.

    _____

> **Exercise 2**  **Recognizing Compound Prepositions.**  Underline the compound preposition in each of the following sentences. Then rewrite the sentence using a different one-word or compound preposition.

**EXAMPLE:** The ski chalet is <u>on top of</u> the mountain. _____The ski chalet is on the mountain.____

1. The broken lawnmower is in back of the barn.

   _____

2. In front of the entrance is a large warning notice.

   _____

3. The new highway passes next to the foothills.

   _____

4. In addition to the application, you must include a reference.

   _____

5. A very slow bus was ahead of our car.

   _____

**17.2** # Prepositions Used in Sentences • Practice 1

**Prepositional Phrases**   A prepositional phrase is a group of words that begins with a preposition and ends with a noun or pronoun, called the object of the preposition.

| PREPOSITIONAL PHRASES | |
|---|---|
| **Prepositions** | **Objects of Prepositions** |
| at | home |
| before | dinner |
| beyond | the *horizon* |
| inside | the haunted *house* |
| according to | the *rules* |
| on top of | the misty *mountain* |

**Preposition or Adverb?**   Some words can be used as either prepositions or adverbs. A preposition begins a prepositional phrase and has an object. Adverbs do not.

| Adverbs | Prepositions |
|---|---|
| The dog stayed *behind*. | The dog stayed *behind* the house. |
| An animal hid *inside*. | An animal hid *inside* the barn. |

▶ **Exercise 1**   **Identifying Prepositional Phrases.**   Underline each *preposition* and circle its *object*.

**EXAMPLE:** He searched <u>among</u> the (bushes) .

1. Let's put the lamp next to the table.
2. Susan is singing tonight in place of Martha.
3. John can run the mile in record time.
4. The next restaurant is just around the corner.
5. The package will not arrive until tomorrow.
6. The bus is expected within an hour.
7. Because of our excellent pitching, we have a winning season.
8. He moved quickly toward the open door.
9. Since our last meeting, many things have happened.
10. A large cat sunned itself outside the window.

▶ **Exercise 2**   **Distinguishing Between Prepositions and Adverbs.**   On the line at the right, write whether the underlined word is an *adverb* or a *preposition*.

**EXAMPLE:** We moved the lawn chairs <u>inside</u>.   *adverb*

1. Leave your books <u>behind</u> the desk. _____
2. Leave your books <u>behind</u>. _____
3. We finished our work and went <u>outside</u>. _____
4. <u>Outside</u> the house, the flowers were in full bloom. _____
5. We expected his answer <u>before</u> noon. _____
6. I wanted to speak to you <u>before</u>, but there wasn't time. _____
7. I poked my head up and looked <u>around</u>. _____
8. <u>Around</u> 6:00 P.M., we'll begin to eat. _____
9. He saw an Easter egg <u>underneath</u> the bushes. _____
10. To repair the hole in the bridge, we'll have to climb <u>underneath</u>. _____

# 17.2 Prepositions Used in Sentences • Practice 2

▶ **Exercise 1** **Identifying Prepositional Phrases.** A prepositional phrase appears in each of the following sentences. Underline the preposition and circle the object of the preposition.

**EXAMPLE:** The pigeon cage is <u>on</u> the (roof).

1. What do you expect to buy in the village?
2. The climbing party approached the Rockies by means of the Platte River.
3. This novel is a romantic tale of the Old South.
4. In the morning the cattle train continued its journey.
5. The trunk in the attic contains Grandma's old dresses.
6. Behind the door is the boiler room.
7. The sailboat turned and headed into the sun.
8. Between us, Glenn and I finished the apple pie.
9. The children were riding on top of a tired, old donkey.
10. The newspaper reporter stationed herself in front of the grandstand.

▶ **Exercise 2** **Distinguishing Between Prepositions and Adverbs.** In each pair of sentences, one sentence contains a word used as a preposition; the other sentence contains the same word used as an adverb. Find the word that appears in both sentences. If the word acts as a preposition, write the prepositional phrase. If the word acts as an adverb, write *adverb*.

**EXAMPLE:** The gas station is down the road. _____*down the road*_____

She examined the vase and then put it down. _____*down* adverb_____

1. Aunt Stacy told us about her army experiences. _____

Tired as he was, he walked about for a few more minutes. _____

2. She tried to call us before, but couldn't get us. _____

He runs several miles each morning before breakfast. _____

3. The rowboat was found underneath the bridge. _____

To repair the car, they crawled underneath. _____

4. "Come along," said my aunt. _____

The surveyors walked along the creek. _____

5. Deer will sometimes come near. _____

Near the old library is a Civil War statue. _____

▶ **Writing Application** **Writing Sentences with Prepositional Phrases.** Write a sentence using each preposition. Underline the preposition and circle the object.

**EXAMPLE:** inside _____*I searched <u>inside</u> my (closet) to find my favorite sweater.*_____

1. above _____

2. after _____

3. beside _____

4. during _____

5. from _____

**18.1** # Conjunctions • **Practice 1**

**Coordinating Conjunctions**  A conjunction connects words or groups of words. Coordinating conjunctions connect words or groups of words that are similar: two or more nouns, two or more verbs, two or more prepositional phrases, or even entire sentences.

| COORDINATING CONJUNCTIONS | | | |
|---|---|---|---|
| and | for | or | yet |
| but | nor | so | |

**Correlative Conjunctions**  Correlative conjunctions always come in pairs and, like coordinating conjunctions, connect similar kinds of words or groups of words.

| CORRELATIVE CONJUNCTIONS | |
|---|---|
| both ... and | not only ... but also |
| either ... or | whether ... or |
| neither ... nor | |

▷ **Exercise 1**  **Identifying Conjunctions.**  Underline the conjunctions in the sentences below. In the blank, write whether the conjunction is coordinating or correlative.

**EXAMPLE:** My brother and I are twins.  ___coordinating___

1. The novel was long, but very interesting. _____
2. Neither the living room nor the dining room needs painting. _____
3. You can reach me at home or at my office. _____
4. Both the band and the choir are performing out of town. _____
5. The man had a scarred yet appealing face. _____
6. I want to go swimming, but I have to work. _____
7. Whether we win or lose depends on you. _____
8. He saw neither his mother nor his father in the grandstands. _____
9. Not only is our street the longest in town, but it is also the most beautiful. _____
10. I am studying and do not wish to be disturbed. _____

▷ **Exercise 2**  **Using Conjunctions in Sentences.**  Fill in each blank with an appropriate conjunction.

**EXAMPLE:** He left after school ___and___ went home.

1. I enjoy English _____ math is very difficult.
2. _____ the kitchen _____ the family room has been cleaned.
3. The tulips in the garden were red _____ purple.
4. I want to join the Drama Club _____ the band this year.
5. _____ we change our strategy _____ we will lose the game.
6. _____ my brother _____ my sister have red hair.
7. The fighter was beaten _____ still proud.
8. I will not be at work today _____ I have to be out of town.
9. A kite _____ a record would be a nice present.
10. I wonder _____ blue _____ green is the best color for our house.

## 18.1 Conjunctions • Practice 2

▶ **Exercise 1**  **Recognizing Coordinating Conjunctions.**  Circle the coordinating conjunction in each of the following sentences. Then underline the word or group of words connected by the conjunction.

**EXAMPLE:** He likes to draw pictures of lions (and) tigers.

1. Andrew and Jane live far apart.
2. I have to take my medicine before breakfast or before dinner.
3. What is the connection between lightning and thunder?
4. My family is looking for a large yet inexpensive house.
5. I will be late getting home, for I have to make several stops.
6. Wind and rain lashed the Florida coastline.
7. I would like to bake cookies, but I am missing a few ingredients.
8. In the morning and in the evening, traffic backs up at this light.
9. The dancer was thin but strong.
10. You have a choice of cotton, wool, or polyester.

▶ **Exercise 2**  **Recognizing Correlative Conjunctions.**  Circle the correlative conjunction in each of the following sentences. Then underline the two words or groups of words connected by the conjunction.

**EXAMPLE:** He lost (not only) his watch (but also) his wallet.

1. She will pay her tuition either by check or by money order.
2. Both Anne and Barbara volunteered to decorate the hall.
3. I will either buy or make her birthday card.
4. Not only were the rebels short on men, but they were also short on supplies.
5. She asked whether football or baseball was my favorite sport.
6. Neither flowers nor candy seems an appropriate gift.
7. The girls invited both Manuel and Pat to the dance.
8. Not only will they attend, but they will also bring five guests.
9. We expect them either in the evening or in the early morning hours.
10. That afternoon Robert was neither swimming nor diving.

▶ **Exercise 3**  **Writing Sentences Using Conjunctions.**  Complete each sentence, keeping the conjunctions in the positions shown.

**EXAMPLE:** I will be here whether ____*you win*____ or ____*you lose*____ .

1. Either _____ or _____ .
2. I wonder whether _____ or _____ .
3. Not only _____ , but _____ also _____ .
4. Yesterday, _____ and _____ .
5. Neither _____ nor _____ .

# 18.2 Interjections • Practice 1

**Recognizing Interjections**  An interjection expresses feeling or emotion.

| Interjection | Emotion |
|---|---|
| oh, good heavens | surprise |
| aw, darn, oh, no | disappointment |
| ouch | pain |
| wow, goodness | joy |
| uh | hesitation |
| tsk | impatience |

**Exercise 1**   **Using Interjections.**   In each blank, write an appropriate interjection for the feeling shown in parentheses.

**EXAMPLE:**  (Pain)! That really hurts.  _____Ouch_____

1. (Surprise), I didn't expect to see you here. _____

2. (Impatience), I wish you'd hurry up. _____

3. (Hesitation), I don't know the answer. _____

4. (Joy)! What a great present. _____

5. (Pain)! I cut my finger. _____

6. (Surprise)! We won the game. _____

7. (Hesitation), I don't know which way to go. _____

8. (Joy), that was a terrific movie. _____

9. (Pain), I bumped my head. _____

10. (Disappointment), we're late again. _____

**Exercise 2**   **Adding Interjections to Sentences.**   Fill in each blank with an appropriate interjection. Use commas or exclamation marks as punctuation.

**EXAMPLE:**  _____Wow!_____  We had a fabulous trip.

1. I can't figure out, _____, where we are.

2. _____ I just banged my knee.

3. _____ I didn't think the paper was due today.

4. _____ I can't wait all day.

5. _____ The picnic has been rained out again.

6. _____ That's the biggest balloon I've ever seen.

7. _____ I'm so happy you're here for a visit.

8. _____ That was a close call.

9. _____ There isn't enough snow to go skiing.

10. _____ You must be kidding.

# 18.2 Interjections • Practice 2

**▶ Exercise 1** **Recognizing Interjections.** Rewrite each of the following sentences using an appropriate interjection in place of the feeling shown in parentheses.

**EXAMPLE:** ____(Disappointment)____, we lost again.
           _Aw, we lost again._

1. ____(Joy)!____ I'm so glad you're here.

   _____

2. ____(Impatience)____, you're never ready on time.

   _____

3. ____(Pain)!____ Does that sting.

   _____

4. ____(Hesitation)____, I don't know what to say.

   _____

5. ____(Surprise)____, I can't believe you said that.

   _____

**▶ Writing Application** **Using Interjections in Sentences.** Write five sentences of your own, each using one of the following interjections. Use commas or exclamation marks as punctuation.

**EXAMPLE:** darn
           _Darn! It's been raining ever since we arrived._

1. whew _____

   _____

2. good grief _____

   _____

3. well _____

   _____

4. ouch _____

   _____

5. oh _____

   _____

# 19.1 The Basic Sentence • Practice 1

**The Two Basic Parts of a Sentence**   A sentence must contain a subject and a verb. The subject is the word or group of words that answers the question *Who?* or *What?* before the verb. The verb tells what the subject does, what is done to the subject, or the condition of the subject.

| Subject | Verb |
|---------|------|
| Dorothy | dove off the board. |
| The truck | was hit by a snowball. |
| He | looks bored. |

**Using Subjects and Verbs to Express Complete Thoughts**   A group of words expresses a complete thought if it has a subject and verb, can stand by itself, and make sense.

| Incomplete Thoughts | Complete Thoughts |
|---------------------|-------------------|
| | S           V |
| the deer on the hill | The *deer is climbing* the hill. |
| | S   V |
| was beautiful at sunset | The *sky was* beautiful at sunset. |

▶ **Exercise 1**   **Identifying Subjects and Verbs.**   In each of the following sentences, underline the subject once and the verb twice.

**EXAMPLE:** The sailors boarded the ship.

1. Shakespeare wrote the play *Macbeth.*
2. We saw the Lincoln Memorial in Washington.
3. Bob sang a solo in the Christmas pageant.
4. The dog looks very old and tired.
5. Doves flew over the city.
6. They are skating at the indoor rink.
7. The building was destroyed in the earthquake.
8. That quarterback is being tackled from behind.
9. An unexpected visitor delayed our departure.
10. This salad was made with vegetables from my garden.

▶ **Exercise 2**   **Recognizing Sentences.**   Read the items below. If the item is a sentence, write *sentence* in the blank. If the item is an incomplete thought, write *incomplete* in the blank.

**EXAMPLE:** The long day's march. _____*incomplete*_____

1. We ate lunch along a cool stream. _____
2. Vincent painted that mural on the wall. _____
3. Our new library with so many books. _____
4. Walked in the door one hour late. _____
5. I miss my old job at the restaurant. _____
6. A large red fox with its young. _____
7. Dana mailed another letter to her pen pal. _____
8. Slid into third base ahead of the throw. _____
9. A day sunbathing on the beach. _____
10. They went swimming along the reef. _____

## 19.1 The Basic Sentence • Practice 2

▶ **Exercise 1**  **Recognizing Subjects and Verbs.**  Underline the subject once and the verb twice in each of the following sentences.

**EXAMPLE:** The new <u>antenna</u> <u><u>gives</u></u> us better reception.

1. Our school offers a recreation program.
2. An eagle soared above the valley at dusk.
3. My old hammer disappeared from the drawer.
4. We visited Fisherman's Wharf in San Francisco.
5. Her sunburn caused her great discomfort.
6. The Parthenon is being eroded by air pollution.
7. The antique train chugged along the track.
8. Rossini wrote the opera *William Tell.*
9. This yellow ribbon comes in three widths.
10. The farmhouse is built entirely of stone.

▶ **Exercise 2**  **Recognizing Sentences.**  If a group of words is a sentence, write *sentence*. If a group of words expresses an incomplete thought, add words to make a sentence. Then underline the subject once and the verb twice in each new sentence.

**EXAMPLE:**  A single rose on the bush.    *A single <u>rose</u> <u><u>bloomed</u></u> on the bush.*

1. Rain pelted the travelers.

   _____

2. The pastry shop in town.

   _____

3. The new coach of the basketball team.

   _____

4. Stood at the top of the stairs.

   _____

5. The girl in the yellow dress.

   _____

6. Grew in the desert.

   _____

7. Two visitors from Hartford.

   _____

8. Between you and me.

   _____

9. Decided to stay in the park.

   _____

10. Music is my only hobby.

   _____

# 19.2 Complete Subjects and Predicates
## • Practice 1

**Recognizing Complete Subjects and Predicates**  The complete subject of a sentence consists of the subject and any words related to it. The complete predicate of a sentence consists of the verb and any words related to it.

| Complete Subjects | Complete Predicates |
|---|---|
| Mark Twain | worked on a riverboat. |
| The large, shiny car | rounded the bend in the road. |
| All the members of the family | ate dinner. |
| Carol | slept. |

**Exercise 1**  **Identifying Complete Subjects and Predicates.**  In the following sentences, underline the complete subject once and the complete predicate twice.

**EXAMPLE:**  Our school newspaper won a prize in the contest.

1. We are learning about careers in forestry.
2. Roger's room was filled with miniature soldiers.
3. The dentist worked in his office all day.
4. Bill created crossword puzzles for the newspaper.
5. The temperature hit 100°F on that July day.
6. We were given a tour of the museum.
7. The elephants in the circus are well trained.
8. You will find our house on Main Street.
9. The aquarium was filled with fish.
10. My favorite restaurant is going to close.

**Exercise 2**  **Adding Parts to Sentences.**  Each item below is missing either a complete subject or a complete predicate. Add the missing part on the line to create a complete sentence.

**EXAMPLE:**  Boats of all sizes _____ *could be seen in the harbor* _____.

1. The old, wooden fort _____.
2. _____ washed up along the beach.
3. Two tiny sparrows _____.
4. A loud cheer _____.
5. _____ had almost reached the finish line.
6. _____ let out a piercing yell.
7. A man with a crooked nose _____.
8. The golden retriever's puppies _____.
9. _____ moved through the crowd toward the podium.
10. A tall, mysterious woman _____.

# 19.2 Complete Subjects and Predicates
## • Practice 2

**Exercise 1** **Recognizing Complete Subjects and Predicates.**   Underline the subject once and the verb twice in each of the following sentences. Then draw a vertical line between the complete subject and the complete predicate.

**EXAMPLE:** The <u>player</u> with the red hat | <u>is</u> the captain.

1. A tall stranger appeared on the stage.
2. This painting by Velázquez is extremely valuable.
3. The ship's watertight doors close automatically.
4. The smiling governor shook hands with all her guests.
5. Fire spread through the entire forest.
6. The people in the stands and on the field applauded loudly.
7. Our newly elected mayor took the oath of office.
8. This small engraving is a masterpiece of its type.
9. Costa Brava is an area of seaside resorts in Spain.
10. The fresh vegetables cooked rapidly in the wok.

**Writing Application**   **Developing Complete Subjects and Predicates.**   The first word in each item is a noun or pronoun that can be used as a subject. The second word is a verb. Develop each item into a complete subject and predicate by adding details to the subject and verb.

**EXAMPLE:**  storm swept
_____ *A violent storm swept across the lake.* _____

1. story begins

   _____

   _____

2. path leads

   _____

   _____

3. bus rumbled

   _____

   _____

4. each is

   _____

   _____

5. sister decided

   _____

   _____

# 19.3 Compound Subjects and Compound Verbs • Practice 1

**Compound Subjects**   A compound subject is two or more subjects that have the same verb and are joined by a conjunction such as *and* or *or*.

| COMPOUND SUBJECTS |
|---|
| Pines and spruces are both evergreen trees. |
| Clothes or records make perfect gifts. |

**Compound Verbs**   A compound verb is two or more verbs that have the same subject and are joined by a conjunction such as *and* or *or*.

| COMPOUND VERBS |
|---|
| Jill wrote and performed her own music. |
| He will play golf or jog on Saturday. |

▶ **Exercise 1**   **Identifying Compound Subjects.**   Underline each compound subject in these sentences.

**EXAMPLE:** Pam and Kathy have a birthday next week.

1. The house and the barn were painted red.
2. Lemons, limes, and oranges are citrus fruits.
3. On Saturday afternoon, my sister and I visited the zoo.
4. Paintings and sculpture can be found in the museum.
5. My mother or father will take me to the game.
6. Jewelry and pottery were on sale at the bazaar.
7. Cows and horses grazed on the hillsides.
8. During the storm, lightning, thunder, and heavy rains occurred.
9. July or August is a perfect month for a vacation at the shore.
10. Washington and Oregon are states located in the northwest.

▶ **Exercise 2**   **Recognizing Compound Verbs.**   Circle the compound verbs in the sentences below.

**EXAMPLE:** We (danced) and (sang) at the party.

1. The quarterback will run or will pass on the play.
2. She sat on the couch and read her history assignment.
3. The sun rose and shone brightly over the countryside.
4. I ate a sandwich and drank a glass of milk for lunch.
5. We wrote a script and took pictures for our own slide presentation.
6. Bill coached the team and played in the outfield.
7. We mowed the lawn, pruned the bushes, and cleaned the garage before dinner.
8. Tomorrow I will go downtown and buy a new coat.
9. The kite twisted and turned in the wind.
10. You will be surprised and may be pleased by my news.

# 19.3 Compound Subjects and Compound Verbs • Practice 2

**Exercise 1**  **Recognizing Compound Subjects.**   Each sentence contains a compound subject. Underline the words in each compound subject.

**EXAMPLE:** June and Ken moved to California.

1. Lou and Tony are working at the supermarket.
2. During the storm, the teacher and the class waited under an awning.
3. A bus or train can be used to reach the museum.
4. Austria and Hungary were once united.
5. Lettuce, tomatoes, and cucumbers are the chief ingredients in his salad.

**Exercise 2**  **Recognizing Compound Verbs.**   Each sentence contains a compound verb. Underline the words in each compound verb.

**EXAMPLE:** Jane Austen began a final book but died before its completion.

1. Arnie walks or takes the bus to school.
2. Dad planted a Japanese maple twenty years ago and has cherished it ever since.
3. My friends often go to the movies and have a pizza afterward.
4. The architect surveyed the land, asked questions, and began to draw her plans.
5. Later, Lucy washed her hair and settled down with a book.

**Exercise 3**  **Recognizing Compound Subjects and Compound Verbs.**   Each sentence contains a compound subject, a compound verb, or both. Underline the compound subjects and the compound verbs. Then label the underlined words *compound subject* and *compound verb* as in the example.

**EXAMPLE:** The boy in the navy coat and the boy in the green blazer are teammates.
            *compound subject*

1. Adobe bricks and other artifacts were found in the ruins. _____
2. The trip began in New Guinea and continued with stops in Australia and New Zealand.

   _____
3. Lisa and Sandy both draw and paint well. _____
4. Richard picked two quarts of red and black currants and made sherbet from them.

   _____
5. Peanuts, pretzels, and popcorn are American favorites. _____
6. Rodgers and Hammerstein wrote shows together but also worked with other partners.

   _____
7. The snakes escaped from the cage and slithered away. _____
8. Haiti and Martinique are both countries in the Caribbean. _____
9. The dripping ice sculpture trembled, shook once, and collapsed in a heap. _____
10. Prize livestock and homemade foods were at the fair. _____

# 19.4 Hard-to-Find Subjects • Practice 1

**Subjects in Orders and Directions**  In sentences that give orders or directions, the subject is understood to be *you.*

| Orders or Directions | With Understood *You* Added |
|---|---|
| Listen to me. | (You) listen to me. |
| When cooking rice, follow the directions on the box. | When cooking rice, (you) follow the directions on the box. |

**Subjects in Questions**  In questions, the subject often follows the verb. Such questions begin with *what, which, whose, when, where, why, or how.* To find the subject, change the question into a statement.

| Questions | Reworded as Statements |
|---|---|
| What are you studying in English class? | You are studying what in English class. |
| Where is she going today? | She is going where today. |
| When will the governor arrive? | The governor will arrive when. |

▶ **Exercise 1**   **Finding the Subject in Orders and Directions.**   Write the subject of each sentence in the blank. If the subject is an understood (you), put an arrow (↑) where the subject belongs in the sentence.

**EXAMPLE:**  Girls, ↑ sit down. _____(you)_____

1. After turning onto Main Street, drive for one mile. _____
2. Team, watch carefully. _____
3. Bob always turns off the television. _____
4. Class, look at the board. _____
5. When riding your bicycle in traffic, be careful. _____
6. Don't feed the animals in that cage. _____
7. Carol, please give me your homework. _____
8. The warm breezes were a sign of spring. _____
9. After breakfast, feed the dog. _____
10. Mark, please stop talking. _____

▶ **Exercise 2**   **Finding Subjects in Sentences.**   Rewrite each question as a statement. Underline the subject.

**EXAMPLE:**  Who is the captain of this team? _____The captain of this team is who?_____

1. What movie are they showing today? _____
2. When is the doctor arriving? _____
3. Whose exhibit won first prize? _____
4. Where does he keep the flour? _____
5. What are we having for dinner? _____
6. Did you see Carol at the party? _____
7. Can you finish the homework assignment tonight? _____
8. In which direction is the park? _____
9. When will the play begin? _____
10. Has the jury reached a verdict? _____

# 19.4 Hard-to-Find Subjects • Practice 2

**Exercise 1**  **Recognizing Subjects That Give Orders or Directions.**  Underline or write the subject of each of the following sentences. Seven of the ten sentences give orders or directions.

**EXAMPLE:** Tom, help me milk the cows. _____(you)_____

1.  Remove the cassette carefully. _____
2.  Sylvia, give the dog a bath. _____
3.  You should take only one piece of pie. _____
4.  Check the windows and the doors for leaks. _____
5.  After finishing your homework, help Father. _____
6.  A blanket of snow gently covered the lawn. _____
7.  Tom, pile these boxes against the wall. _____
8.  Stop the traffic! _____
9.  The dictionary had been misplaced for a week. _____
10. Soldiers, take your posts immediately. _____

**Exercise 2**  **Finding the Subjects in Questions.**  Underline the subject in each of the following sentences.

**EXAMPLE:** How did you lose your shoes?

1.  Where is the encyclopedia?
2.  Have they visited the town hall yet?
3.  Which rooms will be redecorated?
4.  Whose science project finally won?
5.  Are blueberries in season now?
6.  What will you do with these packages?
7.  Who planned last year's picnic?
8.  How should I draw the solid bars on this graph?
9.  Have the judges reached a decision?
10. When will we read Poe's short stories?

# 19.4 Sentences Beginning with *There* or *Here*
## • Practice 1

**Subjects in Sentences Beginning with *There* or *Here***   *There* or *here* is never the subject of a sentence. Such sentences are usually in inverted order. Reword them to find the subject.

| Sentences Beginning with *There* or *Here* | Reworded with Subjects Before Verbs |
| --- | --- |
| There are three games left to play. | Three games are left to play. |
| Here is your purse. | Your purse is here. |

▶ **Exercise 1**   **Identifying Subjects in Sentences Beginning with *There* or *Here*.**   Underline the subject in each sentence.

**EXAMPLE:** Here is the answer to your question.

1. There are two ducks on the pond this morning.
2. Here is the recipe.
3. Here comes our new principal.
4. There were no upsets in this election.
5. There could be a storm tomorrow.
6. Here is a picture of the animal with its young.
7. There are some beautiful flowers growing in the field.
8. Here is your father now.
9. Here was a great civilization.
10. There will be no more flights to Chicago today.

▶ **Exercise 2**   **Writing Sentences Beginning with *There* or *Here*.**   Write sentences beginning with *there* or *here* using the subjects in parentheses.

**EXAMPLE:** (train) _____*Here comes the train now.*_____

1. (game) _____
2. (career) _____
3. (deer) _____
4. (balloons) _____
5. (house) _____
6. (book) _____
7. (dog) _____
8. (farm) _____
9. (sun) _____
10. (mother) _____

# 19.4 Sentences Beginning with *There* or *Here*
## • Practice 2

▶ **Exercise 1**  **Finding the Subject in Sentences Beginning with *There* and *Here*.**  Underline the subject in each of the following sentences.

**EXAMPLE:**  There is no <u>excuse</u> for such sloppiness.

1. Here comes the express bus now.
2. There was another phone call for you an hour ago.
3. There have been three strikes in less than five years.
4. Here is some strawberry shortcake for dessert.
5. There goes the last train to the city.
6. There is an exciting new play on Broadway.
7. Here are the tickets to the hockey game.
8. There in the valley are the Mayan ruins.
9. There, smiling proudly, stands the winner of the ribbon.
10. Here is the money for your haircut.

▶ **Writing Application**  **Writing Sentences with Subjects in Various Positions.**  Write five sentences by following the directions. Underline the subject in each sentence.

**EXAMPLE:**  Use *Did* to begin a question.

   *Did you return my library books?*

1. Use *Are* to begin a question.

   _____

   _____

2. Use *Here* to begin a sentence.

   _____

   _____

3. Use *Which* to begin a question.

   _____

   _____

4. Use *Choose* to begin an order.

   _____

   _____

5. Use *There* to begin a sentence.

   _____

   _____

# 19.5 Direct Objects • Practice 1

**Direct Objects** A direct object is a noun or pronoun that receives the action of a verb. Direct objects can be compound, having two or more words. A direct object is one type of complement, which is a word or group of words that completes the meaning of a subject and verb.

| DIRECT OBJECTS |
| --- |
| DO |
| They landed their spacecraft on Mars. |
| COMPOUND |
| DO          DO |
| In the garden, we planted bulbs and seeds . |

▶ **Exercise 1** **Identifying Direct Objects.** Underline the verb in each sentence. Circle the direct object.

**EXAMPLE:** She hoisted the (sails) on the schooner.

1. The two boys dug a hole in the sand.
2. Michelangelo painted those magnificent murals on the ceiling.
3. I deposited my savings in the bank.
4. Next week we will watch a solar eclipse.
5. The wind blew my hat into the air.
6. Every month the moon orbits Earth.
7. Sandra made a beautiful necklace out of shells.
8. Before breakfast, I usually read the newspaper.
9. During the hike, we washed our clothes in a stream.
10. Karen opened a new account at the department store.

▶ **Exercise 2** **Recognizing Compound Direct Objects.** Write the nouns or pronouns of each compound direct object on the blanks at right.

**EXAMPLE:** We watched acrobats and clowns at the circle. _____*acrobats, clowns*_____

1. I left my clothes and my lunch in the locker. _____
2. She has written two books and three articles on astronomy. _____
3. We will have toast and cereal for breakfast. _____
4. Mrs. Henderson teaches French and Spanish at the junior high school. _____
5. The pirates placed the gold and jewels in a treasure chest. _____
6. I washed the car and the dog this afternoon. _____
7. We carried towels, an umbrella, and a cooler to the beach. _____
8. Karl scored a touchdown and an extra point in the game. _____
9. We saw mountains and deserts during our western trip. _____
10. They grow corn and potatoes on the farm. _____

# 19.5 Direct Objects • Practice 2

**Exercise 1** **Recognizing Direct Objects.** Each of the following sentences contains a direct object. Underline each direct object.

**EXAMPLE:** She tapped the <u>window</u> gently.

1. The visitor rang the bell twice.
2. Beethoven wrote only one opera.
3. She ate spaghetti for lunch.
4. My mother reads at least two books a month.
5. Phillis Wheatley wrote poetry about her life as a slave.
6. This morning Father skipped breakfast.
7. This tree produces hazelnuts.
8. She wrote original music for the show.
9. The steamer blew its whistle during the storm.
10. The kitchen clock uses only batteries.

**Exercise 2** **Recognizing Compound Direct Objects.** Each of the following sentences contains a compound direct object. Underline only the nouns or pronouns that make up each compound direct object.

**EXAMPLE:** We saw several <u>yaks</u>, <u>tigers</u>, and <u>lions</u> at the zoo.

1. My family visited Toronto and Ottawa.
2. Marge helped him and me with our homework.
3. He bakes delicious breads, cookies, and cakes.
4. My older sister teaches biology and chemistry at school.
5. We found Bill and her at the lake.
6. I will read *The Pearl* and *Death Be Not Proud* this summer.
7. Yesterday Martha got a vaccination and a checkup.
8. We can choose ice cream, fruit, or pie for dessert.
9. Barbara is touring Colombia and Panama this month.
10. Did the workers receive any praise or rewards?

# 19.5 Distinguishing Direct Objects • Practice 1

**Direct Object, Adverb, or Object of a Preposition?**   A direct object is a noun or pronoun that receives the action of a verb. A direct object is never an adverb, or the noun or pronoun at the end of a prepositional phrase.

| DIRECT OBJECT, ADVERB, OBJECT OF PREPOSITION |
|---|
| DO |
| *With a Direct Object:* Carol played the \|trumpet\|. |
| ADV |
| *With an Adverb:* Carol played brilliantly. |
| PREP PHRASE |
| *With a Prepositional Phrase:* Carol played in the parade. |
| DO        ADV        PREP PHRASE |
| *With all three:* Carol played the \|trumpet\| brilliantly in the parade. |

▶ **Exercise 1**   **Distinguishing Direct Objects, Adverbs, and Objects of Prepositions.**   In the sentences below, circle each direct object, draw a line under each adverb, and draw two lines under each prepositional phrase.

**EXAMPLE:** I quickly drank the ( juice ) with my lunch.

1. She left her keys in the car.
2. I threw a pebble into the pond.
3. Bob moved quickly down the field.
4. They are drilling wells in the ocean floor.
5. I can see Jupiter with my telescope.
6. The tiny bird flew effortlessly into the air.
7. That green lizard eats insects.
8. The school bought new chairs and tables for the classrooms.
9. The plane landed safely on the runway.
10. Please sit in your seat.

▶ **Exercise 2**   **Using Direct Objects in Sentences.**   Write a sentence using each word as a direct object. Underline the direct object.

**EXAMPLE:** skates       *I sold my skates for ten dollars.*

1. alligator _____
2. club _____
3. water _____
4. radio _____
5. clouds _____
6. football _____
7. flower _____
8. hamburger _____
9. book _____
10. present _____

## 19.5 Distinguishing Direct Objects • Practice 2

**Exercise 1** **Distinguishing Direct Objects, Adverbs, and Objects of Prepositions.** Underline each direct object in the following sentences. Circle any adverbs or prepositional phrases. Not every sentence has all three.

**EXAMPLE:** He dropped the snake (quickly) (into the sack) .

1. She touched the rabbit in the cage.
2. I asked my father often about the surprise.
3. Merri put the stamp on the letter.
4. Richard reminded Al repeatedly about the rehearsal.
5. He took his daughter with him to England.
6. Winifred watched the gently falling snowflakes outside her window.
7. The children gleefully built a snowman in front of the house.
8. The family quickly harvested the vegetables from their backyard garden.
9. Wanda simmered the meat gently in her large stewpot.
10. Don imaginatively added oregano to the bread dough.

**Exercise 2** **Using Direct Objects, Adverbs, and Objects of Prepositions.** Fill in the blank in each sentence with an appropriate word performing the function stated in parentheses.

**EXAMPLE:** After dinner, Sam sat ____contentedly____ by the fire. (Adverb)

1. Sarah overcame many _____ in her efforts to succeed. (Direct Object)
2. The locusts _____ attacked the crops in the field. (Adverb)
3. Travelers come to the _____ by train, car, and bus. (Object of a Preposition)
4. George took the _____ outside and chopped down the cherry tree. (Direct Object)
5. Have you read the latest book by _____? (Object of a Preposition)
6. The house was so _____ cleaned that it seemed to sparkle. (Adverb)
7. The three friends took a walk in the _____. (Object of a Preposition)
8. Noises from the woods seemed _____ close. (Adverb)
9. Isabel wore her red _____ to the movies. (Direct Object)
10. The smoke from the fire added to _____ in the air. (Object of a Preposition)
11. Sam was too busy to be bothered with _____. (Object of a Preposition)
12. Sharon bought a _____ for her sister's birthday. (Direct Object)
13. Mia _____ pushed her little sister on the swing. (Adverb)
14. The ducks ate the _____ we had brought for them. (Direct Object)
15. Vinnie practiced _____ with his water-polo team. (Adverb)

# 19.5 Direct Objects in Questions • Practice 1

**Direct Objects in Questions**   A direct object in a question is sometimes near the beginning of the sentence, before the verb. To locate the direct object, reword the question as a statement.

| Questions | Reworded as Statements |
|---|---|
| DO<br>What did you cook for dinner? | DO<br>You did cook what for dinner. |
| DO<br>Which horse are you training for the show? | DO<br>You are training which horse for the show. |
| DO<br>Whom did she take with her? | DO<br>She did take whom with her. |

▶ **Exercise 1**   **Identifying Direct Objects in Questions.**   Underline each direct object in these sentences.

**EXAMPLE:** Which movie did you see last night?

1. What instructions do I need for the project?
2. Whose lawn are we mowing today?
3. Which song will you play in the recital?
4. Whose novel are you reading in class?
5. What can we do about this problem?
6. Whom did you see at the park?
7. Which trail will you ski tomorrow?
8. What should I take for a cold?
9. Whose bicycle are you riding?
10. What items are you buying from the catalog?

▶ **Exercise 2**   **Writing Questions with Direct Objects.**   Complete these questions. Make sure the underlined word is used as a direct object.

**EXAMPLE:** What clothes _____are you packing for the trip?_____

1. What _____
2. Which birds _____
3. What Christmas carols _____
4. Whom _____
5. Which poem _____
6. Whose house _____
7. Which dress _____
8. What language _____
9. Whose guitar _____
10. Which team _____

## 19.5 Direct Objects in Questions • Practice 2

> **Exercise 1**  **Finding Direct Objects in Questions.**  Underline each direct object in the following questions.

**EXAMPLE:** What should we take with us to the picnic?

1. Whom did your sister invite to the party?
2. Which coat will you wear tonight?
3. What will you do with the twenty dollars?
4. What shall I buy?
5. Which groups will they audition for the dance?
6. Whom has Julie chosen as co-captain?
7. Whose radio did they borrow yesterday?
8. What effect did the aspirin have on the pain?
9. Which windows did the sonic boom break?
10. Which story will she read to us this evening?

> **Writing Application**  **Writing Sentences with Direct Objects.**  Write five sentences, one for each of the following patterns. You may add any additional words or details as long as you keep the assigned pattern.

**EXAMPLE:**  direct object + helping verb + subject + verb
          *What did you just say?*

1. subject + action verb + direct object

   _____

2. adjective + direct object + helping verb + subject + verb

   _____

3. subject + action verb + direct object + adverb

   _____

4. subject + action verb + direct object + prepositional phrase

   _____

5. subject + action verb + direct object + adverb + prepositional phrase

   _____

# 19.5 Indirect Objects • Practice 1

**The Indirect Object** An indirect object is a noun or pronoun that comes after an action verb and before a direct object. It names the person or thing that receives something or for which something is done. Like direct objects, indirect objects can be compound.

```
                    INDIRECT OBJECTS
                IO           DO
       Bob gave  me  sailing lessons .
                IO           DO
       I sent my friend a long letter .
              IO      IO       DO
       Give the dog and cat some water .
```

▶ **Exercise 1** **Recognizing Indirect Objects.** Circle the indirect objects in the sentences below. Some sentences have compound indirect objects.

**EXAMPLE:** Tell ( me ) your name, please.

1. She bought me some cotton candy at the fair.
2. Following the game, we gave the other team a cheer.
3. I left Mom a message so she wouldn't worry.
4. The company offered my father a promotion.
5. Will you bring my brother and me some souvenirs of your trip?
6. The robin fed its young a big meal.
7. Tom loaned Howard some money for lunch.
8. I sent him a telegram on Friday.
9. Paul, show your aunt and uncle your blue ribbon.
10. Mr. Fowler taught us the fundamentals of algebra.

▶ **Exercise 2** **Using Indirect Objects in Sentences.** Use each word in parentheses as an indirect object in a sentence.

**EXAMPLE:** (me) _____Carla gave me some help with the homework._____

1. (you) _____
2. (mother, father) _____
3. (her) _____
4. (them) _____
5. (brother, sister) _____
6. (horse) _____
7. (friends) _____
8. (partner) _____
9. (uncle, aunt) _____
10. (waiter, waitress) _____

# 19.5 Indirect Objects • Practice 2

**Exercise 1** **Recognizing Indirect Objects.** Each of the following sentences contains a direct object and an indirect object. Underline each indirect object.

**EXAMPLE:** I sent <u>her</u> flowers for her birthday.

1. Yesterday Mother bought me a new dress.
2. After two meetings, we finally gave our club a name.
3. Senator Lawton gave Mary the award.
4. Can he really get the boys tickets for the game?
5. I can show you the stamp album now.
6. Our teacher sent the principal an invitation.
7. I will draw her a map of directions to the restaurant.
8. The President sent Congress an important message.
9. Can you lend me a dollar?
10. The entire class wrote our representative a letter.

**Exercise 2** **Recognizing Compound Indirect Objects.** Each of the following sentences contains a compound indirect object. Underline only the nouns or pronouns that make up each compound indirect object.

**EXAMPLE:** Have you told your <u>brother</u> and <u>sister</u> the news?

1. Our parents brought Rafael and Maria souvenirs from Venice, Italy.
2. Our teacher gave Jimmy and her a pass to the dean.
3. Did you tell your mother and your father the whole story?
4. Ask the doctor and the nurse that question.
5. Give each flower and plant some fertilizer.
6. Dana wrote Brian and Matthew a letter.
7. Will you show Max and Gail those strange stones?
8. In the morning, Mollie told Willy and Jeff the news.
9. I am selling Mark and John my coin collection.
10. Why don't you lend Ellie and Sue your tapes?

# **19.5** Distinguishing Indirect Objects • Practice 1

**Indirect Object or Object of a Preposition?**   An indirect object never follows the preposition *to* or *for* in a sentence.

| Indirect Object | Prepositional Phrase |
|---|---|
| IO        DO | DO        PREP PH |
| I gave Carol the magazine . | I gave the magazine to Carol . |
| IO        DO | DO        PREP PH |
| Jim bought himself a present . | Jim bought a present for himself . |

▶ **Exercise 1**   **Distinguishing Between Indirect Objects and Objects of Prepositions.**   In each blank, write whether the underlined word is an indirect object or the object of a preposition.

**EXAMPLE:** The Pilgrims left us a rich heritage. _____*indirect object*_____

1. The rock star gave me his autograph. _____

2. I cooked a gourmet meal for myself. _____

3. Richard brought a beautiful bouquet to his parents. _____

4. Let's give Mr. Keith three cheers. _____

5. The manager offered me a job for the summer. _____

6. Bill left a message for Sheila at the office. _____

7. After working so hard, Carol prepared a special treat for herself. _____

8. My grandmother sent me two tickets for the opera. _____

9. I made a delicious sandwich for myself. _____

10. She sent us a year's subscription to *Time*. _____

▶ **Exercise 2**   **Writing Sentences with Indirect Objects and Objects of Prepositions.**   Rewrite each sentence above. Change indirect objects to objects of prepositions. Change objects of prepositions to indirect objects.

**EXAMPLE:**   *The Pilgrims left a rich heritage for us.*

1. _____
2. _____
3. _____
4. _____
5. _____
6. _____
7. _____
8. _____
9. _____
10. _____

# 19.5 Distinguishing Indirect Objects • Practice 2

▶ **Exercise 1**  **Distinguishing Between Indirect Objects and Objects of Prepositions.**  The sentences below contain either an indirect object or an object of a preposition. Underline each indirect object. Circle each object of a preposition.

**EXAMPLE:** Mel gave his dog a bone.     Mel gave a *bone* to his (dog).

1. The boys will show us the lake.
2. I found the keys for them.
3. Every Saturday Pete makes pizza for his family.
4. Certainly, I will tell her the answer.
5. I gave my ring to my younger sister.
6. Have you given the instructions to them yet?
7. She promised him another chance.
8. They are preparing a picnic basket for themselves.
9. Why don't you buy Amy a soda?
10. Terry happily delivered the package to them.

▶ **Writing Application**  **Writing Sentences with Indirect Objects.**  Write five sentences of your own according to the following directions.

**EXAMPLE:** Write a sentence using *me* as an indirect object.
_____*She gave me the last piece of paper in her notebook.*_____

1. Write a sentence using *them* as an indirect object.

   _____

   _____

2. Write a sentence with a compound indirect object connected by *and.*

   _____

   _____

3. Change *her,* the object of the preposition in the following sentence, into an indirect object: I gave the message to *her.*

   _____

   _____

4. Write a sentence using *girls* as an indirect object.

   _____

   _____

5. Write a sentence with a compound indirect object connected by *or.*

   _____

   _____

# 19.5 Subject Complements • Practice 1

**Predicate Nouns and Pronouns** A predicate noun or pronoun follows a linking verb and renames or identifies the subject of the sentence. A predicate noun or pronoun is a subject complement.

| PREDICATE NOUNS AND PRONOUNS |
| --- |
| PN |
| Samuel Clemens was Mark Twain. (*Mark Twain* renames *Samuel Clemens*.) |
| P |
| The winners will be they. (*They* identifies *winners*.) |

**Predicate Adjectives** A predicate adjective follows a linking verb and describes the subject of the sentence. A predicate adjective is also a subject complement.

| PREDICATE ADJECTIVE |
| --- |
| PA |
| The sea is so calm today. (*Calm* describes *sea*.) |
| PA |
| Barbara looks very unhappy. (*Unhappy* describes *Barbara*.) |

**▶ Exercise 1** **Identifying Predicate Nouns and Pronouns.** Underline the predicate nouns and pronouns in these sentences.

**EXAMPLE:** Mavis is president of the class.

1. Sacramento is the capital of California.
2. This should be an easy test.
3. Redwoods are evergreen trees.
4. The Nile River was the center of an ancient civilization.
5. Nigeria is a country in Africa.
6. The team captain is she.
7. Dinosaurs are extinct beasts.
8. This novel should be a best-seller.
9. Babe Ruth was a great baseball player.
10. The peacock is certainly a beautiful bird.

**▶ Exercise 2** **Recognizing Predicate Adjectives.** Underline each predicate adjective in these sentences.

**EXAMPLE:** The milk tastes sour to me.

1. That dress looks perfect on you.
2. *Call of the Wild* was very powerful.
3. This perfume smells familiar to me.
4. Next Thursday, the moon will be full.
5. Betsy seems very quiet today.

# 19.5 Subject Complements • Practice 2

▶ **Exercise 1** **Recognizing Predicate Nouns and Pronouns.** Underline each predicate noun or predicate pronoun in the following sentences.

**EXAMPLE:** The largest continent is Asia.

1. The losers will be they.
2. *The City Boy* is the title of a book by Herman Wouk.
3. This should be the correct address.
4. The capital of Turkey is Ankara.
5. In Greek mythology, Athena was the goddess of wisdom.
6. One plant with supposedly magical powers is the mandrake.
7. A little knowledge is a dangerous thing.
8. The Amazon has always been the most famous river in South America.
9. Lichens are primitive plants.
10. The name of those fruit flies is drosophila.

▶ **Exercise 2** **Recognizing Predicate Adjectives.** Underline each predicate adjective in the following sentences.

**EXAMPLE:** The milk tasted sour.

1. The new recipe for chili looks interesting.
2. St. Stephen's Cathedral in Vienna is absolutely majestic.
3. The sky became dark before the storm.
4. Of all the girls, she is the most athletic.
5. Because of the weather, the flight will be hazardous.
6. After winning, he was dizzy with excitement.
7. The sound from that speaker seems tinny.
8. The valley is particularly peaceful in the spring.
9. That roast duck smells delicious.
10. The climate there is unusually mild all year round.

# 19.5 Compound Subject Complements
## • Practice 1

**Compound Subject Complements**  A linking verb may be followed by two or more predicate nouns, predicate pronouns, or predicate adjectives joined by *and*.

| COMPOUND SUBJECT COMPLEMENTS |
|---|
| PN        PRED PRON |
| The new co-captains are [Randy] and [I]. |
| PA        PA |
| This year's harvest will be [rich] and [bountiful]. |

▶ **Exercise 1**  **Identifying Compound Subject Complements.**  Underline the compound subject complements in each sentence.

**EXAMPLE:** After the exam, I felt <u>tired</u> but <u>relieved</u>.

1. In the eye of the hurricane, the weather was sunny and calm.
2. Two beautiful vacation spots are Florida and Jamaica.
3. The water felt cool and refreshing against my skin.
4. The beaches here look soft and luxurious.
5. The green salad tasted fresh and crisp.
6. My best friends are Ralph and Dawn.
7. Two of the cheerleaders are Charlotte and I.
8. That Mexican dish smells tangy and delicious.
9. A day at a museum can be fun and rewarding.
10. Among the world's greatest painters are Renoir and Van Gogh.

▶ **Exercise 2**  **Writing Sentences with Compound Subject Complements.**  Complete each sentence with a compound subject complement.

**EXAMPLE:** My favorite possessions are _____*a radio and a baseball*_____ .

1. The American flag is _____.
2. Some animals seen in the forest are _____.
3. My experience at camp was _____.
4. Two of Dickens's novels are _____.
5. The Santa Fe Trail was _____.
6. The flowers in our garden smell _____.
7. Having lost my way in the woods, I felt _____.
8. Among the world's best athletes are _____.
9. This dinner tastes _____.
10. Our new car looks _____.

# 19.5 Compound Subject Complements
## • Practice 2

> **Exercise 1** **Recognizing Compound Subject Complements.**  Underline each part of each
subject complement in the following sentences.

**EXAMPLE:** The best grain is either <u>wheat</u> or <u>rye</u>.

1. After the ice storm, the path was smooth and slick.
2. That woman is both a talented musician and a lyricist.
3. The main course is either beef or veal.
4. Two Spanish cities on the sea are Barcelona and Cádiz.
5. This time the desert appeared vast and treacherous.
6. The saxophonists in the band are Luis and she.
7. The colors of the banner will be orange, green, and purple.
8. The trip up the coast was neither smooth nor scenic.
9. Over the years, the statue has turned old and gray.
10. Lincoln was a fine writer and storyteller.

> **Writing Application**  **Writing Sentences with Subject Complements.**  Write sentences
using the following subjects and verbs. Include the type of subject complement given in parentheses.
Add details you think are needed.

**EXAMPLE:** flowers are (compound predicate noun)

> _My favorite flowers are carnations and roses._

1. cheerleaders are (compound predicate nouns)

_____

_____

2. cupcakes look (predicate adjective)

_____

_____

3. dog is (predicate noun)

_____

_____

4. roads were (compound predicate adjectives)

_____

_____

5. musicians are (compound predicate pronouns)

_____

_____

# 20.1 Prepositional Phrases (Adjective) • Practice 1

**Phrases That Act as Adjectives** An adjective phrase is a prepositional phrase that modifies a noun or pronoun by telling what kind or which one.

| Adjectives | Adjective Phrases |
|---|---|
| Richard wore a *striped* tie. | Richard wore a tie *with stripes*. (What kind of tie?) |
| A *red-faced* policeman directed traffic. | A policeman *with a red face* directed traffic. (Which policeman?) |

▶ **Exercise 1** **Recognizing Adjective Phrases.** Underline the adjective phrases in these sentences and circle the word each phrase modifies.

**EXAMPLE:** The (house) on the corner was deserted.

1. Dad made a pitcher of orange juice.
2. Have you read Aesop's fable about the fox and the grapes?
3. A thing of beauty is a joy forever.
4. I wrote an essay about my summer vacation.
5. *The Belle of Amherst* is a play about Emily Dickinson.
6. The bicycle with the flat tire is mine.
7. The kitten chased a ball of yarn.
8. The tree beside the garage was planted here last year.
9. A boy from New Orleans has the seat beside me.
10. The capital of this country is New Delhi.

▶ **Exercise 2** **Adding Adjective Phrases to Sentences.** Fill in each blank in these sentences with an appropriate adjective phrase.

**EXAMPLE:** We bought a balloon _____*with pink polka dots*_____.

1. The name _____ is Daisy.
2. I saw birds _____ perched in the tree.
3. Do you have time for a game _____?
4. I want that new shirt _____.
5. We purchased three tickets _____.
6. Tom read a story _____ to his younger brother.
7. All the great political leaders _____ gathered for a meeting.
8. Cancel my subscription _____.
9. I'd like a cup _____ with my lunch.
10. Did you figure out the answer _____?

## 20.1 Prepositional Phrases (Adjective) • Practice 2

**Exercise 1**   **Identifying Adjective Phrases.**   Each of the following sentences contains at least one prepositional phrase used as an adjective. Underline each adjective phrase and draw an arrow pointing from it to the word it modifies.

**EXAMPLE:** Noise from aircraft may damage houses near busy urban airports.

1. He drank a whole quart of milk.
2. My aunt is the president of the charity.
3. Grandfather told a story about Maine.
4. The stamp on that envelope is extremely rare.
5. The city of Damascus is several thousand years old.
6. A visitor from Italy showed slides of Rome and Florence.
7. Is this the road to the exhibit?
8. The box of nails in the cellar spilled all over.
9. The dot in the center of the map is Lake Zaragosa.
10. The room in the back of the house is mine.
11. Please place this bowl of fruit on the table.
12. The flowers by the window are called dahlias.
13. The cat with the long fur is my favorite one.
14. The calendar on the wall has photographs by Ansel Adams.
15. The photograph of Half Dome is one of his most famous ones.

**Exercise 2**   **Using Adjective Phrases.**   Fill in each blank with an appropriate adjective phrase.

**EXAMPLE:** Our soccer team won the game _____ *in the last minute of play.* _____

1. Marlon, _____, realized that he owed his aunt a letter.
2. Jeanine looked at the puppy _____.
3. The truck _____ is huge.
4. The police officers _____ ordered everyone out.
5. _____, Marco and Roseanne walked in the park.
6. Jacob's bicycle has a scratch _____.
7. Cecily, _____, wished for a puppy.
8. In the afternoon, you can get a ticket _____.
9. Skip's friend _____ visited this afternoon for two hours.
10. This morning, let's visit the home _____.
11. The curtain rose, and the actor _____ began to speak.
12. The gymnast _____ jumped into the air.
13. Julia ate a bowl _____.
14. Dan threw the ball over the fence _____.
15. The hikers _____ began walking up the steep trail.

#  **20.1** **Prepositional Phrases** (Adverb) • **Practice 1**

**Phrases That Act as Adverbs**   An adverb phrase is a prepositional phrase that modifies a verb, adjective, or adverb. Adverb phrases point out where, in what manner, or to what extent.

| Adverbs | Adverb Phrases |
|---|---|
| He painted the boat *carefully*. | He painted the boat *with care*. (Painted in *what manner*?) |
| Leave the radio *there*. | Leave the radio in *your room*. (Leave *Where*?) |

> **Exercise 1**   **Recognizing Adverb Phrases.**   Underline the adverb phrases in these sentences and circle the word that each phrase modifies.

**EXAMPLE:**  He (hung) his clothes in the closet.

1. Anne was upset about her long homework assignment.
2. The French army retreated down the valley.
3. In a panic, she ran out.
4. The goalie stopped the ball in front of the net.
5. Bob always arrives late for work.
6. We feel optimistic about our chances for victory.
7. The plane flew from Detroit to Miami.
8. With a broad smile, the politician acknowledged the cheers of the crowd.
9. Thunder rumbled across the sky.
10. I will answer your question in a moment.

> **Exercise 2**   **Writing Sentences with Adverb Phrases.**   Write a sentence using the adverb phrase in parentheses.

**EXAMPLE:**  (in time)  _____Will we reach the airport in time?_____

1. (in the past) _____
2. (at sunset) _____
3. (across the desert) _____
4. (under the sea) _____
5. (with the election results) _____
6. (in the morning) _____
7. (after school) _____
8. (down the river) _____
9. (close to the finish line) _____
10. (over the bridge) _____

# 20.1 **Prepositional Phrases** (Adverb) • **Practice 2**

▶ **Exercise 1**  **Identifying Adverb Phrases.**   Each of the sentences contains at least one prepositional phrase used as an adverb. Underline each adverb phrase and draw an arrow from it to the word it modifies.

**EXAMPLE:**  By chance they always lived near busy urban airports.

1. The trout stream winds through the forest.

2. Alice was early with her science report.

3. At dawn they prepared for the rescue attempt.

4. She seems happy with her new job.

5. At the hotel the visitor learned about the delay.

6. The astronauts arrived late for the test run.

7. In a well-prepared speech, Larissa explained her decision.

8. We piled flowers and other decorations near the station wagon.

9. From the doctor's office, she drove to the library.

10. Our coach is happy about our victory.

▶ **Writing Application**  **Writing Sentences with Prepositional Phrases.**   Write sentences using the given prepositional phrases as adjectives or adverbs, according to the instructions in parentheses. Underline each phrase and draw an arrow from it to the word it modifies.

**EXAMPLE:**  through the city (as an adverb phrase)

   *The river flows through the city.*
_____

1. in the afternoon (as an adverb phrase)

   _____

   _____

2. on the hanger (as an adjective phrase)

   _____

   _____

3. in the white shoes (as an adjective phrase)

   _____

   _____

4. to the museum director (as an adverb phrase)

   _____

   _____

5. near cool water (as an adverb phrase)

   _____

   _____

#  **20.1** **Appositives in Phrases • Practice 1**

**Appositive Phrases**  An appositive is a noun or pronoun placed after another noun or pronoun to identify, rename, or explain the preceding word. An appositive phrase is an appositive with its modifiers.

| Appositives | Appositive Phrases |
|---|---|
| The main character, *Tom Sawyer*, appeals to me. | Tom Sawyer, *the main character,* appeals to me. |
| We stopped at the capital of Virginia, *Richmond*. | I like St. Louis, *Gateway to the West.* |
| The salad consisted of two vegetables, *lettuce and tomatoes*. | These two states, *one on the East Coast and one on the West Coast*, are my favorites. |

▶ **Exercise 1**  **Recognizing Appositives.**  Circle each appositive in the sentences below. Underline the word it renames.

**EXAMPLE:**  A former President, ⟨Gerald Ford⟩ , spoke at graduation.

1. That artist, Picasso, is one of the most famous of the twentieth century.
2. The coach, Mr. Sawyer, explained the play.
3. The nation's largest state, Alaska, is my home.
4. We climbed that mountain, Pike's Peak, yesterday.
5. We saw Arthur Miller's play, *Death of a Salesman*, on Broadway.
6. The poet Walt Whitman wrote during the nineteenth century.
7. The famous artist, Winslow Homer, sketched Civil War soldiers.
8. They stayed in the capital, Austin, for two days.
9. We ate at my favorite restaurant, Smiley's.
10. These composers, Chopin and Mozart, died when they were still young men.

▶ **Exercise 2**  **Identifying Appositive Phrases.**  Underline the appositive phrases in these sentences. Circle the words they explain.

**EXAMPLE:**  We bought a new ⟨car⟩, a green Chevrolet.

1. Thomas Jefferson, our third President, also served as Secretary of State.
2. Have you ever been to Washington, D.C., the nation's capital?
3. "The Star-Spangled Banner," our national anthem, was written by Francis Scott Key.
4. The magazine article compared two animals, the lynx and the bobcat.
5. Jenny, the class speaker, is a Native American.
6. We watched the horse, a dappled mare, gallop away.
7. Audie Murphy, a real war hero, starred in that movie about World War II.
8. Ulysses Grant, commander of the Union armies, later became President.
9. Thursday, the day after tomorrow, is Thanksgiving.
10. We planted two trees, a red maple and a Douglas fir, in the schoolyard.

## 20.1 Appositives in Phrases • Practice 2

**Exercise 1** **Identifying Appositives and Appositive Phrases.** Underline each appositive or appositive phrase in the following sentences and draw an arrow pointing from it to the word it renames.

**EXAMPLE:** The winner, one of five semifinalists, will be announced tomorrow.

1. The singer Marilyn Horne has a magnificent mezzo-soprano voice.

2. He owns just one car, a Packard.

3. Her home, an old Victorian mansion, was destroyed in the fire.

4. Stephen Crane's poem "A Learned Man" is among my favorites.

5. Houston, a city of opportunity, has attracted many newcomers.

6. The composer Mozart wrote many pieces while still a child.

7. Her shoes, brown and white Indian moccasins, were handmade.

8. We were introduced to the leading man—a tall, strange, scowling person.

9. The desserts—chocolate pudding, peach pie, and fruit salad—are all delicious.

10. The English writer Virginia Woolf had a sister who was a respected painter.

**Writing Application** **Writing Sentences with Appositives.** Write sentences of your own, each using one of the following words or phrases as an appositive.

**EXAMPLE:** an American writer

_____Pearl Buck, an American writer, spent many years in China._____

1. my favorite city

_____

_____

2. an exciting group

_____

_____

3. a beautiful sight

_____

_____

4. the coach

_____

_____

5. a green vegetable

_____

_____

**20.1** # Participles • **Practice 1**

**Participles**   A participle is a form of verb that is often used as an adjective.

| Present Participles | Past Participles |
| --- | --- |
| A *barking dog* kept me awake.<br>*Listening,* I learned some useful information. | The *harvested* corn sat in the silo.<br>The freshly *baked* bread smelled wonderful. |

▶ **Exercise 1**   **Identifying Present and Past Participles.**   Underline the participles in these sentences. Circle the words that the participles modify.

**EXAMPLE:**  This is a <u>settled</u> (area) of the state.

1. Silver City was an expanding community.
2. I ran my finger across the polished surface.
3. Laughing, I fell off my chair.
4. She was a known liar.
5. The convicted criminal received a life sentence.
6. I love the taste of roasted chestnuts.
7. The sunken treasure may never be found.
8. The defeated army surrendered on the battlefield.
9. A whistling sound shattered the silence.
10. We live in a restored barn on the edge of town.

▶ **Exercise 2**   **Writing Sentences with Participles.**   Use each of the participles listed below in a sentence.

**EXAMPLE:**  twisted _____*A twisted smile crossed his face.*_____

1. toasted _____
2. running _____
3. worried _____
4. roaring _____
5. written _____
6. singing _____
7. dented _____
8. surprised _____
9. falling _____
10. lost _____

# 20.1 Participles • Practice 2

**Exercise 1** **Identifying Present and Past Participles.** Underline the participle in each sentence. Then draw an arrow to the word that the participle modifies.

**EXAMPLE:** I learned much from the growing baby.

1. The burning logs were soon only embers.
2. The detective examined the marked bill.
3. What is the asking price for this vase?
4. The sheriff said the outlaw is a dangerous man.
5. The broken lamp can be repaired.
6. This is a frightening turn of events.
7. The spoiled cheese has turned green.
8. The pitcher was applauded by the cheering crowd.
9. Charlotte, a growing city, offers a rich past as well.
10. After the tournament, she became a well-known athlete.
11. Josie believes in the power of the written word.
12. Did you see the skater's amazing leaps?
13. A well-trained dog can be a big help to a family.
14. As a growing child, Alicia needs her vitamins.
15. Exhausted, the runner barely made it to the finish line.

**Exercise 2** **Using Participles.** Fill in the blank in each sentence with an appropriate participle.

**EXAMPLE:** The ____determined____ child took her first step.

1. Terrie turned her _____ face toward her best friend.
2. _____, Kristen tried to figure out the difficult math problem.
3. Barry's _____ eyes gave him a friendly appearance.
4. The _____ stars seemed extra bright that night.
5. _____, the ballerina sprained her ankle.
6. The _____ horse was moving faster than the train.
7. A raisin is nothing more than a _____ grape.
8. Wendy heard some _____ news this morning.
9. The carefully _____ garden was a riot of color.
10. The _____ walls contrasted with the ones that had paper on them.
11. _____, Suzie listened to the creaking of the old house.
12. The _____ fans stayed on their feet for a full five minutes.
13. A _____ customer returned this cheese.
14. You can store _____ jars in the cabinet.
15. The _____ turkey took hours to thaw.

# 20.1 Participles in Phrases • Practice 1

**Participial Phrase**   A participial phrase is a present or past participle that is modified by an adverb or adverb phrase or that has a complement. The entire phrase acts as an adjective in a sentence.

| PARTICIPIAL PHRASES |
|---|
| *Running rapidly*, Todd won the race. |
| The child, *overcome with fear*, began to cry. |
| The leopard, *stalking its prey*, advanced slowly. |

**Exercise 1**   **Identifying Participial Phrases.**   Underline the participial phrase in each sentence. Circle the word that the phrase modifies.

**EXAMPLE:** Looking around the room, ( I ) noticed something missing.

1. We found a gold coin buried in the sand.
2. The ruins of Troy, untouched for centuries, were eventually discovered.
3. The explorer, exhausted by his journey, collapsed in the hospital.
4. Separated from its parents, the baby chick soon lost its way.
5. Known for its spectacular vistas, the Grand Canyon is a popular tourist attraction.
6. On the banks of the river stands an ancient castle, shrouded in mystery.
7. The soldiers, marching with heavy packs, soon became tired.
8. Glistening with dew, the grass looked lush and beautiful.
9. *The Three Musketeers*, written by Alexandre Dumas, is a great adventure story.
10. The fire engines, speeding through the city, stopped all other traffic.

**Exercise 2**   **Writing Sentences with Participial Phrases.**   Fill in the blank in each sentence with an appropriate participial phrase.

**EXAMPLE:** The river, _____*overflowing its banks*_____, flooded the entire community.

1. _____, I see a bright future for you.
2. I listened to the orchestra _____.
3. _____, we entered the discount store.
4. The dog, _____, scared away the intruder.
5. She saw smoke _____.
6. We looked up at the clouds _____.
7. _____, Steve finished the project.
8. That beautiful portrait, _____, hangs in the museum.
9. _____, Bob stayed home from school.
10. _____, he saw many colorful fish.

# 20.1 **Participles in Phrases • Practice 2**

▶ **Exercise 1**  **Recognizing Participial Phrases.**  Each of the following sentences contains a participial phrase. Underline each participial phrase and draw an arrow from it to the word it modifies.

**EXAMPLE:** On the table I saw several packages wrapped in gold paper.

1. The girl smiling shyly is my cousin from Florida.

2. Troubled by the news, Glenn phoned his parents.

3. Mrs. Grant, waiting for the right moment, whisked the fly out the window.

4. He found the ring hidden in a trunk.

5. Gliding swiftly, the canoe approached the rapids.

6. The *Twentieth Century Limited*, redecorated for the occasion, began its last run.

7. Noted for its mountains, Banff National Park is a popular resort.

8. I spoke to the runner, holding his side in pain.

9. Greeting the guests, the mayor shook dozens of hands.

10. The ancient mammals, frozen for centuries in ice, were well preserved.

▶ **Writing Application**  **Writing Sentences with Participial Phrases.**  Write five sentences using the given participial phrases. Underline each participial phrase and draw an arrow from it to the word it modifies.

**EXAMPLE:** standing on a ladder

Standing on a ladder, the painter could reach the ceiling.

1. shivering in the cold air

   _____

   _____

2. examining the contract closely

   _____

   _____

3. holding a colorful bouquet of flowers

   _____

   _____

4. entering the room

   _____

   _____

5. responding to the question

   _____

   _____

## 20.2 Adjective Clauses • Practice 1

**Recognizing Adjective Clauses**   A clause is a group of words with its own subject and verb. An independent clause can stand by itself as a complete sentence. A subordinate clause cannot stand by itself as a sentence. An adjective clause is a subordinate clause that modifies a noun or pronoun.

| ADJECTIVE CLAUSES |
|---|
| She wore a sweater *that was made of wool.* (*What kind* of sweater?) |
| This store, *which opened in 1900,* is still very popular. (*Which* store?) |
| I met the woman *who was just elected senator.* (*Which* woman?) |
| George Washington slept in the house *that is located at the corner.* (*Which* house?) |
| Remember the days *when mini-skirts were popular.* (*Which* days?) |

▶ **Exercise 1**   **Identifying Adjective Clauses.**   Underline the adjective clause in each sentence.

**EXAMPLE:**   Here is the girl who will be your baby sitter.

1.  That was the era when Prohibition was the law.
2.  This is a novel which I highly recommend to you.
3.  The paintings that you saw in the museum were original works by Degas.
4.  The taiga, which is an evergreen forest, stretches across Canada.
5.  The usher to whom you gave your tickets is my sister.
6.  A satellite, which will be used for weather forecasting, has just been placed in orbit.
7.  The time since we last met has passed quickly.
8.  The playwright whose work we are reading is William Shakespeare.
9.  The movie which we will see tonight is supposed to be very funny.
10.  Some of the animals that you saw at the zoo are endangered species.

▶ **Exercise 2**   **Using Adjective Clauses in Sentences.**   Fill in each blank with an appropriate adjective clause.

**EXAMPLE:**   The tree _____*that grows behind the town hall*_____ is two hundred years old.

1.  The song _____ was written by Cole Porter.
2.  The man _____ is my grandfather.
3.  Abraham Lincoln was the President _____.
4.  Those were the days _____.
5.  Let me give you a recipe _____.
6.  Shakespeare is the author _____.
7.  Chicago, _____, is a large city.
8.  Thomas Edison, _____, was a genius.
9.  With that telescope, you can see stars _____.
10.  Now, I understand the problems _____.

# 20.2 **Adjective Clauses** • **Practice 2**

▶ **Exercise 1** **Identifying Adjective Clauses.** Underline the adjective clause in each of the following sentences.

**EXAMPLE:** The lake <u>where we swim</u> is a hundred feet deep in the center.

1. He is the pitcher whom we saw the last time.

2. *Kabloona*, which describes a Frenchman living among the Eskimos, was written by Gontran De Poncins.

3. A *tsunami* is a huge wave that is caused by an earthquake or volcanic eruption.

4. Is this the teacher who also makes silver jewelry?

5. In her talk, the ambassador described Luxembourg, which has changed greatly.

6. The man whom you want lives across the street and three houses down.

7. A movie that I will never forget is *Zorba the Greek*.

8. The house where she lived is now a historic site.

9. This is the travel agent who offers trips to China.

10. The girl whose pen I used is my sister Elizabeth's best friend.

▶ **Writing Application** **Writing Sentences with Adjective Clauses.** Follow the directions to write five sentences that contain adjective clauses. Underline each adjective clause.

**EXAMPLE:** Write a sentence with a clause that begins *whom we chose.*

      *The player <u>whom we chose as team captain</u> is the best athlete on the squad.*

1. Write a sentence with a clause that begins *who always forgets.*

    _____

    _____

2. Write a sentence with a clause that begins *whom I visited recently.*

    _____

    _____

3. Write a sentence with a clause that begins *whose main job was.*

    _____

    _____

4. Write a sentence with a clause that begins *that George and I saw.*

    _____

    _____

5. Write a sentence with a clause that begins *that costs.*

    _____

    _____

# 20.2 Adverb Clauses • Practice 1

**Recognizing Adverb Clauses** An adverb clause is a subordinate clause that modifies a verb, an adjective, or an adverb.

| ADVERB CLAUSES | |
|---|---|
| **Modifying Verbs** | I will leave *when I am ready.* (Will leave *when?*) |
| | The child acted *as if he were unhappy.* (Acted *in what manner?*) |
| | George spoke loudly *so that he could be heard.* (Spoke loudly *why?*) |
| **Modifying an Adjective** | She was late *because her train was delayed.* (Late *why?*) |
| **Modifying an Adverb** | He understands less *than you think.* (Less *to what extent?*) |

▶ **Exercise 1** **Recognizing Adverb Clauses.** Underline the adverb clause in each of these sentences. Circle the word it modifies.

**EXAMPLE:** We met friendly people (wherever) we traveled.

1. We will drive into town after I finish lunch.
2. Although we set out early, we didn't arrive until dark.
3. Before James Madison became President, he served as Secretary of State.
4. If the South had won the Civil War, our nation's history would have been quite different.
5. When Charles de Gaulle became president of France, the country faced a grave crisis.
6. He is better prepared to lead our country than most other politicians are.
7. Many things changed while you were gone.
8. I feel sad because we have to say "good-bye."
9. She can't graduate until she passes this course.
10. Since you left, the baby has grown.

▶ **Exercise 2** **Identifying Adverb Clauses and the Words They Modify.** Underline the adverb clause in each sentence. Circle the word or words it modifies.

**EXAMPLE:** We (can eat) whenever you are ready.

1. This dish tastes delicious because it has so many spices.
2. The Texans defended the Alamo until the last man was dead.
3. If we hurry, we can still catch the first act.
4. She taught us more than the other teachers did.
5. Since you insist, I will tell you my secret.
6. America was still a young country when Andrew Jackson became President.
7. Bob will be happy if you choose him for your team.
8. After the Roman Empire fell, Europe entered the Middle Ages.
9. While we're in Virginia, we should visit Williamsburg.
10. Debby worked carefully so that the project would be done correctly.

## 20.2 Adverb Clauses • Practice 2

▶ **Exercise 1** **Identifying Adverb Clauses.** Underline each adverb clause in the following sentences.

**EXAMPLE:** Before we left for vacation, we put the dog in a kennel.

1. If the book is delivered in time, I will use it for my report.
2. Mike writes to his aunt at least twice a month even though she seldom answers.
3. I will return whenever you need me.
4. Grandma ran for mayor when the incumbent retired.
5. When Fred Astaire started his career, he danced with his sister Adele.
6. Our principal is busier than I have ever seen her.
7. A storm developed after we reached the turnpike.
8. Winston Churchill was better read than were most of the other world leaders of his time.
9. They drove to the park although it was nearby.
10. Fortunately, my brother runs faster than I do.

▶ **Writing Application** **Using Adverb Clauses in Sentences.** Combine each pair of sentences into a single sentence by making one of them an adverb clause. Write the new sentence and underline the adverb clause.

**EXAMPLE:** I will work on my hobby. You want to sleep.

*I will work on my hobby if you want to sleep.*

1. Bob was late to the show. He missed part of the first act.

   _____

   _____

2. The lookout saw the danger. The ship still struck the iceberg.

   _____

   _____

3. They picked two bushels of blueberries. They fell asleep.

   _____

   _____

4. The traffic light suddenly flashed red. We tried to stop the car.

   _____

   _____

5. You want to see the play. Why don't you write away for tickets?

   _____

   _____

# 20.2 Classifying Sentences by Structure
## • Practice 1

**The Simple Sentence**   A simple sentence consists of a single independent clause.

| SIMPLE SENTENCES |
|---|
| *One Subject and Verb:* The alarm sounded. |
| *Compound Subject:* Susan or Jim will go. |
| *Compound Verb:* We laughed and shouted with joy. |
| *Compound Subject and Verb:* Bill and I swam and fished throughout the day. |

**The Compound Sentence**   A compound sentence has two or more independent clauses.

| COMPOUND SENTENCES |
|---|
| I could watch television, or I could begin my chores. |
| Doug builds model airplanes; he flies them too. |

▶ **Exercise 1**   **Recognizing Simple Sentences.**   Underline the subjects and circle the verbs below.

**EXAMPLE:**  I (sent) a telegram to my grandmother.

1. Barbara was an acrobat in the circus.

2. We brought our new dog home from the pound.

3. Vikings settled in England over a thousand years ago.

4. Joyce and Darlene went to camp together.

5. The old house rattled and shook during the storm.

6. Sarah built a birdhouse and put it in the tree.

7. We hiked from sunrise until sunset.

8. Tim and I waved and shouted to attract their attention.

9. My aunt and uncle have retired in Florida.

10. How old are you?

▶ **Exercise 2**   **Distinguishing Between Simple and Compound Sentences.**   In the space at the right, tell whether each sentence is *simple* or *compound*.

**EXAMPLE:** Roger can cook, and he can sew. _____*compound*_____

1. The ancient Egyptians built pyramids for their pharaohs. _____

2. Benjamin Franklin was a scientist; he was also an inventor. _____

3. Carolyn cooked the dinner, so Bill washed the dishes. _____

4. The tornado struck in the morning. _____

5. Where is Tucson located? _____

6. John Adams and his son were both elected President. _____

7. Rusty went inside, and he applied for a job. _____

8. I looked everywhere, but I couldn't find the keys. _____

9. According to the *Iliad*, Priam was king of Troy. _____

10. In tomorrow's game, George will pitch, and Randy will be the catcher. _____

**20.2** # Classifying Sentences by Structure
• **Practice 2**

▶ **Exercise 1**  **Recognizing Simple Sentences.** The following are simple sentences. Underline the subject once and the verb twice. Notice that some of the subjects and verbs are compound.

**EXAMPLE:** Jan opened the envelope and read the letter aloud.

1. Rick and I caught trout under the bridge.

2. The trail left the forest and wound its way up the steep mountain.

3. According to the Bible, Ichabod was born at the hour of the capture of the Ark.

4. Spinach, kale, beans, and peas are all relatively inexpensive.

5. The empty wagon struck the fence and then crashed into the tree.

▶ **Exercise 2**  **Recognizing Compound Sentences.** The following are compound sentences. Underline the subject once and the verb twice in each independent clause.

**EXAMPLE:** Kathleen folded the letters, and Jane sealed the envelopes.

1. James must remember to bring the lantern, or we will have no light in the cabin.

2. The capital of Louisiana is Baton Rouge; other important cities are Shreveport, Lake Charles, and New Orleans.

3. The southern magnolia has huge white flowers; the northern variety has smaller, somewhat pinkish flowers.

4. She is interested in space exploration, so she reads every article and book on the subject.

5. The night sky was clear, but we did not see a single shooting star.

# 20.2 Classifying Sentences by Structure
## • Practice 1

**The Complex Sentence**   A complex sentence consists of one independent clause and one or more subordinate clauses.

| COMPLEX SENTENCES |
| --- |
| SUBORDINATE CLAUSE                    MAIN CLAUSE<br>Although the desert has a harsh climate, \| many creatures live there.<br> MAIN CLAUSE    SUBORDINATE CLAUSE<br>This is the day \| when summer begins. |

**The Compound-Complex Sentence**   A compound-complex sentence consists of two or more independent clauses and one or more subordinate clauses.

| COMPOUND-COMPLEX SENTENCES |
| --- |
| INDEPENDENT CLAUSE    SUBORDINATE CLAUSE    INDEPENDENT CLAUSE<br>Stamp collecting is the hobby \| which I enjoy most, \| and I have a huge collection.<br><br> SUBORDINATE CLAUSE     INDEPENDENT CLAUSE      INDEPENDENT CLAUSE<br>When I finish the laundry, \| I'm going to the market, \| but I'll be back in time for dinner. |

▶**Exercise 1**   **Recognizing Complex Sentences.**   In these complex sentences, underline the subject of the independent clause once and the verb twice. Circle each subordinate clause.

**EXAMPLE:** I showed the class some slides ⟨that I took at camp.⟩

1. I cleaned up the mess that you made.
2. The car, which had run smoothly all day, suddenly stopped.
3. While I was watching the parade, someone stole my wallet.
4. If our school wins, we will be state champions.
5. The soldiers, who had not eaten all day, were famished by nightfall.

▶**Exercise 2**   **Distinguishing Between Complex and Compound-Complex Sentences.**   Write whether each sentence is *complex* or *compound-complex* in the space at the right.

**EXAMPLE:** This experiment which we are conducting is difficult, and you must follow all the instructions carefully.   *compound-complex*

1. England once ruled a large empire which included countries in many parts of the globe. _____
2. Robert E. Lee, who commanded the Confederate armies, was a West Point graduate, and he also served in the Mexican War. _____
3. When Pericles ruled Athens, it was one of the greatest city-states in Greece, but women had no part in its government. _____
4. If you read about Charlemagne, you will discover that he was a brilliant ruler. _____
5. Spain and Portugal, which were great sea powers, led the earliest explorations of the new world, yet they later lost much territory to other countries. _____

# 20.2 Classifying Sentences by Structure
## • Practice 2

▶ **Exercise 1**   **Recognizing Complex Sentences.**   The following are complex sentences. Underline the subject once and the verb twice in each clause. Then put parentheses around each subordinate clause.

**EXAMPLE:** Alan is smarter (than we realized).

1. The main road was closed after the bridge collapsed.
2. The actress whom I admire the most is Carol Burnett.
3. We continued our vacation trip when the dense fog lifted.
4. If you are not happy with their work, you can wallpaper the room yourself.
5. The cactus will grow if you do not overwater it.

▶ **Exercise 2**   **Recognizing Compound-Complex Sentences.**   The following are compound-complex sentences. Underline the subject once and the verb twice in each clause. Then put parentheses around each subordinate clause.

**EXAMPLE:** The mountains are now barren, but the valleys remain fertile (because they are irrigated).

1. If she can pack quickly she can leave with me, but I must leave exactly in an hour.
2. The roads were closed after the storm struck, and they are still dangerous now.
3. After we fell asleep, raccoons invaded our campsite, but we awoke and chased them away.
4. I will help you if I can, yet I know little about making jelly.
5. Sarah called home because she was late for dinner, but no one answered.

▶ **Exercise 3**   **Identifying the Structure of Sentences.**   Identify the structure of each of the following sentences as *simple, compound, complex,* or *compound-complex.*

**EXAMPLE:** We waited at the curb so that we could see the President. ____*complex*____

1. After two days of rain, the sun finally appeared. _____
2. Since he learned to cook, he has made one rich dish after another. _____
3. He will need a day of rest after he returns from Spain. _____
4. Draw a map, and I will try to follow it. _____
5. Where have you put our movie reels? _____
6. The ship that we visited in the harbor is a French destroyer from World War II. _____
7. I will plant the tulips, or Jessie will plant them. _____
8. The phone stopped ringing before I could answer it. _____
9. Circe, according to Greek legend, changed the companions of Odysseus into pigs. _____
10. Tanya dives better than I do, but I can swim faster. _____

# 21.1  The Four Functions of Sentences • Practice 1

**The Four Types of Sentences**   A declarative sentence states an idea and ends with a period.

| DECLARATIVE SENTENCES |
|---|
| They waited at the station for the bus. |
| In the fall, the trees will lose their leaves. |

An interrogative sentence asks a question and ends with a question mark.

| INTERROGATIVE SENTENCES |
|---|
| To whom did you give the book? When will you get it back? |

An imperative sentence gives an order or a direction and ends with a period or an exclamation mark.

| IMPERATIVE SENTENCES |
|---|
| Turn left at the stoplight. Listen to me! |

An exclamatory sentence conveys strong emotion and ends with an exclamation mark.

| EXCLAMATORY SENTENCES |
|---|
| Our school won first prize! What excitement there was! |

▶ **Exercise 1**   Recognizing the Four Types of Sentences.   On the blank at the right of each sentence, write whether it is *declarative, interrogative, imperative,* or *exclamatory.*

**EXAMPLE:** The cat chased its tail. _____*declarative*_____

1. Leave my house, immediately! _____
2. What should we cook for the party? _____
3. What great ideas you have, Paul! _____
4. We are reading Shakespeare's *Hamlet.* _____
5. After finishing our model airplane, we wanted to fly it. _____
6. Will you be in school tomorrow? _____
7. Apollo was the Greek god of the sun. _____
8. Answer the questions carefully. _____
9. In which state do you live? _____
10. Sara wears contact lenses. _____

▶ **Exercise 2**   Writing the Four Types of Sentences.   On the space at the right, write the type of sentence shown in the parentheses.

**EXAMPLE:** (declarative) _____*Kurt built a table out of pine.*_____

1. (declarative) _____
2. (exclamatory) _____
3. (interrogative) _____
4. (imperative, strong command) _____
5. (imperative, mild command) _____

# 21.1 The Four Functions of Sentences • Practice 2

**Exercise 1** **Identifying the Four Types of Sentences.** Read each of the following sentences carefully and identify it as *declarative, interrogative, imperative,* or *exclamatory.* After each answer write the appropriate punctuation mark for that sentence.

**EXAMPLE:** Do you want to go to the movies _____*interrogative*  ?_____

1. The lynx can be found in North America and Asia _____
2. Remove your shoes, please _____
3. Which topic will you choose for the report _____
4. Watch out for spiders _____
5. Will you agree to sing _____
6. Proper care of your teeth is important _____
7. In Roman legend, Remus is the twin brother of Romulus _____
8. Give us the names now _____
9. What a terrible movie we saw _____
10. Are you ready to go _____

**Writing Application** **Writing Sentences with Different Uses.** Write five sentences of your own according to the directions given for each of the following items.

**EXAMPLE:** Write an imperative sentence that does not end with a period.
_____*Watch out!*_____

1. Write a question beginning with *Who.*

_____

_____

2. Write an exclamatory sentence expressing happiness.

_____

_____

3. Write a declarative sentence about Emily Dickinson.

_____

_____

4. Write an imperative sentence that begins with the verb *Finish.*

_____

_____

5. Write a declarative sentence about your state.

_____

_____

# 21.2 Shortening Sentences That Are Too Long
## • Practice 1

**Shortening Rambling Sentences**  Separate rambling compound sentences into two or more shorter sentences.

| Rambling Sentence | Shorter Sentences |
|---|---|
| Janice is an enthusiastic basketball player, *and* she is the top-scoring player on our team, *but* unfortunately, she will not be able to play in tomorrow's game, *for* her sprained ankle is not completely healed. | Janice is an enthusiastic basketball player, *and* the top-scoring player on our team. Unfortunately, she will not be able to play in tomorrow's game, *for* her sprained ankle is not completely healed. |

**Shortening Complicated Sentences**  Separate complicated complex sentences into shorter sentences.

| Complicated Complex Sentence | Shorter Sentences |
|---|---|
| The train stopped at the small station, *which* was a few miles from the center of the city, *because* it was a local run that picked up passengers *who* chose to ride in the late morning. | The train stopped at the small station, *which* was a few miles from the center of the city. It was a local run *that* picked up passengers *who* chose to ride in the late morning. |

▶ **Exercise 1**  **Shortening Rambling Compound Sentences.**  Rewrite each compound sentence to make two or more shorter sentences.

1. Daniel hurriedly packed his books, and he quickly put on his coat, and he raced down the stairs, for he was meeting his friend Charles after school, and they were going shopping for computer games, and they wanted to get to the store at least an hour before it closed.

_____

_____

_____

2. Emily knew she could spend the afternoon chatting with her friend Alexandra, or she could help her mother weed the garden and tend the plants, but instead she chose to spend the time alone in her room, for she wanted to write in her diary.

_____

_____

_____

▶ **Exercise 2**  **Shortening Complicated Complex Sentences.**  Rewrite each sentence to make two or more shorter sentences.

1. Anita was getting ready to leave for school when Helen called to tell her not to forget her American history project, which was due on the teacher's desk the first thing in the morning, even though history class didn't meet until later that afternoon.

_____

_____

_____

2. My cousin, who attends college in Massachusetts, is studying chemistry because he wants to work in a laboratory which is filled with interesting equipment that he can use to perform ingenious experiments that lead to improvements in our daily lives.

_____

_____

_____

# 21.2 Shortening Sentences That Are Too Long
## • Practice 2

▷ **Exercise 1**  **Shortening Rambling Compound Sentences.**  Rewrite each rambling compound sentence that follows to make two or three shorter sentences.

**EXAMPLE:** He rose from bed, and he stretched wearily, and he tried to shake the cobwebs from his mind, but eight weeks of steady work had exhausted him, and he tumbled back into bed and pulled up the covers.

*He rose from bed, and he stretched wearily. He tried to shake the cobwebs from his mind, but eight weeks of steady work had exhausted him. He tumbled back into bed and pulled up the covers.*

1. Joyce wished to enter medical school, so she joined a premedical society at college, and in addition, she worked as a volunteer in an emergency room at the university hospital, and she also worked every other Saturday in a convalescent home for elderly people.

   _____

   _____

   _____

2. A shirt begins as yarn of one or more colors, and then it is woven into a roll of fabric, and next it is sent to a factory, and there it is cut and sewn, and finally it is shipped with other manufactured shirts to a clothing store.

   _____

   _____

   _____

3. The canyon was narrow and winding, and at the bottom a stream trickled over greenish rocks, and on either side of the stream, the walls of the canyon thrust up hundreds of feet toward the racing clouds, and some parts of the cliffs had crumbled into the river, and other parts were pocked with caves carved out by the wind and storms.

   _____

   _____

   _____

▷ **Exercise 2**  **Shortening Complicated Complex Sentences.**  Each of the following is a complicated complex sentence. On a separate sheet of paper, rewrite each sentence to make two or three shorter sentences, changing words as necessary.

1. Although we crossed the Mojave Desert late in the afternoon, we could hardly stand the extreme heat because we did not have air conditioning in the car, which would have allowed us to close the windows instead of suffering the fiery blasts that blew in as we drank water from our cooler and sped east.

2. The old movie that I love most is *Shane* with Alan Ladd who played the role of Shane because Shane is a farmhand with a mysterious past who tries to give up his life as a gunfighter until he becomes involved in a conflict between farmers and a cruel rancher, which is settled when Shane decides to risk his life and fight again to save the family he loves.

3. Even though more carpooling would improve traffic conditions, it alone would not cut down on the congestion that clogs the highways and creates smog because for one reason not everyone can commute with other people is that they often have very different work schedules.

# 21.3 Using Different Sentence Openers
## • Practice 1

**Sentence Openers**   Use different sentence openers, including subjects, adjectives and adverbs, phrases, and clauses.

| DIFFERENT SENTENCE OPENERS |
| --- |
| *Subject: Michelle* owns a black horse. |
| *Adjective: Adventuresome,* the traveler set off alone. |
| *Adverb: Triumphantly,* the hero rode through the city. |
| *Phrase: To express her gratitude,* Susan sent a note. |
| *Clause: Unless I am mistaken,* the movie starts at seven-thirty. |

▶ **Exercise 1**   **Using Different Sentence Openers.**   Rewrite each sentence so that it begins with an adjective, an adverb, a phrase, or a clause.

**EXAMPLE:** We can make an earlier train if we hurry.
            *If we hurry, we can make an earlier train.*

1. Andrew listened to music before he went to sleep.

   _____

2. The enthusiastic tennis player looked for an opponent.

   _____

3. We had a picnic under some shady trees.

   _____

4. The hikers, feeling tired, sat down to rest.

   _____

5. You should bring your bathing suit although it may be too cool to go swimming.

   _____

6. Ira was asked to head the committee since he is a qualified leader.

   _____

7. He repeatedly asked the stewardess when the plane was due to land.

   _____

8. The satisfied customer left the store with a heavy parcel.

   _____

9. The dog, seeing his master approach, ran to greet him.

   _____

10. Carol generously offered to share her lunch with her friend.

    _____

▶ **Exercise 2**   **Varying Sentence Openers Within a Passage.**   On another sheet of paper rewrite the paragraph below, using a variety of sentence openers.

(1) Samuel Adams was quite successful in politics, even though he was unsuccessful in business. (2) This fearless organizer helped form the Sons of Liberty in 1765. (3) He helped plan the Boston Tea Party to protest British trade policies. (4) He urged the colonies to move towards independence when he served as a delegate to the Continental Congress. (5) Adams proudly signed the Declaration of Independence.

# 21.3 Using Different Sentence Openers
## • Practice 2

▶ **Exercise 1** **Using Different Sentence Openers.** Rewrite each of the sentences by moving a word, phrase, or clause.

**EXAMPLE:** They felt more secure after the first play-off game.
_____After the first play-off game, they felt more secure._____

1. Mr. Wu called the police just after his store was robbed.

_____

_____

2. The curious chimpanzee explored the house.

_____

_____

3. The doorbell rang at exactly midnight.

_____

_____

4. Their air-conditioning system failed to operate during the intense heat spell this summer.

_____

_____

5. Clara attended school for five more years to become a veterinarian.

_____

_____

▶ **Writing Application** **Varying Sentence Openers.** The following passage contains a series of sentences that all begin with subjects. Look for different openers for *most* of the sentences. Rewrite the paragraph using a variety of sentence openers to produce a more interesting passage.

(1) The game was tied as it headed into the bottom of the ninth. (2) The pitcher, taking careful aim, delivered a curve ball, and the first batter singled. (3) The first batter then moved to second base because of a wild pitch. (4) The second batter next took a ball, and the man on base stole third. (5) The pitcher then struck out the second batter. (6) The third batter walked after only four pitches. (7) The fourth batter, with a powerful swing, hit a long fly ball. (8) The right fielder caught the ball though the sun was in his eyes. (9) The man on third base was tagged out trying to reach home. (10) The game entered the tenth as the excitement grew.

_____

_____

_____

_____

_____

_____

_____

_____

_____

_____

_____

# 21.3 Improving Short Sentences • Practice 1

**Adding Details**    Add details to the subject, verb, or complement of short sentences.

| ADDING DETAILS TO A SHORT SENTENCE | |
| --- | --- |
| *Details Added to the Subject:* | The customer purchased a bicycle. *The woman customer in the jogging outfit* purchased a bicycle. |
| *Details Added to the Verb:* | The children returned home. *At the end of the day*, the children *happily* returned home. |
| *Details Added to the Complement:* | Kate cooked dinner. Kate cooked a delicious dinner *with fresh vegetables from the garden*. |

**Sentence Combining**    Improve two or more short choppy sentences by combining them into a longer simple sentence, a compound sentence, or a complex sentence.

| COMBINING SHORT SENTENCES |
| --- |
| *Short, Choppy Sentences:* Henry enjoys good music. He attends concerts often. *A Longer Simple Sentence:* To enjoy good music, Henry attends concerts often. *A Compound Sentence:* Henry enjoys good music, and he attends concerts often. *A Complex Sentence:* Because he enjoys good music, Henry attends concerts often. |

> **Exercise 1**    **Adding Details to Short Sentences.**    Expand each sentence below according to the directions given in parentheses.

**EXAMPLE:**  Diana was watching a movie. (Add to the verb.)
       *Nearby, Diana was intently watching a movie.*

1. The airplane landed. (Add to the verb.)

   _____

2. The scientist spoke to them. (Add to the subject.)

   _____

3. Katherine read them a story. (Add to the complement.)

   _____

> **Exercise 2**    **Combining Short Sentences.**    Combine each pair of sentences below. Follow the instructions given in parentheses.

**EXAMPLE:**  We sat by the river. We watched the calm waters. (Change the first sentence into a phrase.)
       *Sitting by the river, we watched the calm waters.*

1. He spoke frankly. He said he opposed the plan. (Change the first sentence to a phrase.)

   _____

2. Bruce understands the procedure. He still makes mistakes. (Write a compound sentence with *but*.)

   _____

3. She heard the startling news. She rushed to the telephone. (Write a complex sentence with *when*.)

   _____

# **21.3** Improving Short Sentences • Practice 2

**▶ Exercise 1** . **Adding Details to Short Sentences.** Each of the following items contains a short sentence followed by three details. Rewrite each sentence, adding the three details.

**EXAMPLE:** Their barn caught fire.
      a. empty     b. in the middle of the night    c. old
      *In the middle of the night, their old, empty barn caught fire.*

1. The couch needs to be re-covered.
    a. in the playroom    b. ragged    c. by a professional

    _____

    _____

2. Carnations brightened the room.
    a. blue and green    b. placed on the night stand    c. hospital

    _____

    _____

3. Dad could not start the engine.
    a. using all his patience and wisdom    b. after it overheated    c. old truck's

    _____

    _____

**▶ Exercise 2** **Combining Short Sentences.** Combine the short sentences using the method given in parentheses.

**EXAMPLE:** The birds perched on the bobbing boat. They looked like passengers with skinny necks. (Make the first sentence a phrase.)

    *Perched on the bobbing boat, the birds looked like passengers with skinny necks.*

1. She began her career as a laboratory technician. She worked at Huntington General Hospital. (Make the second sentence a phrase.)

    _____

    _____

2. Clint admired my poster collection. He offered to buy five posters. (Join the sentences with *and* to form a compound sentence.)

    _____

    _____

3. At the shore we bodysurfed. We played volleyball in the afternoon. (Join the sentences using a compound verb.)

    _____

    _____

4. The company changed its package design. Sales increased sharply. (Join the sentence with *when* to form a complex sentence.)

    _____

    _____

5. Our television's reception was poor. We added a cable adapter. (Join the sentences with *because* to form a complex sentence.)

    _____

    _____

# 21.4 Correcting Sentence Fragments • Practice 1

**Recognizing Fragments**   A fragment is a group of words that does not express a complete thought.

| Fragments | Sentences |
|---|---|
| in the middle of the lake | A large raft sat *in the middle of the lake.* |
| the plane on the runway | *The plane on the runway* has developed problems with its engines. |
| wonder where I left my notebook | I *wonder where I left my notebook.* |
| raising its paw | The dog *raising its paw* is a spaniel. |
| when we were driving home | *When we were driving home,* a storm began. |

▶ **Exercise 1**   **Recognizing Sentence Fragments.**   Write whether each group of words is a *sentence* or a *fragment*.

**EXAMPLE:**  If I begin planning now. _____*fragment*_____

1.  As I gazed at the tree. _____

2.  In the afternoon, we had a picnic. _____

3.  The long, wooden table. _____

4.  When we arrived at our destination. _____

5.  After I have saved enough money. _____

6.  We fished for hours, but caught nothing. _____

7.  Dad always rises very early in the morning. _____

8.  While Harold was still a boy. _____

9.  During the Olympic competition. _____

10.  Under the eaves of the house. _____

▶ **Exercise 2**   **Identifying Sentence Fragments.**   In the items below, underline each sentence once and each fragment twice.

**EXAMPLE:**  Dragging himself along the ground.

1.  I couldn't see the house in the fog.

2.  With all its colors flying.

3.  In the last chapter of the book.

4.  Since September, I have grown five inches.

5.  Since I started school this fall.

6.  If he could have one wish.

7.  She couldn't understand the strange language.

8.  We talked.

9.  Beyond the little village.

10.  Will take many years.

# 21.4 Correcting Sentence Fragments • Practice 2

▶ **Exercise 1** **Recognizing Sentence Fragments.** Each of the following word groups is either a sentence or a fragment. Write *F* if it is a fragment and *S* if it is a complete sentence. If it is a *fragment*, write a complete sentence using the fragment.

**EXAMPLE:** Firefighters climbing ladders. ___*F*___

_____*Firefighters climbing ladders reached the top of the building.*_____

1. Near the new traffic light. _____

_____

2. A car jumping the curb. _____

_____

3. The motor turned over. _____

_____

4. Tried all day to contact them. _____

_____

5. Since she speaks Spanish well. _____

_____

6. The roof of the old auditorium. _____

_____

7. Everyone accepted the decision. _____

_____

8. At the bottom of the well. _____

_____

9. Finished my shopping for the holidays. _____

_____

10. Unless they answer by tomorrow. _____

_____

11. The bicycle in front of the store. _____

_____

12. The governor standing on the new platform. _____

_____

13. The man suffering from the heat. _____

_____

14. In hot weather a cold drink often helps. _____

_____

15. Completed the project in an hour. _____

_____

# 21.4 Correcting Fragments (Phrases, Clauses)
## • Practice 1

**Phrase Fragments**  A phrase should not be capitalized and punctuated as if it were a sentence.

| Phrase Fragments | Complete Sentences |
|---|---|
| *during the storm* | A shutter blew off the house *during the storm.* |
| *looking across the street* | *Looking across the street,* I saw Carol. |
| *to explain my problem* | I tried *to explain my problem.* |

**Clause Fragments**  A subordinate clause should not be capitalized and punctuated as if it were a sentence.

| Clause Fragments | Complete Sentence |
|---|---|
| *that you painted* | I saw the picture *that you painted.* |
| *that was playing at the theater* | She went to the movie *that was playing at the theater.* |
| *when Tom was six* | *When Tom was six,* his family moved to Des Moines. |

▶ **Exercise 1**  **Identifying Phrase Fragments and Clause Fragments.**  Write whether each item is a *phrase fragment*, a *clause fragment*, or a *sentence*.

**EXAMPLE:** With this victory. ___*phrase fragment*___

1. During the night. _____
2. Which opened last week on Broadway. _____
3. After the rodeo had ended. _____
4. When I reach the age of twenty-five. _____
5. Inside that dark cave, a brown bear is hibernating. _____
6. On July 4, 1776. _____
7. I spent an entire day wandering through the beautiful gardens. _____
8. Who arrived from Ireland many years ago. _____
9. Sitting by the window. _____
10. After graduation, Paul is joining the army. _____

▶ **Exercise 2**  **Correcting Fragments.**  Turn five of the fragments you identified in Exercise 1 into sentences.

**EXAMPLE:** ___*The war ended with this victory.*___

1. _____
2. _____
3. _____
4. _____
5. _____

## 21.4 Correcting Fragments (Phrases, Clauses)
### • Practice 2

▶ **Exercise 1**　**Changing Phrase Fragments into Sentences.**　Use each of the following phrase fragments in a sentence. You may use the phrase at the beginning, at the end, or in any other position in the sentence. Check to see that each of your sentences contains a subject and verb.

**EXAMPLE:** in the morning after breakfast
_____Sheri took the dog to the kennel in the morning after breakfast._____

1. on the telephone
   _____

2. to think clearly
   _____

3. getting tired
   _____

4. on time to class
   _____

5. found on the beach
   _____

6. waiting at school
   _____

7. drinking cold milk
   _____

8. on last night's news
   _____

9. at breakfast
   _____

10. stung by a bee
   _____

▶ **Exercise 2**　**Changing Clause Fragments into Sentences.**　Use each clause fragment in a sentence. Include an independent clause in each sentence.

**EXAMPLE:** that she wanted to use
_____I lent her the hammer that she wanted to use._____

1. if you write to me soon
   _____

2. who knows the combination to the lock
   _____

3. that he told us
   _____

4. whom they described to the police
   _____

5. although she doesn't speak French too well
   _____

**21.4** # Correcting Run-ons • Practice 1

**Two Kinds of Run-ons**   A run-on is two or more complete sentences that are not properly joined or separated. There are two kinds of run-ons. One is made up of two sentences that run together without any punctuation between them. The other consists of two or more sentences separated only by a comma.

| RUN-ONS | |
|---|---|
| **With No Punctuation** | **With Only a Comma** |
| Your body is supported by the skeletal system it includes bones and joints. | Lewis and Clark headed west, they eventually reached the Pacific. |

▶ **Exercise 1**   **Identifying Run-ons.**   Write whether each item is a *run-on* or a *sentence* in the space at the right.

**EXAMPLE:** The glacier moved southward it covered miles of territory. _____*run-on*_____

1. Hannibal crossed the Alps he had elephants with him. _____

2. They lived on a large plantation, many slaves tended the fields. _____

3. Washington led his troops into battle, they were victorious. _____

4. The Bahama Islands are located in the Atlantic Ocean, Columbus landed there. _____

5. When gold was discovered in California, many people traveled there. _____

6. A cold front moved across the state temperatures fell rapidly. _____

7. During the afternoon of March 7, an important meeting occurred at the capital. _____

8. Trees are not completely helpless, they can protect themselves from insects. _____

9. Richard the Lion-Hearted was king of England he fought in the Crusades. _____

10. Some elderly people remain active, others prefer to sit at home. _____

▶ **Exercise 2**   **Recognizing Run-ons.**   Underline each item that is a run-on.

**EXAMPLE:** The pilot landed the plane in Seattle, it had been a bumpy flight.

1. During the Civil War, brother sometimes fought against brother.

2. Hawaii is located in the Pacific, it is famous for magnificent beaches and lush, tropical foliage.

3. The Vikings established a kingdom in Russia, they were courageous seafarers.

4. Standing on top of the hill was a small horse. It looked like a Shetland pony.

5. Before the ice thaws, we should go skating on the pond again.

6. The economy moves up and down, from good times into recessions and back again.

7. I am reading an interesting novel it was written by Willa Cather.

8. We are organizing a large Labor Day Parade this one will be the biggest in years.

9. The new model car that I am building is a Packard.

10. Watch the news tonight I think you will see something very unusual.

## 21.4 Correcting Run-ons • Practice 2

▶ **Exercise 1**  **Recognizing Run-ons.**  Next to each item, write *S* if the item is a sentence and *RO* if the item is a run-on.

**EXAMPLE:**  At fifteen John Keats began studying medicine, at twenty-one he was encouraged to work as a poet. ___*RO*___

1. On my last trip, I visited Platt National Park in Oklahoma I also spent some time at the Mesa Verde National Park in Colorado. _____

2. There are many famous horses in mythology, probably the most famous is the wooden horse of Troy. _____

3. After overcoming many problems, he finally finished staining the cabinet. _____

4. Saint Genevieve is the patron saint of Paris she is supposed to have prevented Attila the Hun from attacking that city. _____

5. The commuter railroads seem to have little trouble on weekends they run into problems with heavy passenger loads on weekdays. _____

6. The heart is a muscular, cone-shaped organ that maintains the circulation of the blood. _____

7. Some people prefer active sports, others like to watch sports on television. _____

8. Havana is the capital of Cuba it is also the chief port of the West Indies. _____

9. In 1926, Amy Lowell won the Pulitzer Prize for her poetry. _____

10. The side wall of the building collapsed, the next day the rest of the building was torn down. _____

▶ **Exercise 2**  **Recognizing Run-ons.**  Each of the following items is a run-on. If the run-on is made of two sentences without punctuation, write *NP* in the space provided. If the run-on is made of two or more sentences separated by only a comma, write *C* in the space provided.

**EXAMPLE:**  The sale begins on Saturday morning all departments will be affected. ___*NP*___

1. All jackets, sweaters, and coats in the store are on sale the discounts are up to fifty percent. _____

2. Let's shop early, you know I need a new jacket for the winter. _____

3. I've always wanted to get a red jacket with fur trim, of course the fur would have to be fake. _____

4. How about you what kind of jacket would you like to get? _____

5. After we shop, we can eat lunch, let's try that new restaurant on Fourth. _____

6. The restaurant serves pizza, chicken, and salads, I've heard the salads are very good. _____

7. Later we can go to the art museum there's a new photography exhibit. _____

8. Who's your favorite photographer I like Dorothea Lange. _____

9. I have two free passes to the art museum, that's a savings of about ten dollars. _____

10. If it's cold enough, we can wear our new jackets we'll be the best-dressed pair there! _____

# 21.4 Correcting Run-ons • Practice 1

**Three Ways to Correct Run-ons**   There are three easy ways to correct a run-on. Use an end mark to separate a run-on into two statements. Use a comma and a coordinating conjunction to combine two independent clauses into a compound sentence. Use a semicolon to connect two closely related ideas.

| WAYS TO CORRECT RUN-ONS |
| --- |
| **Using End Marks** |
| Have you seen my new costume it looks terrific? |
| Have you seen my new costume? It looks terrific. |
| **Using Commas and Coordinating Conjunctions** |
| My brother will be working this summer I am going to camp. |
| My brother will be working this summer, but I am going to camp. |
| **Using Semicolons** |
| Some people enjoy classical music others prefer jazz. |
| Some people enjoy classical music; others prefer jazz. |

> **Exercise 1**   **Identifying Run-ons.**   Place an *R* after each item if it is a run-on. Place an *S* after each item if it is a sentence.

**EXAMPLE:**  We began to shovel the snow it was very deep.    ___*R*___

1. The cattle stampeded across the plain for fifty miles. _____

2. We expected the senator to arrive tonight she has just returned from Africa. _____

3. Franklin Roosevelt became President in 1933 he served until 1945. _____  .

4. Where are we going when will we arrive? _____

5. I like cereal for breakfast my brother likes eggs and toast. _____

6. When I arrived at the station, my father was there to meet me. _____

7. A team is only as good as its players, we have the best. _____

8. After she graduated from college, Susan joined the Peace Corps. _____

9. Here is the package you ordered it was delivered this morning. _____

10. What can we accomplish with so little time and with so little help? _____

> **Exercise 2**   **Correcting Run-ons.**   Correct five of the run-ons you identified in Exercise 1.

**EXAMPLE:**  ____*We began to shovel the snow. It was very deep.*____

1. _____

2. _____

3. _____

4. _____

5. _____

**21.4** **Correcting Run-ons • Practice 2**

▶ **Exercise 1** **Correcting Run-ons.** Rewrite each of the following run-ons using any of the three methods described in this section.

**EXAMPLE:** Tell the truth, it is easier than lying.
*Tell the truth. It is easier than lying.*

1. I had a terrible day at school, I lost my lunch and stained my shirt with dye during science.

2. An old saying says that a new broom sweeps clean our new coach may thus make a lot of changes.

3. Do you know who was the last President of the United States to serve two full terms, President George Bush served only one term.

4. Nancy loves humorous poems, her favorites are Carroll's "Jabberwocky" and Nash's "The Panther."

5. Finish your homework, then clean your desk.

6. My mother and aunt collect porcelain my brother and I collect coins.

7. Histamines cause itching, some people take antihistamines for relief.

8. Benito Juarez is a national hero in Mexico he helped defeat the French and drive them from his land.

9. Crops are damaged by a variety of pests, spraying them with special insecticides sometimes helps.

10. A silver jubilee celebrates an event that occurred twenty-five years before, Queen Elizabeth II celebrated her silver jubilee in 1977.

**21.4** # Recognizing Misplaced Modifiers • Practice 1

**Misplaced Modifiers**   A modifier should be placed as close as possible to the word it modifies. A modifier placed too far away is called a misplaced modifier. Such a word or phrase seems to modify the wrong word in the sentence.

| MISPLACED MODIFIERS |
|---|
| I chased the balloon *running down the street.*<br>They had a fine dinner in the restaurant *with dessert and coffee.*<br>*Reaching the bottom of the mountain,* the trip was finally over. |

▶ **Exercise 1**   **Recognizing Misplaced Modifiers.**   Underline the misplaced modifiers in each sentence below.

**EXAMPLE:**  Walking along the shore, dark clouds gathered overhead.

1.  I found a quarter walking home.

2.  Sitting on the dock, a school of porpoises appeared.

3.  The snake did not see the approaching mongoose lying in the sun.

4.  Riding his horse in front of them, the soldiers cheered their commander.

5.  Doug bought a book in the store on astronomy.

6.  I saw a film in the theater about Gandhi.

7.  Working all day, the leaves were finally cleared.

8.  We purchased a new car from the dealer with a sunroof.

9.  Looking through the binoculars, the bird was easy to identify.

10.  We found fresh fruits and vegetables shopping in the bazaar.

▶ **Exercise 2**   **Identifying Misplaced Modifiers.**   Write *MM* next to each sentence that has a misplaced modifier and *C* next to each sentence that is correct.

**EXAMPLE:**  Waiting in line, shopping took a long time. ___*MM*___

1.  A new library with three stories will be erected on Main Street. _____

2.  Listening to records, time passed very quickly. _____

3.  I read a magazine at the barbershop about computers. _____

4.  The band marched down Pine Street playing its instruments. _____

5.  We just moved into a house built in 1820 with two fireplaces. _____

6.  Strolling through the fields, the sun began to set. _____

7.  We built a cabinet for the bedroom with three shelves. _____

8.  In school I wrote poetry about my dreams for the future. _____

9.  Looking for a summer job, Bill talked to every storeowner in town. _____

10.  Perched on the birdfeeder, I watched the robin eating seeds. _____

11.  Walking down the aisle, the curtain rose. _____

12.  To play tennis well, a good racquet is needed. _____

13.  If you exercise every day, your health will improve. _____

14.  After visiting Yosemite, other parks seem rather ordinary. _____

15.  Being very tired, the alarm was not heard. _____

# 21.4 Recognizing Misplaced Modifiers • Practice 2

▶ **Exercise 1** **Recognizing Misplaced Modifiers.** Some of the following sentences are correct, but most of them contain a misplaced modifier. Read each sentence carefully and check the placement of the modifiers. If the sentence is correct, write *C*. If the sentence contains a misplaced modifier, write *MM*.

**EXAMPLE:** My brother Richard bought a loaf of bread at the local supermarket that had turned green with mold. _____*MM*_____

1. Crossing the street, the curb was very high. _____
2. She bought a jacket from the catalog with large patch pockets. _____
3. Traveling in Spain, the roof of their house collapsed. _____
4. A beautiful car with whitewalls and a vinyl roof appeared in our driveway. _____
5. Seth found a book in the local library about prehistoric animals. _____
6. Reaching the top of the hill, the town could be clearly seen. _____
7. Worried about her mother, April called home three times. _____
8. Bring the package to me with the green cord. _____
9. Two girls in red bathing suits swam near the dock. _____
10. Father bought a key chain for my sister with a whistle. _____

▶ **Exercise 2** **Recognizing Misplaced Modifiers.** The following paragraph contains ten misplaced modifiers. Write each misplaced modifier on one of the lines beneath the paragraph.

**EXAMPLE:** Staring at the ceiling, the solution finally came to me.

_____*Staring at the ceiling*_____

Walking up the driveway, the tree looked beautiful near the house. It had been decorated for the upcoming holidays the week before. Barbara strolled across the lawn toward the tree wearing a white coat. Shivering a bit, the coat did little to keep her warm. Wearing a pair of open sandals, the dew on the grass got her feet wet. Barking loudly, Barbara heard the dog before she saw it. Running from the side of the house to greet her, Barbara was startled to see the huge Great Dane. Slightly frightened, the dog almost knocked Barbara over. Coming from behind the tree, the dog was calmed down by Alan, who said, "Down, boy!"

1. _____
2. _____
3. _____
4. _____
5. _____
6. _____
7. _____
8. _____
9. _____
10. _____

**21.4** # Correcting Misplaced Modifiers • Practice 1

**Revising Sentences with Misplaced Modifiers**  Among the most common misplaced modifiers are prepositional phrases, participial phrases, and adjective clauses. All are corrected by placing the modifier as close as possible to the word it modifies.

| Misplaced Modifiers | Corrected Sentences |
|---|---|
| Jack wore a coat to the game *with a hood on it.* | Jack wore a coat *with a hood on it* to the game. |
| I found a buried treasure *exploring the cave.* | *Exploring the cave,* I found a buried treasure. |
| We finally located the wrench in the shed *which we needed.* | We finally located the wrench *which we needed* in the shed. |

▶ **Exercise 1**  **Recognizing Misplaced Modifiers.**  Underline the misplaced modifiers in the sentences below.

**EXAMPLE:**  <u>Walking the tightrope</u>, we watched the juggler.

1.  I went to the checkout counter at the bargain store with the green ribbon.

2.  Chattering in the tree, we listened to two squirrels.

3.  Sally put on her coat before she reached the door with the silver buttons.

4.  The rocket left Earth far behind cruising rapidly through space.

5.  I watched the television program when I finished dinner set in Ireland.

6.  Carefully listening with a stethoscope, the boy was examined by the doctor.

7.  The policeman began to chase the thief blowing his whistle.

8.  For his birthday, he received a jacket from his father with a zip-out lining.

9.  Carol visited Bryce Canyon which is located in Utah after school ended.

10.  In six months, the author finished the book writing diligently.

▶ **Exercise 2**  **Correcting Misplaced Modifiers.**  Rewrite the sentences in Exercise 1, correcting the misplaced modifiers.

**EXAMPLE:**  _We watched the juggler walking the tightrope._

1.  _____
2.  _____
3.  _____
4.  _____
5.  _____
6.  _____
7.  _____
8.  _____
9.  _____
10.  _____

# 21.4 Correcting Misplaced Modifiers • Practice 2

▶ **Exercise 1**    **Correcting Misplaced Modifiers.**    Rewrite the sentences to eliminate the misplaced modifiers. Underline the modifier that was misplaced. Then draw an arrow pointing from the modifier to the word it modifies.

**EXAMPLE:** My brother Richard bought a loaf of bread at the local supermarket that had turned green with mold.

    *At the local supermarket, my brother Richard bought a loaf of*

    *bread that had turned green with mold.*

1. The dress had already been purchased that she wanted.

   _____

2. Reaching the park, my aunt was waiting on a bench.

   _____

3. Uncle Ron bought a hat at the bazaar with a green feather.

   _____

4. I read the story when I got home with the surprise ending.

   _____

5. Told to move along, the hissing of the crowd increased.

   _____

6. The famous actor arrived late whom everyone hoped to see.

   _____

7. Walking rather slowly toward the station, the train was almost missed.

   _____

8. Tudor Castle was destroyed by a terrible fire built in 1512.

   _____

9. I received a new television from my mother with remote controls.

   _____

10. The soldiers finally caught the man after a long chase who was spying on them.

    _____

## 21.4 Double Negatives • Practice 1

**The Mistaken Use of Double Negatives** Negative words mistakenly used together are double negatives. Avoid writing sentences with double negatives.

| Double Negatives | Correct Negative Sentences |
|---|---|
| He doesn't trust nobody. | He doesn't trust anybody. He trusts nobody. |
| Sue never said nothing to me about a ride. | Sue never said anything to me about a ride. |
| | Sue said nothing to me about a ride. |

▷ **Exercise 1** **Correcting Double Negatives.** Underline the word in parentheses that is correct in each sentence.

**EXAMPLE:** I didn't notice (any, no) telephone booth.

1. I didn't have (any, no) change to make a phone call.
2. We know Jamie wouldn't do (nothing, anything) wrong.
3. There weren't (any, no) letters in the mailbox when I looked.
4. Nicole wouldn't give me (no, any) help with my math homework.
5. Elsie doesn't tell (no one, anyone) about her problems.
6. These grapes don't have (no, any) seeds.
7. Don't sing (nothing, anything) until you have read it carefully.
8. We went to the zoo, but we didn't see (any, no) koala bears.
9. Jeff wouldn't let (anybody, nobody) help him.
10. I haven't (no, any) money to spend on records.

▷ **Exercise 2** **Using Negatives Correctly.** Write a sentence of your own, correctly using each negative word in parentheses.

**EXAMPLE:** (nothing) _There is nothing we can do about it now._

1. (couldn't) _____
2. (no) _____
3. (nothing) _____
4. (never) _____
5. (won't) _____
6. (nowhere) _____
7. (haven't) _____
8. (nobody) _____
9. (none) _____
10. (not) _____

**21.4**

# Double Negatives • Practice 2

▶ **Exercise 1**   **Correcting Double Negatives.**   The following sentences contain double negatives, which are underlined. Correct each sentence in *two* ways. Write each pair of corrected sentences beneath each incorrect sentence.

**EXAMPLE:**  I didn't see <u>no</u> airplanes.

> _____*I didn't see any airplanes.*_____
> _____*I saw no airplanes.*_____

1. That bicycle factory has<u>n't</u> made <u>nothing</u> for ten years.

   _____

   _____

2. The railroad tracks that run past our yard do<u>n't</u> lead <u>nowhere</u>.

   _____

   _____

3. Do<u>n't</u> eat <u>nothing</u> now, or you won't enjoy your dinner.

   _____

   _____

4. Lillian has<u>n't</u> <u>no</u> place to keep her model train set.

   _____

   _____

5. The Governor has<u>n't</u> shown <u>nobody</u> the speech he is delivering tonight.

   _____

   _____

6. Lonnie has<u>n't</u> played <u>no</u> music with an orchestra.

   _____

   _____

7. These sandals do<u>n't</u> have <u>no</u> straps.

   _____

   _____

8. There were<u>n't</u> <u>no</u> more seats on the bus after we got on.

   _____

   _____

9. I ca<u>n't</u> remember <u>nothing</u> about my dreams last night.

   _____

   _____

10. Sheila would<u>n't</u> give me <u>none</u> of her crackers.

   _____

   _____

**21.4** # Common Usage Problems • **Practice 1**

**Common Usage Problems** Some common usage problems are expressions that you should avoid in your speaking and writing. Others are words that are often confused because of similar spelling or meaning.

| TYPES OF PROBLEMS | |
|---|---|
| Similar Spellings | *advice* and *advise; farther* and *further* |
| Similar Sounds | *accept* and *except; their, there,* and *they're* |
| Misused Pairs | *in* and *into; beside* and *besides* |

▷ **Exercise 1** **Avoiding Some Common Usage Problems.** Underline the word in parentheses that correctly completes each sentence.

**EXAMPLE:** Carla wrote to Dr. Fix-It for (advice, advise) about her problem.

1. As yet, no one (beside, besides) you and me knows about the treasure.
2. We were happy to (accept, except) your invitation.
3. Chemicals used on land can also (affect, effect) life in lakes and streams.
4. Are you sure that you know where this store (is, is at)?
5. The revision is quite different (than, from) the original poem.
6. Everyone (accept, except) Cinderella left for the ball.
7. The reason I got a D on the quiz is (that, because) I studied the wrong chapter.
8. What (affect, effect) will the new regulation have on us?
9. (Beside, Besides) visiting the Lincoln Memorial, we went to the zoo.
10. Did the lawyer (advice, advise) you to sue?

▷ **Exercise 2** **Avoiding Other Common Usage Problems.** Underline the word in parentheses that correctly completes each sentence.

**EXAMPLE:** She got the mail and came back (in, into) the house.

1. I like these jeans, but they are (sort of, rather) expensive.
2. The ballerina needed no (farther, further) urging to make a curtain call.
3. She is a person (who, whom) I greatly admire.
4. This is (the place where, where) the accident occurred.
5. The fox was much (to, too) clever to be caught by the hounds.
6. Whales have to breathe air (like, as) other mammals do.
7. After a poor start, the Penguins won the rest of (they're, their) games.
8. Nancy swam much (farther, further) out than I did.
9. I always thought that Mr. Hotchkiss was (rather, kind of) stingy.
10. The nose of the jet sloped down (as, like) the beak of a bird.

# 21.4  Common Usage Problems • Practice 2

▷ **Exercise 1**  **Avoiding Usage Problems.**  For each of the following sentences, write the correct form in the blank from the choices in parentheses.

**EXAMPLE:** I can't _____accept_____ this check for a million dollars. (accept, except)

1. When I asked you for _____, I didn't expect a lecture. (advice, advise)
2. Do you know where the public telephones _____? (are, are at)
3. Everyone _____ Elsie burst out laughing at the burned pancakes. (accept, except)
4. The reason I spoke up was _____ you were absolutely right. (because, that)
5. Praise had an unusual _____ on the new puppy. (affect, effect)
6. Marcie never forgot the day when her puzzle was _____ for the math club's newsletter. (accepted, excepted)
7. The weather always _____ Zack's state of mind. (affects, effects)
8. I have finally discovered where your secret hiding place _____. (is, is at)
9. The Highway Patrol _____ motorists to stay off the roads today. (advices, advises)
10. Gil's reason for leaving at nine was _____ he had an early class. (because, that)

▷ **Exercise 2**  **Avoiding Usage Problems.**  For each of the following sentences, write the correct form in the blank from the choices in parentheses.

1. You need to explain your idea _____. (farther, further)
2. This parakeet is different _____ the others because it can already speak. (from, than)
3. The decorations around their windows indicate that these buildings are _____ old. (kind of, rather)
4. The Frisbees were _____ the trunk of the car. (in, into)
5. Carol is the girl who just sat down _____ Nancy. (beside, besides)
6. I was _____ upset after I stepped on the bee. (sort of, rather)
7. This newspaper is entirely different _____ the way it used to be. (from, than)
8. _____ visiting the Statue of Liberty, we're going to Radio City today. (Beside, Besides)
9. I think the country store is _____ than five miles away. (farther, further)
10. The young father tiptoed _____ the baby's room to close the window. (in, into)

▷ **Exercise 3**  **Avoiding Usage Problems.**  For each of the following sentences, write the correct form in the blank from the choices in parentheses.

1. This trunk is _____ I keep my old toys. (the place where, where)
2. It takes _____ people to ride a seesaw. (too, two)
3. In his skin-diving outfit, my father looked exactly _____ a frog. (as, like)
4. The rabbit _____ we saw had ears of different colors. (that, whom)
5. _____ are two sets of twins in that family. (There, They're)
6. Late fall is _____ slightly sour apples taste best. (the time when, when)
7. _____ the twig is bent, so grows the tree. (As, Like)
8. The person _____ won the contest has not yet claimed the prize. (that, which)
9. _____ few people know how to do their own home repairs. (Too, To)
10. Their mother called to say that _____ coming to the party. (their, they're)

# 22.1 The Four Principal Parts of Verbs (Regular)
## • Practice 1

**Regular Verbs**   A verb has four principal parts: the present, the present participle, the past, and the past participle. The past and past participle of a regular verb are formed by adding *-ed* or *-d* to the present form. Most verbs are regular.

| PRINCIPAL PARTS OF REGULAR VERBS | | | |
|---|---|---|---|
| **Present** | **Present Participle** | **Past** | **Past Participle** |
| join | (am) joining | joined | (have) joined |
| like | (am) liking | liked | (have) liked |

▶ **Exercise 1**   **Recognizing the Principal Parts of Regular Verbs.**   Identify the principal part used to form the underlined verb in each sentence below.

**EXAMPLE:** Peter's family is moving to Canada.   _____*present participle*_____

1. Barbara and Lee filled the fish tank with fresh water. _____
2. The President is holding a press conference tomorrow. _____
3. My brother is enrolling in college in the fall. _____
4. Canadians pronounce the letter "zed." _____
5. Have the judges announced the winner? _____
6. We had hoped for better weather for our Field Day. _____
7. The head chef personally prepared each dish. _____
8. The first guests had already arrived. _____
9. We are planning a trip to Yellowstone Park next summer. _____
10. I have not finished my report yet. _____

▶ **Exercise 2**   **Using the Principal Parts of Verbs.**   Fill in each blank with the correct form of the verb in parentheses.

**EXAMPLE:** The detective had _____*hoped*_____ for a few more clues. (hope)

1. This week, the library is _____ at noon on Saturdays. (close)
2. The letter carrier _____ the package this morning. (deliver)
3. After the long dry spell, we _____ the rain yesterday. (welcome)
4. The jury has still not _____ a verdict. (reach)
5. Her uncle was _____ impatiently at the airport. (wait)
6. Michelle and Paul sometimes _____ piano duets together. (play)
7. Jess has still not _____ his lines for the play. (learn)
8. Sergeant Broudy _____ life-saving at last week's meeting. (demonstrate)
9. The witness has _____ to testify. (refuse)
10. What has _____ at the meetings? (happen)

# 22.1 The Four Principal Parts of Verbs (Regular)
## • Practice 2

▶ **Exercise 1** **Recognizing the Principal Parts of Regular Verbs.** The verb or verb phrase in each of the following sentences is underlined. Identify the principal part used to form each verb.

**EXAMPLE:** Ginny is painting a portrait of her sister. _____present participle_____

1. Chris filled the flower pot with pebbles and soil. _____
2. We are visiting the state legislature tomorrow. _____
3. Roberto is joining the photography club. _____
4. Has Denise mentioned her vacation plans to you? _____
5. Hot meals always taste better on a cold day. _____
6. I had climbed the hill too late for the fireworks. _____
7. The lifeguards cleaned the pool every day last summer. _____
8. Why was Steve dancing down the hill? _____
9. I have not typed my essay yet. _____
10. Kate is planning a surprise party for her brother. _____

▶ **Exercise 2** **Using the Principal Parts of Regular Verbs.** In the blank space, write the correct form of the verb given in parentheses.

**EXAMPLE:** They have _____looked_____ everywhere for the missing piece. (look)

1. After the long train ride yesterday, we _____ in relief. (sigh)
2. Before he left, Kevin _____ Jane to visit him soon. (ask)
3. Tracy _____ in the parade last Thursday. (march)
4. We have _____ about the noise repeatedly. (complain)
5. Last week, the boys _____ Easter Eggs across the lawn. (roll)
6. I am _____ that sonata in the music recital. (play)
7. Had you _____ him before he stood up? (notice)
8. After I _____ the floor last week, I never wanted to see another piece of wood. (polish)
9. Last winter the wind _____ down the old tree. (knock)
10. Rodney and Meg will _____ their geography project. (start)

# 22.1 The Four Principal Parts of Verbs (Irregular)
## • Practice 1

**Irregular Verbs** The past and past participle of an irregular verb do not follow the pattern for spelling verbs by adding *-ed* or *-d* to the present form.

| PRINCIPAL PARTS OF IRREGULAR VERBS | | | |
|---|---|---|---|
| **Present** | **Present Participle** | **Past** | **Past Participle** |
| become | (am) becoming | became | (have) become |
| begin | (am) beginning | began | (have) begun |
| bring | (am) bringing | brought | (have) brought |
| choose | (am) choosing | chose | (have) chosen |
| drink | (am) drinking | drank | (have) drunk |
| hurt | (am) hurting | hurt | (have) hurt |
| lead | (am) leading | led | (have) led |
| write | (am) writing | wrote | (have) written |

▶ **Exercise 1** **Completing the Principal Parts of Irregular Verbs.** Write the missing principal parts of the following irregular verbs.

**EXAMPLE:** ___lose___  ___am losing___  ___lost___  ___(have) lost___

1. _____  _____  _____  (have) held

2. _____  (am) riding  _____  _____

3. set  _____  _____  _____

4. _____  _____  swung  _____

5. throw  _____  _____  _____

6. _____  _____  _____  (have) sunk

7. _____  (am) breaking  _____  _____

8. _____  (am) fighting  _____  _____

9. shake  _____  _____  _____

10. _____  _____  caught  _____

▶ **Exercise 2** **Using the Principal Parts of Irregular Verbs.** Fill in each blank with the correct verb form from the choices in parentheses.

**EXAMPLE:** Nancy had never ___ridden___ a horse before. (rode, ridden)

1. The soprano _____ the Canadian national anthem and then ours. (sang, sung)
2. Terry _____ faster than anyone else in the tryouts. (swam, swum)
3. The two old friends had _____ each other since childhood. (knew, known)
4. By that time, most of the others had _____ home. (went, gone)
5. The bubble _____ as it hit the ceiling. (burst, busted)
6. The storm has _____ down several big trees. (blew, blown)
7. The movie had already _____ when we got to the theater. (begin, begun)
8. Yesterday, our dog _____ home someone's lunch bag. (brang, brought)
9. Have you _____ a topic for your report yet? (chose, chosen)
10. The pitcher _____ a few more warm-up pitches. (throwed, threw)

# 22.1 The Four Principal Parts of Verbs (Irregular)
## • Practice 2

▶ **Exercise 1**  **Completing the Principal Parts of Irregular Verbs.**  Write the missing principal parts for the following irregular verbs.

**EXAMPLE:**

| Present | Present Participle | Past | Past Participle |
|---|---|---|---|
| begin | beginning | began | begun |

| | Present | Present Participle | Past | Past Participle |
|---|---|---|---|---|
| 1. | teach | _____ | _____ | _____ |
| 2. | _____ | _____ | cost | _____ |
| 3. | _____ | giving | _____ | _____ |
| 4. | _____ | _____ | _____ | worn |
| 5. | _____ | catching | _____ | _____ |
| 6. | fly | _____ | _____ | _____ |
| 7. | _____ | _____ | _____ | burst |
| 8. | _____ | _____ | went | _____ |
| 9. | _____ | paying | _____ | _____ |
| 10. | shake | _____ | _____ | _____ |
| 11. | _____ | _____ | lost | _____ |
| 12. | _____ | _____ | _____ | lain |
| 13. | _____ | swearing | _____ | _____ |
| 14. | say | _____ | _____ | _____ |
| 15. | _____ | _____ | found | _____ |
| 16. | _____ | _____ | _____ | frozen |
| 17. | _____ | _____ | got | _____ |
| 18. | ride | _____ | _____ | _____ |
| 19. | _____ | springing | _____ | _____ |
| 20. | _____ | _____ | _____ | put |
| 21. | _____ | growing | _____ | _____ |
| 22. | sink | _____ | _____ | _____ |
| 23. | _____ | _____ | _____ | broken |
| 24. | _____ | _____ | fought | _____ |
| 25. | _____ | leading | _____ | _____ |

▶ **Exercise 2**  **Supplying the Correct Principal Part of Irregular Verbs.**  In the blank space, write the correct past or past participle form of the verb given in parentheses.

**EXAMPLE:** You should have ____brought____ your radio with you. (bring)

1. After a spectacular career as a chef, my uncle _____ down his tall hat and favorite spoon and retired. (lay)

2. We always thought that he should have _____ his own restaurant. (buy)

3. Jay _____ into the parking lot and announced that we were already late. (drive)

4. Emily has always _____ early to exercise before going to school. (rise)

5. The snow _____ all day, creating drifts that were taller than we were. (fall)

# 22.2 The Six Tenses of Verbs • Practice 1

**The Basic Forms of the Six Tenses**  A tense is a form of a verb that shows when something happens or when something exists.

| BASIC FORMS OF THE SIX TENSES OF *BREAK* | | | |
|---|---|---|---|
| **Tense** | **Basic Form** | **Tense** | **Basic Form** |
| **Present** | I break | **Present Perfect** | I have broken |
| **Past** | I broke | **Past Perfect** | I had broken |
| **Future** | I will break | **Future Perfect** | I will have broken |

**Conjugating the Basic Forms of the Six Tenses**  A conjugation is a list of the singular and plural forms of a verb in a particular tense. An important verb to learn to conjugate is the verb *be*. It is the most common and the most irregular verb.

▶ **Exercise 1**  **Identifying the Basic Forms of Verbs.**  Identify the tense of each underlined verb in the following sentences.

**EXAMPLE:** The hikers had lost their way in the fog. _____past perfect_____

1. We have just finished our rehearsal. _____
2. With this tail wind, the plane will arrive early. _____
3. The audience listened closely to the speaker. _____
4. Mr. Waldner has brought some samples for us to look at. _____
5. Frannie and I walk to school most of the time. _____
6. At first Lisa had been nervous about playing in public. _____
7. By next week, the workers will have finished the job. _____
8. The pitcher threw six fast balls in a row. _____
9. Only local trains stop at this station. _____
10. We will send you a postcard from London. _____

▶ **Exercise 2**  **Supplying the Correct Tense.**  Fill in each blank with the verb form called for in parentheses.

**EXAMPLE:** The moon _____will be_____ full tomorrow night. (be, *future*)

1. The bus _____ at this corner. (stop, *present*)
2. The new school _____ open for several years now. (be, *present perfect*)
3. Volunteers _____ a truckload of scrap paper. (collect, *past perfect*)
4. Carrie _____ out to the raft and back. (swim, *past*)
5. Next time I _____ not _____ so many pancakes. (eat, *future*)
6. Our team _____ yesterday's game. (win, *past*)
7. Frank feels confident that he _____ the test. (pass, *future*)
8. Suzie _____ to win last week's race. (hope, *past perfect*)
9. I _____ the book by the end of next week. (finish, *future perfect*)
10. I _____ Howard at the front of the line. (see, *present*)

# 22.2 The Six Tenses of Verbs • Practice 2

▶ **Exercise 1** **Identifying the Basic Forms of Verbs.** The verb in each of the following sentences is underlined. Identify the tense of each verb.

**EXAMPLE:** Our elegant sand castle has partly collapsed. _____present perfect_____

1. I had wondered why you wrote that strange letter. _____
2. Lawrence will drive to Pasadena with his family next week. _____
3. My sisters always hold on to the railing at the skating rink. _____
4. By the end of the next lap, she will have swum one mile today. _____
5. Jeanne has visited Japan but not China. _____
6. Mrs. Vronsky's parrots sing arias from operas. _____
7. I listened to them sing last week. _____
8. Franklin had underlined every misspelled word in his composition. _____
9. What will you do with your snowshoes in Florida? _____
10. I have never met anyone as shy as Chuck. _____

▶ **Exercise 2** **Supplying the Correct Tense.** In the blank space, supply the basic form of the verb as directed in parentheses.

**EXAMPLE:** Diane _____bought_____ theater tickets for Thursday. (buy, *past*)

1. Martie _____ the harsh overhead light with track lights. (replace, *future*)
2. I _____ to read this book about five times. start, *present perfect*)
3. My father once _____ a boa constrictor as a pet. (buy, *past*)
4. Angela often _____ that she lives in a different time and place. (imagine, *present*)
5. She _____ to invent a time-travel machine when she was younger. (want, *past perfect*)
6. They all _____ the ending by now. (guess, *future perfect*)
7. That actor _____ in the same play for the last four years. (be, *present perfect*)
8. The swimming pool _____ more to build than the house. (cost, *past*)
9. Cora always _____ our costumes for Halloween. (make, *present*)
10. We _____ the dinosaur exhibit before it was opened to the public. (see, *past perfect*)

▶ **Writing Application** **Using the Basic Form of the Six Tenses.** Write six sentences of your own for each of the following verbs. Use a different tense of the verb in each of your sentences. Use a separate sheet of paper if necessary.

**EXAMPLE:** take
_____I take our dog out for a run every day._____
_____I took a picture of the new building._____
(and so on)

1. do

_____

_____

_____

2. speak

_____

_____

_____

# 22.2 The Six Progressive Forms of Verbs
## • Practice 1

**The Progressive Forms of the Six Tenses**   Each tense has a progressive form. The present participle is used to make all six progressive forms.

| PROGRESSIVE FORMS OF THE SIX TENSES OF *BREAK* | | | |
|---|---|---|---|
| **Tense** | **Progressive Form** | **Tense** | **Progressive Form** |
| **Present** | I am breaking | **Present Perfect** | I have been breaking |
| **Past** | I was breaking | **Past Perfect** | I had been breaking |
| **Future** | I will be breaking | **Future Perfect** | I will have been breaking |

**Conjugating the Progressive Forms of Verbs**   To conjugate the progressive forms of a verb, add the present participle of the verb to a conjugation of the basic forms of *be*.

▶ **Exercise 1**   **Identifying the Tenses of Progressive Forms of Verbs.**   Identify the tense of each underlined verb.

**EXAMPLE:** We <u>are running</u> out of popcorn. ___*present*___

1. We <u>have been living</u> here for five years now. _____
2. Stan <u>was hoping</u> to get a letter from his friend. _____
3. The workers <u>had been striking</u> for nearly a month. _____
4. They <u>will be arriving</u> late tomorrow night. _____
5. My sister <u>is teaching</u> a course on computers. _____
6. The crew <u>had been painting</u> scenery most of the day. _____
7. In June, I <u>will have been going</u> to school eight years. _____
8. The Penguins <u>were leading</u> by six points at the half. _____
9. The same movie <u>has been playing</u> there for weeks. _____
10. I <u>will be rooting</u> for you in the tournament. _____

▶ **Exercise 2**   **Supplying the Correct Tense.**   Fill in each blank with the form of the verb called for in the parentheses.

**EXAMPLE:** The bus ___*will be leaving*___ any minute now. (leave, *future progressive*)

1. My sister _____ driving instruction. (take, *future progressive*)
2. The Riordans _____ us next week. (visit, *future progressive*)
3. Nick _____ a large reward. (expect, *past perfect progressive*)
4. Mr. Nelson _____ for mayor. (run, *present progressive*)
5. Alicia's friends _____ a farewell party. (give, *past progressive*)
6. The team _____ the game. (win, *past progressive*)
7. I _____ for three hours before my supervisor arrives. (work, *future perfect progressive*)
8. Joe _____ for hours to find the solution. (struggle, *present perfect progressive*)
9. Ann _____ to break the endurance record. (try, *present progressive*)
10. Ronald _____ for a long time before he decided to watch television. (study, *past perfect progressive*)

# 22.2 The Six Progressive Forms of Verbs
## • Practice 2

▶ **Exercise 1**  **Identifying the Progressive Forms of Verbs.**  Identify the tense of each of the following verbs.

**EXAMPLE:** will have been waiting _____*future perfect*_____

1. has been going _____
2. is running _____
3. will be eating _____
4. had been exploring _____
5. was explaining _____
6. have been staying _____
7. are fixing _____
8. had been thinking _____
9. will be having _____
10. have been giving _____
11. were chopping _____
12. am agreeing _____
13. will have been taking _____
14. will be studying _____
15. have been competing _____
16. was working _____
17. is putting _____
18. had been paying _____
19. will have been making _____
20. have been sailing _____

▶ **Exercise 2**  **Supplying the Correct Tense.**  In the blank space, supply the progressive form of the verb as directed in parentheses.

**EXAMPLE:** Janine _____*was trying*_____ to tell you about the election. (try, *past progressive*)

1. Otis _____ houses all summer. (paint, *present perfect progressive*)
2. I _____ when you called. (cook, *past progressive*)
3. Anita _____ the yearbook cover. (design, *future progressive*)
4. The Reeses _____ our neighborhood newsletter for seven years next month. (publish, *future perfect progressive*)
5. I _____ Uncle Dal at the other end of the table. (put, *present progressive*)
6. Actually, I _____ about my new CDs. (think, *past progressive*)
7. Renee _____ Italian secretly for three months when her grandmother finally agreed to teach her. (learn, *past perfect progressive*)
8. The concert _____ soon. (start, *future progressive*)
9. Carlos _____ a diary since he was nine years old. (keep, *present perfect progressive*)
10. Jake _____ to live in the mountains for years before his family finally moved to Colorado last July. (want, *past perfect progressive*)

# 22.3 Glossary of Troublesome Verbs • Practice 1

**Troublesome Verbs** Some problems with verbs arise when the wrong principal part is used. Other problems occur when the meanings of certain pairs of verbs are confused.

| TROUBLESOME VERBS | |
| --- | --- |
| **Incorrect Uses** | **Correct Uses** |
| Eliot *busted* the vase. | Eliot *broke* the vase. |
| Grandfather *should of* come with us. | Grandfather *should have* come with us. |
| The builders *are lying* the foundation for the house. | The builders *are laying* the foundation for the house. |

▶ **Exercise 1** **Avoiding Problems with Troublesome Verbs.** Circle the correct verb from the choices in parentheses.

**EXAMPLE:** I ((saw), seen) your picture in the morning paper.

1. In another minute, the child would have (drowned, drownded).

2. The dough should (raise, rise) for about twenty more minutes.

3. We should (have, of) painted this corner first.

4. I can't play the tape because my tape recorder is (busted, broken).

5. You mean I (did, done) the wrong page of math homework?

6. The sitter carefully (lay, laid) the baby in the crib.

7. Now I wish that I had (went, gone) with you.

8. (Sit, Set) the picnic basket over there in the shade.

9. There (isn't, ain't) any use in denying that we are lost.

10. Marco Polo (saw, seen) many strange sights in his travels.

▶ **Exercise 2** **Using Troublesome Verbs Correctly.** Write an original sentence for each of the following verb forms.

**EXAMPLE:** done ___*I have done most of my homework already.*___

1. set _____

2. raise _____

3. lay _____

4. drowned _____

5. burst _____

6. gone _____

7. isn't _____

8. seen _____

9. sat _____

10. done _____

# 22.3 Glossary of Troublesome Verbs • Practice 2

**▶ Exercise 1** **Avoiding Problems with Troublesome Verbs.** For each of the sentences, choose the correct verb from the choices in parentheses and write it in the blank.

**EXAMPLE:** ____Aren't____ you ready to leave yet? (Ain't, Aren't)

1. He _____ the experiment four times before he got any results. (did, done)
2. The heavy orchestration _____ out the singer's delicate voice. (drownded, drowned)
3. The piñata _____ open, showering the children with dozens of toys. (bust, burst)
4. Cyril _____ ahead to save us a place at the movies. (gone, has gone)
5. After all, it _____ easy to find ten seats together on Saturday night. (isn't, ain't)
6. Sally has turned in a hand-written essay because her computer is _____. (busted, broken)
7. It seems as if everyone in this school _____ to the same summer camp. (went, gone)
8. I don't like my spaghetti to be _____ in tomato sauce. (drowned, drownded)
9. They _____ convinced that we need a new television set. (ain't, aren't)
10. You _____ a great job with the set for the variety show. (done, have done)

**▶ Exercise 2** **Avoiding Problems with Troublesome Verbs.** For each of the following sentences, choose the correct verb from the choices in parentheses and write it in the blank.

1. The Greens are _____ a new wood floor in their dining room. (laying, lying)
2. Do you realize that you _____ won that race with more training? (could of, could've)
3. I _____ a shooting star a second ago. (seen, saw)
4. The assembly will _____ when the judge enters the courtroom. (rise, raise)
5. Then everyone will _____ down when she says, "Be seated." (set, sit)
6. Gil _____ many strange plants on his various field trips. (has seen, seen)
7. A Druid shrine once _____ somewhere in these hills. (laid, lay)
8. There is absolutely no need for you to _____ your voice. (raise, rise)
9. Every morning, Laurie _____ her parakeet on a special swing next to the dining-room table. (sets, sits)
10. I should _____ looked him straight in the eye and said, "None of your business." (of, have)

**▶ Exercise 3** **Avoiding Problems with Troublesome Verbs.** For each of the following sentences, choose the correct verb from the choices in parentheses and write it in the blank.

1. My aunt always used to say, "I'll be there if the sun is shining and the creeks don't _____." (raise, rise)
2. Maybe we should _____ turned left instead of right at that intersection. (have, of)
3. I almost _____ in the wading pool in a freak accident last week. (drownded, drowned)
4. Aside from embarrassing me, the experience really _____ me no harm. (did, done)
5. The radio station had to shut down because its transmitter was _____. (busted, broken)
6. The children _____ on their backs to look at the stars. (lay, laid)
7. _____ down and take a look at this puzzle. (Sit, Set)
8. He _____ finished peeling the potatoes yet. (isn't, aren't)
9. Cassie _____ to find a tow truck. (gone, went)
10. I _____ one at that gas station we passed a few miles back. (had seen, seen)

**23** # The Three Cases of Personal Pronouns
### • Practice 1

**The Three Cases of Personal Pronouns**  Pronouns have three cases: nominative, objective, and possessive.

| CASE FORMS OF PERSONAL PRONOUNS | | |
|---|---|---|
| **Case** | **Use in Sentence** | **Forms** |
| Nominative | Subject of a Verb<br>Predicate Pronoun | I, we; you; he, she, it, they |
| Objective | Direct Object<br>Indirect Object<br>Object of a Preposition | me, us; you; him, her, it, them |
| Possessive | To Show Ownership | my, mine; our, ours; your, yours;<br>his, her, hers, its, their, theirs |

▶ **Exercise 1**  **Identifying Pronoun Case.**  Write the case of each underlined pronoun in the space to the right.

**EXAMPLE:** The judges awarded her a blue ribbon. _____objective_____

1. The audience gave them a standing ovation. _____
2. As usual, the first one to finish was he. _____
3. The yellow house with the brown shutters is theirs. _____
4. They will probably need our help after all. _____
5. The notebook with the checkered cover is his. _____
6. This bike is Terry's; mine is red and white. _____
7. If anyone deserves an apology, it is you. _____
8. Paul takes his radio with him everywhere. _____
9. Carla and I were born on the same day. _____
10. The speaker's reply surprised us. _____

▶ **Exercise 2**  **Identifying Pronoun Case.**  Write the case of each underlined pronoun.

**EXAMPLE:** Mrs. Wang helped them with their makeup. _____objective_____

1. The tornado was heading right toward us. _____
2. Rachel and she have been friends since childhood. _____
3. The principal gave Tom and me a warning. _____
4. The players bring their own rackets. _____
5. I must write her a thank-you note. _____
6. Of course it was he who hid the birthday cake. _____
7. Ms. Sanchez took us on a tour of the automobile manufacturing plant. _____
8. Don't forget to bring your camera along. _____
9. Linda and he are in charge of refreshments. _____
10. Dad will drive them to school tomorrow. _____

# 23 The Three Cases of Personal Pronouns
## • Practice 2

**▶ Exercise 1  Identifying Case.** In each blank space, identify the case of the personal pronoun that is underlined in each of the following sentences.

**EXAMPLE:** Didn't Richard give her the directions?    _objective_

1. After an hour of cleaning flounder, Winnie lost her taste for fish. _____
2. He dedicated the book to his children. _____
3. Spring came at last; a month of rain came with it. _____
4. Show me the trick that you learned. _____
5. The last people in the auditorium were Ian and I. _____
6. Carlos saw her once again at the foot of the staircase. _____
7. At least the land is ours, no matter what happens to the house. _____
8. The twins stopped crying when Rolfie swung them both in the air. _____
9. She would like to learn how to ski down the intermediate slope. _____
10. Does any one of you know how to write a sonnet? _____
11. As Harry walked up the winding staircase, he felt more and more curious. _____
12. After eating too much, Gwendolyn felt that her waistband was too tight. _____
13. "This bracelet belongs to me!" said Sheree, as she snatched it from Lois. _____
14. Reuben said that it didn't matter to him if Sean came along. _____
15. "Is it your turn or mine?" asked Boris, pointing to the trash can. _____

**▶ Exercise 2  Identifying Case.** The following passage contains eighteen personal pronouns. Underline each personal pronoun and write it on a line in the appropriate column.

**EXAMPLE:** I bought four baseball tickets.

| Nominative Case | Objective Case | Possessive Case |
|---|---|---|
| I | _____ | _____ |

Jodie looked out at the members of her audience. They stared back at her. "Oh, no!" Jodie thought. "I have forgotten my lines!" As Jodie looked at her director, he pretended to be watering a plant. "Ah!" thought Jodie. Immediately, she walked to the table and took the plant off it, saying, "Let me give you some water."

Then Sam walked onto the stage, speaking his line. "If I had my way, we would get rid of that plant. Three of them have not done well. Their needs are not being met."

The director smiled from the sidelines. His play would be fine.

| Nominative Case | Objective Case | Possessive Case |
|---|---|---|
| _____ | _____ | _____ |
| _____ | _____ | _____ |
| _____ | _____ | _____ |
| _____ | _____ | _____ |
| _____ | _____ | _____ |
| _____ | _____ | _____ |
| _____ | _____ | _____ |
| _____ | _____ | _____ |

# 23 Cases of Personal Pronouns (Nominative, Objective) • Practice 1

**The Nominative Case**  Use the nominative case for the subject or predicate pronoun.

| USES OF THE NOMINATIVE CASE | |
|---|---|
| Subject | *They* folded the parachutes carefully.<br>Luis and *she* received the most votes. |
| Predicate Pronoun | Was that *she* who just called?<br>The two pianists are Betsy and *he*. |

**The Objective Case**  Use the objective case for a direct object, an indirect object, and the object of a preposition.

| USES OF THE OBJECTIVE CASE | |
|---|---|
| Direct Object | The class elected *her*.<br>The Penguins beat *us* by two points. |
| Indirect Object | Our neighbor gave *us* two free tickets.<br>The judges awarded *them* duplicate prizes. |
| Object of a Preposition | You may leave the message with Ellen or *her*.<br>Do you have an extra ticket for *me*? |

▶**Exercise 1**  **Identifying Pronouns in the Nominative Case.**  Circle the correct nominative pronoun from the choices in parentheses. Then write *S* (for subject) or *PP* (for predicate pronoun) to indicate its use.

**EXAMPLE:** The first person to volunteer was ((she), her).  ____PP____

1. Elena and (he, him) went to a party on Saturday night. _____

2. Is that (she, her) already? It's still very early. _____

3. (They, Them) are the best in the class in most subjects. _____

4. You and (I, me) know the recipe for meatloaf. _____

5. The co-captains are Tom and (he, him). _____

6. Maria and (she, her) stayed up too late last night. _____

7. "It could have been (he, him)," Mary said thoughtfully. _____

8. (Her, She) and I have been friends for a long time. _____

9. Angie and (he, him) are eating apples in the garden. _____

10. The Halls and (us, we) contributed to the Red Cross. _____

▶**Exercise 2**  **Identifying Pronouns in the Objective Case.**  Circle the objective pronoun from the choices in parentheses. Then write *DO* (for direct object), *IO* (for indirect object), or *OP* (for object of a preposition) to indicate its use.

**EXAMPLE:** The class sent (she, (her)) a get-well card.  ____IO____

1. Please come to the supermarket with Mom and (I, me). _____

2. Two witnesses identified (he, him) during the trial. _____

3. Had you met (she, her) before the party last night? _____

4. Mom gave (they, them) some good advice about the problem. _____

5. Leave Jim and (he, him) a shopping list and the car keys. _____

# 23 Cases of Personal Pronouns (Nominative, Objective) • Practice 2

▶ **Exercise 1** **Using Personal Pronouns in the Nominative Case.** Complete each of the following sentences by writing an appropriate nominative pronoun. Then indicate how each pronoun is used in the sentence.

**EXAMPLE:** ____We____ think that this photograph is best. ____subject____

1. _____ cannot remember what happened. _____
2. It must be _____; no one else would arrive this late in the evening. _____
3. Willard and _____ will set up the tent. _____
4. The door creaked open, and a voice from outside said, "It is _____." _____
5. The maples are turning red; soon _____ will be losing their leaves. _____
6. When Bart's dog was sent to those groomers, _____ came back looking embarrassed and bald. _____
7. The person who did this is _____. _____
8. My contest entry was postmarked early, but _____ got lost in the mail. _____
9. When the wind blows this way, _____ can hear the music. _____
10. The first people to speak after the announcement were Tony and _____.
_____

▶ **Exercise 2** **Using Personal Pronouns in the Objective Case.** Complete each of the following sentences by writing an appropriate objective pronoun. Then indicate how each pronoun is used in the sentence.

**EXAMPLE:** Why didn't Edwin invite ____me____ to this dinner? ____direct object____

1. If Mark and Susie leave now, who will go with _____? _____
2. Teresa showed _____ the sealed envelope containing the secret formula. _____
3. This speech was drafted for _____ by a new member of the staff. _____
4. When you catch the brass ring, throw _____ at that large painted clown. _____
5. Unfortunately, John made a mistake and told _____ the plans for the surprise party. _____
6. The helicopter lifted Jo and _____ high up over the city. _____
7. The donation was a secret between Tracy and _____. _____
8. As the song went on and on, Kit made faces at _____. _____
9. The man in the ticket booth sold _____ four seats for the 9:30 show. _____
10. Chris hugged the baby girl and then set _____ down in the crib. _____

# 23 Cases of Personal Pronouns (Possessive)
## • Practice 1

**The Possessive Case**   Use the possessive case of personal pronouns to show possession before nouns. Also use certain possessive pronouns by themselves to show possession.

| USES OF THE POSSESSIVE CASE | |
|---|---|
| Before Nouns | The cat licked *its* paws. |
| | *Our* team was far behind. |
| Alone | Here is your pen; this one is *mine*. |
| | The notebook on the table is *hers*. |

> **Exercise 1**   **Using Personal Pronouns in the Possessive Case.**   Write the correct word from the choices in parentheses to complete each sentence.

**EXAMPLE:** Steve, may I borrow ____*your*____ binoculars? (your, yours)

1.  Neither of these raincoats is _____. (my, mine)

2.  Eric forgot _____ lunch money again. (he, his)

3.  _____ is the package with the red bow on it. (Your, Yours)

4.  The cat arched _____ back and hissed. (it's, its)

5.  The two suspects claimed that the money was _____. (their's, theirs)

6.  Please return that book to _____ proper place on the shelf. (its, it's)

7.  Is this fielder's glove _____? (your's, yours)

8.  The boy hid near the pirates and overheard _____ plans. (them, their)

9.  _____ is the racket with the plaid cover. (Her's, Hers)

10. Surely that bus turning the corner must be _____. (our, ours)

> **Exercise 2**   **Using All Three Cases.**   Complete each sentence with the appropriate pronoun form. The number in parentheses tells which set of pronouns to choose from for each sentence.

(1) I, me, my, mine    (3) he, him, his; it, its    (4) we, us, our, ours
(2) you, your, yours       she, her, hers       (5) they, them, their, theirs

**EXAMPLE:** The coach took Rosa aside and complemented ____*her*____ on her play. (3)

1.  It was _____ who left the message earlier. (1)

2.  The white rowboat with the green trim is _____. (4)

3.  When we saw Mr. Anders, we told _____ about the leaking faucet. (3)

4.  I am sure that the tan van we passed was _____. (5)

5.  You and _____ should play doubles more often. (1)

6.  Alex asked me to ride with Terry and _____. (3)

7.  _____ is the white house on the corner, isn't it? (2)

8.  The witch asked the children into her house and gave _____ milk and cookies. (5)

9.  The most surprised of all were Mrs. Dugan and _____. (1)

10. Betsy and _____ won the girls' doubles tournament. (3)

                                             

# 23 Cases of Personal Pronouns (Possessive)
## • Practice 2

**Exercise 1**   **Using Personal Pronouns in the Possessive Case.**   For each of the following sentences, choose the correct word from the choices in parentheses and write it in the blank.

**EXAMPLE:** Now that Kim has gone away to school, this room is all ____*yours*____ . (yours, your's)

1. The dog eats _____ food as if there were no tomorrow. (it's, its)
2. Kip has difficulty keeping _____ shoelaces tied. (his', his)
3. The boat is _____ , but we can use it. (theirs, their's)
4. How many of these albums are _____? (our's, ours)
5. Rita said that some of the records are _____ . (hers, her's)
6. Every other poem in the literary magazine is _____! (your's, yours)
7. _____ my problem, not David's. (Its, It's)
8. I wrote the melody, but the lyrics are _____ . (his', his)
9. I always forget which house is _____ . (your's, yours)
10. The thermometer reached _____ highest point for the year today. (its, it's)

**Exercise 2**   **Checking the Case of Personal Pronouns.**   Many of the underlined pronouns in the following sentences are incorrect. Circle each error and write the form of the pronoun that should be used in the blank. For sentences without any errors, write *correct*.

**EXAMPLE:** Here are <u>your</u> clothes and <u>your</u> books; this room must be ⬭your's⬭ . ____*yours*____

1. The singers in the opening number will be Patty, Maxine, and <u>me</u>. _____
2. Aunt Bertie trained the cat and changed <u>it's</u> habits. _____
3. When <u>our</u> grandmother arrived, the conductor helped <u>her</u> off the train. _____
4. The judges couldn't choose between <u>her</u> and <u>I</u>. _____
5. <u>You</u> will be happy to hear that the assignment is now <u>yours</u>. _____
6. Delia showed José and <u>I</u> the diagrams. _____
7. <u>Its</u> the first house on the left in that block. _____
8. It was <u>he</u> who ate <u>my</u> pie. _____
9. Elijah and Clarice could not believe that <u>their's</u> was the winning ticket. _____
10. Kevin, Larry, and <u>me</u> are studying together. _____

# 24.1 Agreement Between Subjects and Verbs
## • Practice 1

**The Number of Nouns and Pronouns**  The number of a word can be either singular or plural. Singular words indicate one. Plural words indicate more than one.

| NUMBER OF NOUNS AND PRONOUNS | | |
|---|---|---|
| | **Singular** | **Plural** |
| Nouns | table | tables |
| | fox | foxes |
| | wife | wives |
| | goose | geese |
| Pronouns | I, you, he, she, it, this | we, you, they, these |

**The Number of Verbs**  A subject must agree with its verb in number. Most verb forms can be used with either singular or plural subjects. However, third-person forms of verbs in the present tense and some forms of the verb *be* change to agree in number with their subjects. Third-person singular verbs usually end in *-s*.

| SINGULAR AND PLURAL VERBS IN THE PRESENT TENSE | | |
|---|---|---|
| **Singular** | | **Plural** |
| First and Second Person | Third Person | First, Second, and Third Person |
| (I, you) stand | (he, she, it) stands | (we, you, they) stand |
| (I, you) seem | (he, she, it) seems | (we, you, they) seem |

| SINGULAR FORMS OF THE VERB *BE* | | | |
|---|---|---|---|
| am | is | was | has been |

▷ **Exercise 1**  **Recognizing the Number of Nouns and Pronouns.**  Label each word below S (for singular) or P (for plural).

**EXAMPLE:** knives _____P_____

1. they _____
2. dish _____
3. teeth _____
4. I _____
5. box _____

6. women _____
7. it _____
8. dress _____
9. miles _____
10. we _____

▷ **Exercise 2**  **Recognizing the Number of Verbs.**  Circle the verb form in parentheses that agrees in number with each noun or pronoun. Then write in the blank whether the verb is S (singular) or P (plural).

**EXAMPLE:** they ( seem , seems) _____P_____

1. geese (swim, swims) _____
2. this (is, are) _____
3. I (was, were) _____
4. the brain (is, are) _____
5. These (cost, costs) _____

6. it (has been, have been) _____
7. she (want, wants) _____
8. the actress (play, plays) _____
9. mice (creep creeps) _____
10. we (think, thinks) _____

# 24.1 Agreement Between Subjects and Verbs
## • Practice 2

▶ **Exercise 1**  **Recognizing the Number of Nouns and Pronouns.**   Indicate whether each of the following words is *singular* or *plural*.

**EXAMPLE:** children ____*plural*____

1. they _____
2. I _____
3. both _____
4. feet _____
5. me _____
6. oxen _____
7. these _____
8. river _____
9. goose _____
10. it _____

11. brain _____
12. this _____
13. forest _____
14. she _____
15. person _____
16. cousins _____
17. princess _____
18. fireplace _____
19. automobile _____
20. knight _____

▶ **Exercise 2**  **Recognizing the Number of Verbs.**   Write the verb in parentheses that agrees in number with the pronoun. After each answer write whether the verb is singular or plural.

**EXAMPLE:** they (meets, meet) ____*meet, plural*____

1. he (say, says) _____
2. we (is, are) _____
3. it (was, were) _____
4. she (wait, waits) _____
5. I (is, am) _____
6. we (has, have) _____
7. he (has been, have been) _____
8. they (is, are) _____
9. it (is, are) _____
10. they (forgives, forgive) _____

# 24.1 Agreement Between Subjects and Verbs
## • Practice 1

**Agreement with Singular and Plural Subjects**   A singular subject must have a singular verb. A plural subject must have a plural verb. A prepositional phrase that comes between a subject and its verb does not affect subject-verb agreement.

| SUBJECT-VERB AGREEMENT | |
|---|---|
| **Singular** | **Plural** |
| Mom *enjoys* bowling. | *We* all *enjoy* bowling. |
| *He was* here a minute ago. | *They were* here a minute ago. |
| One *box* of dishes *was* damaged. | Two *boxes* of clothing *are* missing. |

▷ **Exercise 1**   **Checking to See If Subjects and Verbs Agree.**   Write *correct* in the spaces after the sentences below, if the subjects and verbs agree. If a verb does not agree with its subject, write the correct form of the verb in the space.

**EXAMPLE:** One of the problems are really hard. ___*is*___

1. Computers solve hard problems quickly. _____
2. This recipe for brownies call for semisweet chocolate. _____
3. Streets with even numbers are all one-way. _____
4. Tomatoes grow best in sunny places. _____
5. Books on science is on these shelves. _____
6. The jewels in the shop window looks very expensive. _____
7. Water with no antifreeze in it freezes at 0° Celsius. _____
8. Most of the students at this school rides the bus. _____
9. That angel fish look really hungry. _____
10. One of the pieces of the puzzle are missing. _____

▷ **Exercise 2**   **Making Verbs Agree with Singular and Plural Subjects.**   Complete each sentence by writing the correct verb form from the choices in parentheses. Then label each sentence *S* if the subject is singular or *P* if it is plural.

**EXAMPLE:** The puzzles in this book ___*are*___ tricky. (is, are) ___*P*___

1. This key _____ both doors. (open, opens) _____
2. The members of the committee _____ often. (disagree, disagrees) _____
3. The player with the least points _____. (win, wins) _____
4. Pollution _____ air, water, and land. (affect, affects) _____
5. The bell for the front door _____ out of order. (is, are) _____
6. The score after six innings _____ four to two. (was, were) _____
7. Bananas _____ best in warm, moist climates. (grow, grows) _____
8. The shelves of the old general store _____ always crowded. (was, were) _____
9. The workers at the mill _____ planning to strike. (is, are) _____
10. One of the paintings in the exhibit _____ very valuable. (is, are) _____

# 24.1 Agreement Between Subjects and Verbs
## • Practice 2

**Exercise 1** **Making Verbs Agree with Singular and Plural Subjects.**  For each of the following sentences, choose the correct verb from the choices in parentheses and write it in the blank.

**EXAMPLE:** The lines of this table  *follow*  the style of the late Victorian period. (follows, follow)

1. The air _____ become stale since we shut the windows. (has, have)
2. Moss usually _____ on the north side of trees. (grows, grow)
3. The eggplants in our garden _____ particularly large this summer. (is, are)
4. The children in this photograph _____ uncomfortable. (looks, look)
5. The lace on these dresses _____ handmade. (was, were)
6. The newspapers in this collection _____ back to the Revolutionary War. (dates, date)
7. An acre of trees and meadows _____ the little church. (surrounds, surround)
8. The numbers next to the lines on this map _____ the number of miles between each interchange. (indicates, indicate)
9. The guests at the meeting _____ wearing name tags. (is, are)
10. The handwriting in these bills and letters _____ to belong to the same person. (seems, seem)
11. This year, the safety record of the employees _____ excellent. (is, are)
12. The past three presidents of the drama club _____ all been girls. (has, have)
13. The members of the jury _____ upset at some of the testimony. (seems, seem)
14. A cloud of locusts _____ the fields of corn. (approach, approaches)
15. The color of the couches and chairs _____ picked up in the wallpaper. (is, are)

**Exercise 2** **Making Verbs Agree with Singular and Plural Subjects.**  Write the correct form of the verb to complete each of the following sentences. If the subject is singular, circle *singular subject*; if the subject is plural, circle *plural subject*.

**EXAMPLE:** The cold air  *sweeps*  in from the Northwest. (sweeps, sweep)
( (singular subject) , plural subject)

1. The pennies in the fountain _____ the tile with rust. (stains, stain)
(singular subject, plural subject)
2. My friend Gus _____ very good at computer games. (is, are) (singular subject, plural subject)
3. The geese in the barnyard _____ a lot of noise in the afternoon. (makes, make) (singular subject, plural subject)
4. The brackets under the shelf _____ twenty pounds of weight. (supports, support)
(singular subject, plural subject)
5. The carriage for the twins _____ a new spring on the left front wheel. (needs, need)
(singular subject, plural subject)
6. The rugs in the apartment _____ the rooms. (brightens, brighten)
(singular subject, plural subject)
7. The secretary for the attorneys _____ a raise. (wants, want) (singular subject, plural subject)
8. My expenses for the project _____ the budget. (exceeds, exceed)
(singular subject, plural subject)
9. The jaguar, with its beautiful spots, _____ the leopard of Central and South America.
(resembles, resemble) (singular subject, plural subject)
10. The doormen at the hotel _____ guests get taxis. (helps, help)
(singular subject, plural subject)

# 24.1 Agreement with Compound Subjects
### • Practice 1

**Agreement with Compound Subjects**   Two or more singular subjects joined by *or* or *nor* must have a singular verb. When singular and plural subjects are joined by *or* or *nor*, the verb must agree with the closest subject.

| SUBJECTS JOINED BY *OR* OR *NOR* | |
|---|---|
| **Singular Subjects** | Either Dad or Mom *drives* us to school each morning. Neither Bolivia nor Paraguay *has* a seacoast. |
| **Singular and Plural Subjects** | Either an apple or celery sticks *make* a healthful snack. Either celery sticks or an apple *makes* a healthful snack. |

A compound subject joined by *and* must have a plural verb unless the parts are thought of as one thing or are modified by *every* or *each*.

| SUBJECTS JOINED BY *AND* |
|---|
| Pluto and Neptune *are* distant planets. The coach and the players *seem* confident. Spaghetti and meatballs *is* my favorite dish. Every nook and cranny *has been* carefully searched. |

▶ **Exercise 1**   **Making Verbs Agree with Compound Subjects Joined by *Or* or *Nor*.**   Complete each sentence with the verb form in parentheses that agrees with the subject.

**EXAMPLE:**   Neither the truck nor the vans ____*belong*____ to the company. (belong, belongs)

1. A screw or a large nail _____ used to hang the picture. (was, were)
2. Neither the Pied Piper nor the children _____ heard from again. (was, were)
3. A meal or a snack _____ served on each flight. (is, are)
4. Neither the net nor the paddles _____ in the cupboard. (is, are)
5. Angie or her brother _____ dinner every weeknight. (cook, cooks)
6. The manager or her assistants _____ buying trips to New York. (make, makes)
7. A pear or grapes _____ good with that cheese. (taste, tastes)
8. Neither the banks nor the post office _____ open on Columbus Day. (is, are)
9. A nurse or an aide _____ patients' temperatures. (take, takes)
10. Either the witness or the defendant _____ told a lie. (has, have)

▶ **Exercise 2**   **Making Verbs Agree with Compound Subjects Joined by *and*.**   Complete each sentence with the verb form in parentheses that agrees with the subject.

**EXAMPLE:**   Meat, fish, and eggs ____*are*____ good sources of protein. (is, are)

1. Ham and eggs _____ my favorite breakfast. (is, are)
2. Football and soccer _____ from the same ancient game. (come, comes)
3. Every suit and jacket in the store _____ on sale. (is, are)
4. Crossword puzzles and word games _____ new words. (teach, teaches)
5. Both her mother and her father _____ children's books. (write, writes)

# 24.1 Agreement with Compound Subjects
### • Practice 2

> **Exercise 1**  **Making Verbs Agree with Compound Subjects Joined by *or* and *nor*.**  For each of the following sentences, choose the correct verb from the choices in parentheses and write it in the blank.

**EXAMPLE:** Neither the twins nor their dog ____*has*____ managed to stay out of the swimming pool today. (has, have)

1. Either Sam or Lena _____ the car here each day. (drives, drive)
2. I will go, even though neither Leslie nor Bill _____ going. (is, are)
3. Either potatoes or corn _____ good with chicken. (tastes, taste)
4. Neither the front door nor the windows _____ locked. (has been, have been)
5. Neither the texture nor the colors of this fabric _____ well with that hat. (goes, go)
6. Neither the play nor the two movie versions _____ the flavor of the original book. (captures, capture)
7. Neither the subway system nor the bus routes _____ that part of town. (serves, serve)
8. Neither Meg nor Elsa _____ to go to the museum. (wants, want)
9. Neither greeting cards nor wrapping paper _____ sold in this store. (is, are)
10. Either one book or a few articles _____ sufficient background for this report. (is, are)

> **Exercise 2**  **Making Verbs Agree with Compound Subjects Joined by *and*.**  Choose the correct verb from the choices in parentheses and write it in the blank.

**EXAMPLE:** Every singer and dancer on this stage ____*knows*____ how much work the show needs. (knows, know)

1. Pens and pencils _____ poised to write. (was, were)
2. Peanut butter and jelly _____ my favorite combination for sandwiches. (is, are)
3. The books and magazines on the shelf _____ out of order. (was, were)
4. Every boot, shoe, and belt in that store _____ made of leather. (is, are)
5. Cherry pie and apple strudel _____ our choices. (was, were)
6. A prince and princess always _____ happily ever after. (lives, live)
7. Each folder and packet in the files _____ labeled. (was, were)
8. Ducks and geese usually _____ at this park on their way south. (stops, stop)
9. Every worker and manager in our plants _____ suggestions for improvements. (offers, offer)
10. The shops and department stores in this mall _____ paying more rent this year than ever before. (is, are)

> **Exercise 3**  **Checking to See If Subjects and Verbs Agree.**  For each of the following sentences, choose the correct verb from the choices in parentheses and write it in the blank.

**EXAMPLE:** Every cake and pie on these shelves ____*is*____ on sale. (is, are)

1. Neither Sal nor her sisters _____ seen the puppies. (has, have)
2. Pork and beans _____ our favorite campfire food when we were younger. (was, were)
3. The glass in the panes of these Colonial cabinets _____ from England. (comes, come)
4. Each fruit and vegetable in these bins _____ grown on our own farm. (was, were)
5. Either the Capitol or the White House _____ into our schedule. (fits, fit)

# 24.1 Special Problems with Subject-Verb Agreement • Practice 1

**Agreement in Sentences with Unusual Word Order** In most sentences, the subject comes before the verb. Sometimes, however, this normal order is turned around, or inverted. When a subject comes after the verb, the subject and verb must still agree with each other in number.

| AGREEMENT IN SENTENCES WITH INVERTED WORD ORDER | |
|---|---|
| Beginning with *There* | There *are* several *letters* in the mailbox. |
| | There *was* a *knock* on the door. |
| Beginning with *Here* | Here *is* an *example*. |
| | Here *are* the *books* you wanted. |
| In Questions | Why *is* this *door* open? |
| | Where *are* the other *players*? |

▶ **Exercise 1** **Checking Agreement in Sentences with Inverted Word Order.** Complete each sentence with the correct verb form from the parentheses.

**EXAMPLE:** There ____*was*____ only one apple left in the bowl. (was, were)

1. There _____ more tennis balls on the top shelf. (is, are)

2. Why _____ she been acting so strange lately? (has, have)

3. There, beneath that buoy, _____ the sunken ship. (lie, lies)

4. Here _____ the elephants! (comes, come)

5. Where _____ all the customers who love big sales? (is, are)

6. Which events _____ Alicia entered in the track meet? (has, have)

7. How many doughnuts _____ he eaten already? (has, have)

8. There _____ still some points that need to be explained. (is, are)

9. Where _____ the money hidden? (was, were)

10. There _____ your other sneaker behind the sofa. (is, are)

11. Here _____ the stamps from Portugal. (is, are)

12. The experts say there _____ hope for the economy next year. (is, are)

13. Here in this room _____ the solution to the mystery. (lie, lies)

14. Why _____ he called me so late in the evening? (has, have)

15. There _____ three ducks on the lake. (was, were)

▶ **Exercise 2** **Using Inverted Word Order in Sentences.** Write a sentence of your own beginning with the word given. Use verbs in the present tense or *was* or *were*. Circle the subject of each sentence.

**EXAMPLE:** There ____*are many* (records) *to choose from*____ .

1. Here _____ .

2. Where _____ .

3. Why _____ .

4. There _____ .

5. How _____ .

# 24.1 Special Problems with Subject-Verb Agreement • Practice 2

▶ **Exercise 1** **Checking Agreement in Sentences with Inverted Word Order.** Underline the subject in each of the following sentences. Choose the correct verb from the choices in parentheses and write it in the blank space.

**EXAMPLE:** There ____are____ a few new rules in this pamphlet. (is, are)

1. How _____ she learned my name? (has, have)
2. Which records _____ Heather brought with her? (has, have)
3. There _____ many reasons for building a new wing onto the school. (is, are)
4. "Where _____ my three fiddlers?" cried Old King Cole. (is, are)
5. How many times _____ Martin filled his plate? (has, have)

▶ **Exercise 2** **Checking Agreement with Indefinite Pronouns.** For each of the following sentences, choose the correct verb from the choices in parentheses and write it in the blank space.

**EXAMPLE:** Most of the story ____was____ written from a child's point of view. (was, were)

1. Most of the students _____ spelled "encyclopedia" correctly. (has, have)
2. Several of these performing dogs _____ trained abroad. (was, were)
3. _____ any of the participants want to answer that question? (Does, Do)
4. All of the tickets _____ sold before Wednesday. (was, were)
5. Some of the concrete _____ not set yet. (has, have)
6. Everyone _____ when Al puts on his insect costume. (laughs, laugh)
7. All of the ice cream _____ melted. (has, have)
8. Each of the rooms _____ a different period of American history. (represents, represent)
9. Both of the contestants _____ brought good luck charms with them. (has, have)
10. Some of these movies _____ first seen by your grandparents. (was, were)

▶ **Exercise 3** **Checking Special Problems in Agreement.** For each of the following sentences, choose the correct verb from the choices in parentheses and write it in the blank space.

**EXAMPLE:** Most of the breadcrumbs ____were____ blown away by the wind. (was, were)

1. Each of the sliding doors _____. (sticks, stick)
2. What _____ the minimum daily requirement for each team member? (was, were)
3. All of the stamps _____ on the package. (was, were)
4. _____ they realized yet that we were joking? (Hasn't, Haven't)
5. Each of the kittens _____ white patches on its ears. (has, have)
6. Here _____ your concert tickets. (is, are)
7. Everyone _____ some steamed clams. (wants, want)
8. How often _____ they traveled in the West? (has, have)
9. There _____ many strong points in Stella's plan, but it is too expensive. (is, are)
10. Most of the doors in this house _____. (squeaks, squeak)

# 24.2 Agreement Between Pronouns and Antecedents • Practice 1

**Making Personal Pronouns and Antecedents Agree**  A personal pronoun must agree with its antecedent in both person and number. Use a singular personal pronoun to refer to two or more singular antecedents joined by *or* or *nor*.

| PRONOUN-ANTECEDENT AGREEMENT |
| --- |
| My sister just passed *her* driving test. |
| Joan and I agreed to keep *our* secret. |
| Neither Dana nor Ellen was in *her* room when I called. |

**Agreement Between Personal Pronouns and Indefinite Pronouns**  Generally use a singular personal pronoun when its antecedent is a singular indefinite pronoun. When a prepositional phrase follows an indefinite pronoun, the personal pronoun must agree with the indefinite pronoun, not with the object of the preposition.

| AGREEMENT WITH INDEFINITE PRONOUNS | |
| --- | --- |
| **Incorrect** | **Correct** |
| *Each* of the players removed *their* cap. | *Each* of the players removed *his* cap. |
| Does *everybody* have *their* ticket? | Does *everybody* have *his* ticket? |

▶ **Exercise 1**  **Making Pronouns and Antecedents Agree.**  Write an appropriate personal pronoun to complete each sentence.

**EXAMPLE:** Has either Marc or Nate taken _____*his*_____ turn yet?

1. Students should remember to return _____ library books before vacation.

2. Betsy or Lois will lend you _____ racket.

3. My brother and I visited _____ cousins last week.

4. The spectators rose to _____ feet almost as one.

5. Linda's dream is to pilot _____ own plane.

6. Neither Jack nor Luis had much money with _____ .

7. The kitten had a wedge-shaped black spot on _____ forehead.

8. All cast members are expected to know _____ lines by Thursday.

9. Rachel wanted to go to Mexico and try out _____ Spanish.

10. The coach and the players have _____ work cut out for them.

▶ **Exercise 2**  **Making Personal Pronouns and Indefinite Pronouns Agree.**  Underline the pronoun in parentheses that correctly completes each sentence.

**EXAMPLE:** Each of the soldiers pledged (his, their) loyalty.

1. Either of the twins will know (her, their) uncle's address.

2. Before you use one of the encyclopedias, check (its, their) copyright date.

3. Neither of the brothers has ever regretted (his, their) choice.

4. Everyone in the first two classes returned (his, their) books on time.

5. Each of the sisters has (her, their) own version of what happened.

# 24.2 Agreement Between Pronouns and Antecedents • Practice 2

▶ **Exercise 1**  **Making Pronouns and Antecedents Agree.**  For each of the following sentences, fill in the blank with an appropriate pronoun.

**EXAMPLE:** The children had left _____*their*_____ toys all over the living room.

1. Lucy was hoping that _____ name would be chosen.

2. Bob and Chris planned _____ work carefully.

3. Each girl was asked to give _____ own opinion.

4. All pilots are likely to remember _____ first flights.

5. Either Katie or Jenny will ask _____ parents to drive us to the dance.

6. Each boy had to memorize _____ lines for the skit to be given that night.

7. Lisa learned to ski so that _____ could join the teenagers on the slope.

8. Neither Jeremy nor Ian was willing to lend us _____ stereo.

9. Cathy and Linda wanted to try on _____ new uniforms immediately.

10. When they were young, Neil and Sally spent hours playing with _____ blocks.

▶ **Exercise 2**  **Avoiding Shifts in Person and Number.**  Each sentence contains a single error in pronoun-antecedent agreement. Rewrite each sentence correctly, underlining the pronoun that you have changed and its antecedent.

**EXAMPLE:** Each member of the girls' swim team spends much of their free time practicing.

*Each <u>member</u> of the girls' swim team spends much of <u>her</u> free time practicing.*

1. Julio now knows that you can't play in the school band without practicing.

_____

_____

2. Either Curtis or Tim will bring their surfboard today.

_____

_____

3. Each fish in the aquarium acted as if they could not be bothered by our attention.

_____

_____

4. All students should know that you have to register today.

_____

_____

5. The puppies rolled over and kicked its legs.

_____

_____

Name _____ Date _____

 **25.1** # Comparison of Regular Adjectives and Adverbs • Practice 1

**Modifiers with One or Two Syllables**  Most adjectives and adverbs have three degrees of comparison: the positive, the comparative, and the superlative degree. Use -er or more to form the comparative degree and -est or most to form the superlative degree of most one- and two-syllable modifiers. Adding -er and -est is the most common method.

| DEGREES OF MODIFIERS WITH ONE OR TWO SYLLABLES | | | |
|---|---|---|---|
| | Positive | Comparative | Superlative |
| With -er, -est | short | shorter | shortest |
| | quiet | quieter | quietest |
| With more, most | painful | more painful | most painful |
| | brightly | more brightly | most brightly |

**Modifiers with Three or More Syllables**  Use more and most to form the comparative and superlative degrees of all modifiers of three or more syllables.

| DEGREES OF MODIFIERS WITH THREE OR MORE SYLLABLES | | |
|---|---|---|
| Positive | Comparative | Superlative |
| attractive | more attractive | most attractive |
| suddenly | more suddenly | most suddenly |
| memorable | more memorable | most memorable |

▶ **Exercise 1**  **Forming the Comparative and Superlative Degrees of One- and Two-Syllable Modifiers.**  Write the missing forms of each modifier.

**EXAMPLE:**  fast _____*faster*_____   _____*fastest*_____

1. cold      _____   _____

2. _____   _____   most handsome

3. _____   fairer   _____

4. _____   more quickly   _____

5. anxious      _____   _____

▶ **Exercise 2**  **Forming the Comparative and Superlative Degrees of Modifiers with More than Two Syllables.**  Write the comparative and superlative forms of the following modifiers.

**EXAMPLE:**  dangerous _____*more dangerous*_____   _____*most dangerous*_____

1. comfortable   _____   _____

2. ungrateful   _____   _____

3. thoroughly   _____   _____

4. happily   _____   _____

5. carelessly   _____   _____

# 25.1 Comparison of Regular Adjectives and Adverbs • Practice 2

> **Exercise 1** **Forming the Comparative and Superlative Degrees of One- and Two-Syllable Modifiers.** Write the comparative and superlative degrees of the following modifiers. If the degrees can be formed in either way, write the- *er* and- *est* forms.

**EXAMPLE:** gentle          *gentler*          *gentlest*

1. nervous          _____          _____
2. brightly          _____          _____
3. painful          _____          _____
4. slowly          _____          _____
5. quiet          _____          _____

> **Exercise 2** **Forming the Comparative and Superlative Degrees of Modifiers with More Than Two Syllables.** Write the comparative and superlative degrees of the following modifiers.

**EXAMPLE:** beautiful          *more beautiful*          *most beautiful*

1. generous          _____          _____
2. unattractive          _____          _____
3. suddenly          _____          _____
4. capable          _____          _____
5. powerfully          _____          _____

> **Writing Application** **Forming the Comparative and Superlative Degrees of Regular Modifiers.** Write two sentences for each of the following modifiers. Use the comparative degree in the first sentence and the superlative degree in the second.

**EXAMPLE:** quickly

_When the storm approached, Paula responded more quickly than Pete._
_Dave responded the most quickly, running immediately to close the windows._

1. wisely

_____

_____

2. fast

_____

_____

3. cold

_____

_____

4. memorable

_____

_____

5. gracefully

_____

_____

# 25.1 Comparison of Irregular Adjectives and Adverbs • Practice 1

**The Comparative and Superlative of Irregular Modifiers**   Learn the irregular comparative and superlative forms of certain adjectives and adverbs.

| DEGREES OF IRREGULAR ADJECTIVES AND ADVERBS | | |
| --- | --- | --- |
| **Positive** | **Comparative** | **Superlative** |
| bad | worse | worst |
| badly | worse | worst |
| far (distance) | farther | farthest |
| far (extent) | further | furthest |
| good | better | best |
| well | better | best |
| many | more | most |
| much | more | most |

**▶ Exercise 1**   **Recognizing the Degree of Irregular Modifiers.**   Indicate the degree of the underlined word in each of the sentences below.

**EXAMPLE:**  Sam did <u>well</u> in yesterday's race.  _____*positive*_____

1. Roxie has <u>more</u> money than anyone else in her family. _____

2. Joe is the <u>best</u> player on his team. _____

3. We traveled <u>far</u> to find what we were looking for. _____

4. We must discuss this matter <u>further</u>. _____

5. Ralph did <u>badly</u> on his math test. _____

6. Sue said that Jim is the <u>worst</u> dancer she has ever seen. _____

7. <u>Many</u> people feel that securing peace is the President's <u>most</u> important responsibility. _____

8. Lois is a <u>better</u> student than Bruno. _____

9. The field was in <u>better</u> shape than any of the players expected it to be. _____

10. Horace is the <u>most</u> conceited person I know. _____

**▶ Exercise 2**   **Using the Comparative and Superlative Forms of Irregular Modifiers.**   Complete each sentence with the form of the modifier requested in parentheses.

**EXAMPLE:**  The hikers could go no ____*farther*____ . (*far*, comparative)

1. This is the _____ blizzard in many years. (*bad*, superlative)

2. The patient gradually got _____ . (*well*, comparative)

3. Those mountains are _____ away than I thought. (*far*, comparative)

4. The cast gave its _____ performance on opening night. (*good*, superlative)

5. Cars use _____ gas at high speeds. (*much*, comparative)

6. The attorney wished to question the witness _____ . (*far*, comparative)

7. Some people work _____ under pressure. (*well*, superlative)

8. Betsy played _____ than usual because she was nervous. (*badly*, comparative)

9. Beth got the _____ hits of all of us. (*many*, superlative)

10. The third present was the one that pleased me _____ . (*much*, superlative)

# 25.1 Comparison of Irregular Adjectives and Adverbs • Practice 2

**Exercise 1** **Recognizing the Degree of Irregular Modifiers.** In the space provided, indicate the degree of the underlined word in each of the following sentences.

**EXAMPLE:** Uncle Fred's collection of timepieces includes <u>many</u> official railroad clocks. _____positive_____

1. Vinnie enjoyed Monkey Island <u>more</u> than any other part of the zoo. _____

2. How can Maureen sing as <u>well</u> as she does with a head cold? _____

3. The <u>worst</u> suggestion of all was that we paint the gym floor silver for the dance. _____

4. As I read <u>further</u>, I realized why the prime suspect couldn't have committed the crime. _____

5. Caroline's schoolwork has gotten <u>better</u> since she became interested in reading. _____

6. Although the rink was in <u>bad</u> condition, we managed to have a good time ice-skating. _____

7. I thought our team did <u>best</u> in the egg-tossing contest. _____

8. Juan had hiked the <u>farthest</u> when the competition ended. _____

9. Completing the reading list will look <u>good</u> on your record. _____

10. Which of you has eaten the <u>most</u> pudding? _____

**Exercise 2** **Using the Comparative and Superlative Degrees of Irregular Modifiers.** In the blank space in each sentence, write the form of the modifier requested in parentheses.

**EXAMPLE:** The fog seems _____worse_____ this morning. (*bad*, comparative)

1. Sid ran _____ when he lived in the city. (*much*, comparative)

2. The _____ she can do is to disagree with you. (*bad*, superlative)

3. The piano sounds _____ since we removed the tennis ball from its strings. (*good*, comparative)

4. Pluto is the _____ planet from the sun. (*far*, superlative)

5. Terry plays softball even _____ than I do. (*badly*, comparative)

6. I have written _____ stories this week than ever before. (*many*, comparative)

7. My dog behaves _____ just after she has eaten. (*well*, superlative)

8. What surprised me _____ was Sharon's ability to predict the outcome. (*much*, comparative)

9. Our china and glassware fared the _____ at the hands of the third company of movers. (*badly*, superlative)

10. The _____ photograph captured Leroy while he was still standing on the inner tube. (*good*, superlative)

# 25.1 Using the Comparative and Superlative Degrees • Practice 1

**The Comparative and Superlative Degrees**  Use the comparative degree to compare two people, places, or things. Use the superlative degree to compare three or more people, places, or things.

| Comparative | Superlative |
|---|---|
| Alaska is *larger* than Texas. | Alaska is the *largest* of the fifty states. |
| Angie pitches *better* than I do. | Of all the players on our team, Angie pitches *best.* |
| The young deer ran *more gracefully* than its mother. | The young deer ran *most gracefully* of all in the herd. |

▶ **Exercise 1**  **Using the Comparative and Superlative Degrees Correctly.**  Underline the correct form in each sentence.

**EXAMPLE:**  One twin is (taller, tallest) than the other.

1. Only the (more, most) skillful skiers of all use that trail.
2. Luis is the (older, oldest) of five brothers.
3. Air travel is (safer, safest) than travel by car.
4. Tomorrow is the (longer, longest) day of the year.
5. Michelle is the (more, most) adventurous of the twins.
6. Which of these three sketches do you like (better, best)?
7. One of my arms is (longer, longest) than the other.
8. The black and white puppy seems (more, most) frisky than the brown one.
9. Which of the three contestants do you think has the (better, best) chance?
10. Of the two, Nancy is the (more, most) aggressive player.

▶ **Exercise 2**  **Correcting Inappropriate Comparisons.**  In the following sentences, underline any problems in comparisons that you find. Then rewrite each sentence correctly.

**EXAMPLE:**  Rhode Island is the most smallest state.
   *Rhode Island is the smallest state.*

1. Which of the two jars contains the most jellybeans?

_____

2. Nate is the more consistent hitter of all the Bulldogs.

_____

3. Of the two mountains, Mt. Everest is the highest.

_____

4. Which is more bigger, 5/16 or 1/4?

_____

5. These cookies are even worser than the last batch.

_____

# 25.1 Using the Comparative and Superlative Degrees • Practice 2

▶ **Exercise 1** **Correcting Errors in Degree.** Several of the following sentences contain errors in degree. Rewrite the incorrect sentences to correct them. Write *correct* if the sentence contains no errors.

**EXAMPLE:** This ski jump is the highest of the two at Sunrise Lodge.
　　　　　_This ski jump is the higher of the two at Sunrise Lodge._

1. The jester realized more sooner than the rest of the court what the king meant.

_____

2. Which of these two bushes has produced the most roses?

_____

3. Gerri's secrets were safer with Joel than with her friend Kim.

_____

4. I couldn't judge whose work was better—Dean's, Helen's, or Chrisanne's.

_____

5. Yesterday had to be the most hottest day of the year.

_____

6. Which one of your eyes is weakest?

_____

7. Mr. Crespi grew more fonder of that wild rabbit as the summer went on.

_____

8. Of all the sections on the test, I felt most comfortable with the essay question.

_____

9. If I had to choose between beets and sauerkraut, I would say that I dislike beets most.

_____

10. The most worst job Craig ever had to do involved counting bees in a hive.

_____

▶ **Writing Application** **Using the Comparative and Superlative Degrees.** On a separate page, write two sentences for each of the following modifiers. Use the comparative degree in the first sentence and the superlative degree in the second.

**EXAMPLE:** spectacular
　　　　　_The sequel was more spectacular than the original._
　　　　　_The next movie may be the most spectacular of all._

1. silly
2. warm
3. ambitious
4. suddenly
5. wonderful
6. much
7. badly
8. lazy
9. soft
10. colorful

# 25.2 Glossary of Troublesome Adjectives and Adverbs • Practice 1

**Troublesome Adjectives and Adverbs** Several common adjectives and adverbs cause problems. Note the correct uses of those words that have caused you problems.

| TROUBLESOME ADJECTIVES AND ADVERBS | |
|---|---|
| **Adjectives** | bad, good, well (health), fewer (how many), less (how much) |
| **Adverbs** | badly, well, just (no more than) |

▶ **Exercise 1** Using Troublesome Adjectives and Adverbs Correctly. Underline the choice in parentheses that correctly completes each sentence.

**EXAMPLE:** Customers with (fewer, less) than six items can check out here.

1. We (only made, made only) enough punch for twelve guests.

2. Tom felt (bad, badly) about striking out with the bases loaded.

3. My bike runs (good, well) since I got the wheel straightened.

4. The Penguins' chances looked (bad, badly) at the half.

5. A baseball team has (fewer, less) players than a softball team.

6. You use (fewer, less) eggs with this recipe.

7. The blue coat looks very (good, well) on you.

8. This cotton shirt faded very (bad, badly) the first time it was washed.

9. The patient in 203 will soon be completely (good, well).

10. I (just read, read just) the headline, not the news story.

▶ **Exercise 2** Correcting Errors Caused by Troublesome Adjectives and Adverbs. Underline any errors in the use of modifiers in the following sentences. On the line below, rewrite each sentence correctly. If a sentence is correct as written, write *correct* on the line.

**EXAMPLE:** Only give this message to Ellen or Sheila.
      *Give this message only to Ellen or Sheila.*

1. The Penguins had only thirty seconds to score a touchdown.

_____

2. The boys felt badly about their practical joke.

_____

3. Mr. Salvin just assigned the first ten problems, not all twenty-five.

_____

4. The car has been running good since Dad had the tune-up.

_____

5. Only take this medicine with meals.

_____

# 25.2 Glossary of Troublesome Adjectives and Adverbs • Practice 2

**Exercise 1** **Correcting Errors Caused by Troublesome Adjectives and Adverbs.** Most of the following sentences contain errors in the use of modifiers. Identify the errors, and rewrite the sentences in which they appear. Write *correct* if a sentence contains no errors.

**EXAMPLE:** There are less flowers in the garden now.
_____*There are fewer flowers in the garden now.*_____

1. Tony just reached the station one minute before the train pulled out.

   _____

2. Cheryl looks very well with short hair.

   _____

3. I only made two dozen cookies for the party.

   _____

4. There is fewer snow on the ground this winter than last.

   _____

5. He did not deserve to win because he played badly.

   _____

6. You talk good, but you write better.

   _____

7. The bee sting I received yesterday looks badly.

   _____

8. As the day went on, we saw less sky and more clouds overhead.

   _____

9. Cazzie just needs one more plant to make his botany project complete.

   _____

10. Only add a little water; otherwise, it will be impossible to mold the sand.

   _____

**Writing Application** **Using Troublesome Adjectives and Adverbs Correctly.** On your paper write a sentence according to the directions in each of the following items.

**EXAMPLE:** Use *good* with a linking verb.
_____*The performance of the dolphins was especially good.*_____

1. Use *bad* with a linking verb.

   _____

2. Use *well* as an adverb.

   _____

3. Use *less* to modify a noun.

   _____

4. Use *Only* at the beginning of a sentence.

   _____

5. Use *just* to mean "no more than."

   _____

# 26.1 **End Marks** • **Practice 1**

**Uses of the Period**   Use a period to end a declarative sentence—that is, to end a statement of fact or opinion. Use a period to end an imperative sentence—that is, to end a direction or a command. Use a period to end most abbreviations and after initials.

| PERIODS |
| --- |
| *Declarative Sentence:* We will spend our vacation in Massachusetts.<br>*Imperative Sentence:* Be sure to send me a postcard.<br>*Abbreviation:* Dr. (Doctor)<br>*Initials:* J.Q. Adams |

**Uses of the Question Mark**   Use a question mark to end an interrogative sentence—that is, to end a direct question. Use a question mark to end an incomplete question in which the rest of the question is understood.

| QUESTION MARKS |
| --- |
| *Interrogative Sentence:* Did you have a good time?<br>*Incomplete Question:* Joyce wanted to help. But how? |

▶ **Exercise 1**   **Using the Period.**   Add periods where they are needed in the sentences below.

**EXAMPLE:**  We invited Mr F L Hollings to speak to the club
　　　　　 *We invited Mr. F. L. Hollings to speak to the club.*

1. The movie has a happy ending

2. Mrs Jacobson's house on Maple Ave is for sale

3. Kathy Newsome, R N, is working in surgery this week

4. Please deliver this package to T J Mason

5. Pvt Killian handed the paper to the sergeant

6. The person you should speak to is Prof Bell

7. Be sure to wear something green to the St Patrick's Day parade

8. The first name on the petition is S J Murphy

9. Let me know when you are ready to leave

10. *Dr Jekyll and Mr Hyde* was written by R L Stevenson

▶ **Exercise 2**   **Using the Question Mark.**   Add question marks where they are needed in the sentences below.

**EXAMPLE:**  You told me not to use this. Why
　　　　　 *You told me not to use this. Why?*

1. Has Ben replied to your invitation

2. We must have made a wrong turn somewhere. But where

3. Where will the party be And when

4. Audrey loaned you her notebook, didn't she

5. What time is Grandma arriving On what airline

# 26.1 End Marks • Practice 2

▶ **Exercise 1**  **Using the Period.**  In each of the following sentences, some periods are incorrectly used and others are missing. Cross out periods that don't belong and add periods where they are missing.

**EXAMPLE:** The car driven by Dr Michaels. nearly skidded off the road
*The car driven by Dr. Michaels̷ nearly skidded off the road.*

1. Your appointment is. with Mrs Rose Walters on Tuesday morning
2. The letter was addressed to Sgt Jesse Johnson. of Houston, Texas
3. Carla M Carlson. lives at 433 W Fourth St
4. Give the dog a bath. this afternoon
5. This mail belongs to our next-door neighbor. Mr T J Albertson
6. Get up right now and get ready. for school
7. Everything that belonged to the elderly man was willed to his son, Mr Tom. Brady, Jr
8. Listen carefully to what I am. about to tell you
9. Mr and Mrs C J Bello. have invited us to a dinner party
10. In about ten minutes, Dr Nesbaum will. be able to see you
11. The troops were led by Sgt John. Timoney
12. Go to the neighbors. and ask if we can borrow some butter
13. Please give me a few minutes alone. to prepare for the performance
14. Don't make such a fuss
15. The postcard is addressed. to a Mrs Alicia Thomas

▶ **Exercise 2**  **Using the Period and the Question Mark.**  The following sentences do not have periods or question marks. Add the missing periods and question marks.

**EXAMPLE:** Did Mrs M L Richards arrange the benefit
*Did Mrs. M. L. Richards arrange the benefit?*

1. Should I smooth the wet plaster with my hands
2. Did you ask Donald Palmer, Jr, for his opinion
3. Deliver this message to Mrs Allen quickly
4. Col J D Packard, a friend of ours, is stationed in California
5. Dr Jefferson's new assistant is Lee Tomas, R N
6. Where is the movie playing When
7. I've asked you over and over to close the door behind you
8. What time do we have to be at the airport
9. Do you really want to go to that party Why
10. Is it true that you didn't finish the assignment Why not
11. What did Josh say that was so rude
12. Do you think the price of digital camcorders will come down soon
13. Did you really spend eighteen hours creating this toy For what
14. How often do you have to mow the lawn in the summer
15. What gives you the right to make so much noise

# 26.1 End Marks • Practice 1

**Uses of the Exclamation Mark**  Use an exclamation mark to end an exclamatory sentence—that is, to end a statement showing strong emotion. Use an exclamation mark after an imperative sentence if the command is urgent and forceful. Also use an exclamation mark after an interjection expressing strong emotion.

| EXCLAMATION MARKS |
| --- |
| *Exclamatory Sentence:* How I wish I had been there to see it!<br>*Imperative Sentence:* Grab that chair!<br>*Interjection:* Yippee! |

**► Exercise 1**  **Using the Exclamation Mark.**  Add exclamation marks where they are needed in these sentences.

**EXAMPLE:** Run The bus is leaving now
           *Run! The bus is leaving now!*

1. Hey Hands off that button
2. What a spectacular stunt that was
3. Phew That was a close call
4. Hurray We got another hit
5. How delicious this tastes
6. Gosh I never thought of that
7. Leave the building at once
8. Stop that car
9. Help I'm trapped in here
10. What a darling baby he is

**► Exercise 2**  **Using End Marks Correctly.**  On the line after each sentence, write the correct end mark. Add exclamation marks if they are needed within a sentence.

**EXAMPLE:** What time does the movie start _____?_____

1. Call me when you have finished your homework _____
2. I must have left my lunch in my locker _____
3. Who took the message _____
4. You are going on the field trip, aren't you _____
5. Wow What a surprise that was _____
6. Paula plans to enter the essay contest _____
7. How surprised we were to see you there _____
8. Tell Mom I'll be home by nine _____
9. Which of these jackets is yours _____
10. Read all the directions before you begin _____

## 26.1 End Marks • Practice 2

▶ **Exercise 1**  **Using the Exclamation Mark.**  Each of the following items is missing one or more exclamation marks. Add the missing exclamation marks.

**EXAMPLE:**  Stop Don't forget your money
*Stop! Don't forget your money!*

1. Hooray We finally won a game

2. Don't light a match

3. You're late again

4. Oh I have never been so furious at anyone in my life

5. Say That was an unexpected move

6. Take your feet off the table now

7. What an amazing act of courage that was

8. Hey I remember the answer now

9. Wait for me

10. Quick Grab my hand

▶ **Writing Application**  **Using End Marks Correctly in Sentences.**  Write ten sentences of your own that meet the following requirements. Be sure to use the correct end mark after each sentence and after any other word or phrase within your sentences that requires one.

**EXAMPLE:**  a one-word imperative sentence
      *Hurry!*
   _____

1. an urgent command

   _____

2. a statement of opinion containing the abbreviation of a person's social title

   _____

3. a direct question

   _____

4. a mild command

   _____

5. an exclamatory sentence

   _____

6. a statement of opinion

   _____

7. an interjection expressing strong emotion followed by a statement of fact

   _____

8. a declarative sentence followed by an incomplete question

   _____

9. an interrogative sentence followed by an incomplete question

   _____

10. an imperative sentence containing a person's initials

   _____

**26.2** # Commas in Compound Sentences
## • Practice 1

**Commas in Compound Sentences**   Use a comma before the conjunction to separate two independent clauses in a compound sentence.

| COMMAS WITH COMPOUND SENTENCES |
|---|
| Some members wanted to visit Mystic Seaport, but others wanted to go to Old Sturbridge Village. |
| We had been traveling for ten hours, so we were happy to reach the motel. |

▷ **Exercise 1**   **Using Commas with Compound Sentences.**   Add commas where they are needed in these sentences. Not every sentence needs a comma.

**EXAMPLE:** There was something familiar about the man yet I couldn't quite place him.
*There was something familiar about the man, yet I couldn't quite place him.*

1. The teacher repeated the directions but I was still confused.
2. I explained my problem to the librarian and she was able to find exactly what I needed.
3. We arrived early and stayed late.
4. The campers were hot and tired for they had been hiking all day.
5. Alana wanted to explore the cave but her parents had forbidden it.
6. Sam loves coconut cream candies but Andrew won't touch them.
7. We did our best but still lost the game.
8. My brother excels at languages but I am better than he at math.
9. The fossils the explorers found were very valuable yet the coins were worthless.
10. I ironed the shirts and put them back into the closets.

▷ **Exercise 2**   **Writing Compound Sentences.**   Write a compound sentence from each pair of shorter sentences below. Use an appropriate conjunction and correct punctuation.

**EXAMPLE:** Kevin enjoys baseball. Brian prefers soccer.
    *Kevin enjoys baseball, but Brian prefers soccer.*

1. The Browns have a terrific defense. The Bombers' offense is stronger.

   _____

2. Replace the fuse right away. The ice cream in the freezer will melt.

   _____

3. Jodi had better work harder. The coach will throw her off the team.

   _____

4. We had eaten everything in the refrigerator. We were still hungry.

   _____

5. Luis tried out for the lead in the class play. Jed got the part.

   _____

# 26.2 Commas in Compound Sentences
## • Practice 2

**Exercise 1** **Using Commas with Compound Sentences.** A comma has been left out of each of the following sentences. Insert commas where they should be.

**EXAMPLE:** The article was interesting but it did not have the information I needed.
*The article was interesting, but it did not have the information I needed.*

1. I was foolish to have trusted you but I won't make the same mistake again.
2. Alexandra folded the clean laundry and I placed it in the basket.
3. The victims of the hurricane were stunned for they had lost everything.
4. There was no furniture in the tiny cabin nor was there any source of light.
5. He used the back of a spoon to make peaks in the frosting and she pressed grated coconut along the top and sides.
6. Jill missed the flight so we don't expect her to arrive tonight.
7. You can use this free ticket for yourself or you can give it to a friend.
8. No one answered the telephone and it finally stopped ringing.
9. Becky offered a reward for the return of her billfold but not a single person responded to her advertisement in the evening paper.
10. We expected the weather to turn colder yet the day was warm and sunny.
11. The doctor examined the patient carefully but she did not say a word.
12. Drive carefully when you approach the bridge for the road is very narrow there.
13. We arrived at the station twenty minutes early and then we waited in the rain for the train.
14. We can have a picnic at Discovery Park on Saturday or we can go to brunch at your favorite restaurant.
15. An insect like this is very rare so you should be careful not to harm it.

**Exercise 2** **Using Commas.** In the following paragraph, some commas are incorrectly used and others are missing. Cross out commas that don't belong and add commas where they are missing.

**EXAMPLE:** It takes time✗ and money✗ to put on a good party, but all will be wasted if the guests don't show up.

Val was almost ready to give up but she finally, spotted a light in the distance. She had been lost, in the woods for hours, yet she had kept moving. The day had started out beautifully and it had seemed like a good idea to go for a hike. Valerie was a person, who always tried to plan ahead. She had put some provisions in a backpack for she wanted to be prepared for a hike of several hours. She had not counted on being out, for so long. Now she was hungry, and thirsty since she used up her supplies hours ago. The distant light was a signal that all would be well and Valerie hurried toward it.

**26.2** # Commas in a Series, Between Adjectives
### • Practice 1

**Commas Between Items in a Series**   Use commas to separate three or more words, phrases, or clauses in a series.

| SERIES |
|---|
| *Words:* The dish included chicken, cream, and vegetables. |
| *Phrases:* My sneakers are not under my bed, in the closet, or under the couch. |
| *Clauses:* Mom wanted to know where we were going, with whom we were going, and when we would be home. |

**Commas Between Adjectives**   Use commas to separate adjectives of equal rank. Do not use commas to separate adjectives that must stay in a specific order.

| ADJECTIVES | |
|---|---|
| **With Comma** | **Without Commas** |
| The tired, hungry hikers straggled back to camp. | Several tired hikers straggled back to camp. |
| That rock star has had a long, successful career. | The rock star made his first successful record at the age of fifteen. |

▶ **Exercise 1**   **Using Commas with Items in a Series.**   Add commas where they are needed in these sentences. Not all sentences need commas.

**EXAMPLE:** The fire burned all day through the night and into the next day.
*The fire burned all day, through the night, and into the next day.*

1. Seeing the flames, the child ran out of the apartment down the stairs and into the street.
2. Dad asked if we wanted to have meatloaf hamburgers or pizza on Saturday night.
3. The basic ingredients are flour butter and cheese.
4. Poinsettias mistletoe and other holiday plants contain poisons.
5. Bike riding brisk walking and swimming are good forms of exercise.
6. In planning our trip, we discussed where we would go what route we would take and how long we could afford to stay.
7. Pete frosted the cake set the table and blew up the balloons.
8. Marci and Mary Ellen will be roommates next year.
9. The reporter asked how the fire had started when the victims would be housed and what the public could do to help.
10. The doctor recommended plenty of liquids extra rest and a light diet.

▶ **Exercise 2**   **Using Commas Between Adjectives.**   Add commas where they are needed in these sentences. Not all sentences need commas.

**EXAMPLE:** The sun is our nearest brightest star.
*The sun is our nearest, brightest star.*

1. April got a sterling silver bracelet for her birthday.
2. The recording star has a large devoted fan club.
3. The tall lanky outfielder is a powerful hitter.
4. The mayor threw out the traditional first pitch.
5. Dad has several old valuable stamps in his collection.

# 26.2  Commas in a Series, Between Adjectives
## • Practice 2

**Exercise 1**  **Using Commas with Items in a Series.**  Add commas where they are needed.

**EXAMPLE:** Her favorite authors were Tolkien Asimov and Cather.
*Her favorite authors were Tolkien, Asimov, and Cather.*

1. For exercise Robert lifted weights rode a bicycle and did push-ups.
2. Ann was scheduled to take English algebra earth science Spanish and gym.
3. Our small garden plot produced tomatoes lettuce radishes and zucchini.
4. Sharon swept the sidewalk raked the leaves and painted the mailbox.
5. After the movie, I still didn't understand why the crime was committed who did it or whether the criminals were caught.
6. To get there you must walk past the large oak tree over the grassy knoll and along the gravel driveway.
7. To work here you must have a white uniform comfortable shoes a black apron and a white cap.
8. Do you want to bring pretzels salad or soda to the picnic?
9. The best time to go fishing is before dawn just at dawn or several hours before dusk.
10. We had to decide whom we should invite where we would have the reception and what food we would serve.

**Exercise 2**  **Using Commas Between Adjectives.**  In each of the following sentences, two or more adjectives have been underlined. Add commas only in those places where they are needed.

**EXAMPLE:** <u>Many old</u> mansions have been made into apartment houses.

1. This <u>quiet obedient</u> dog is a pleasure to have around.
2. <u>Several shiny</u> spoons were placed to the right of each knife.
3. Mowing the lawn on such a <u>hazy hot humid</u> day was no fun.
4. We heard <u>four sharp trumpet</u> blasts signal the entrance of the royal visitors.
5. The <u>shabby frayed</u> coat hung limply from the child's slender body.

**Writing Application**  **Using Commas That Separate Basic Elements in Your Writing.**  Follow the directions below to write five sentences of your own. Be sure to use commas only where they are needed to separate basic elements in your sentences.

**EXAMPLE:** Write a compound sentence using the conjunction *and*.
_She pitched a fast ball, and the batter swung and missed._

1. Write a sentence containing a series of three prepositional phrases.

_____

2. Write a sentence containing two adjectives of equal rank.

_____

3. Write a sentence containing a series of three nouns.

_____

4. Write a sentence containing two adjectives that must remain in a specific order.

_____

5. Write a compound sentence using the conjunction *but* to join the independent clauses.

_____

# 26.2 Commas That Set Off Added Elements
## • Practice 1

**Commas After Introductory Material**   Use a comma after an introductory word, phrase, or clause.

| INTRODUCTORY MATERIAL | |
|---|---|
| **Words** | Furthermore, you should have read the warning label. |
| | Please, won't you let me go on the class trip? |
| **Phrases** | Throughout the night, we heard the distant sirens. |
| | Annoyed with the delay, Uncle Al became grumpy. |
| **Clauses** | If you ask me, the movie was a waste of time. |
| | Whenever you are ready, we can leave. |

**Commas with Parenthetical Expressions**   A parenthetical expression is a word or phase that is not essential to the meaning of the sentence. Use commas to set off parenthetical expressions.

| PARENTHETICAL EXPRESSIONS | |
|---|---|
| **Names of People Being Addressed** | We know, Lucy, that you tried your best. |
| | Please pass the butter, Jim. |
| **Certain Adverbs** | It seems clear, therefore, that there has been a mistake. |
| | It is not clear how the mistake occurred, however. |
| **Common Expressions** | Several people, in fact, missed the opening number. |
| | This cake will be delicious, I hope. |

▶ **Exercise 1**   **Using Commas After Introductory Material.**   Add commas where they are needed in these sentences.

**EXAMPLE:** Whenever I hear that song I feel happy.
           *Whenever I hear that song, I feel happy.*

1. Lost and frightened the child began to cry.

2. Inside the smallest of the four boxes Sue found a marble egg.

3. After we had examined the crystals more carefully we decided that they were made of salt.

4. Oddly enough that pattern has been discontinued.

5. To be sure we got good seats we arrived at the theater quite early.

6. No I haven't seen Andrew this morning.

7. Having misread the directions we took a wrong turn.

8. Without at least two more people the game will be boring.

9. Frankly we had hoped for a better turn-out.

10. Well where have you been?

▶ **Exercise 2**   **Using Commas with Parenthetical Expressions.**   Add commas where they are needed in these sentences.

**EXAMPLE:** I am sure that our team will win the game Sally.
           *I am sure that our team will win the game, Sally.*

1. Mrs. Wilson I am happy to say will be back in the classroom soon.

2. Did you know Sue that the test has been postponed?

3. Three of the students to be exact received detentions.

4. You should have gotten permission first however.

5. Bart the best choice for class president in fact is Kelly.

# 26.2 Commas That Set Off Added Elements
## • Practice 2

**Exercise 1** **Using Commas with Introductory Material.** Each of the following sentences needs a comma to set off introductory material. Insert the comma where it is needed in each sentence.

**EXAMPLE:** On our flight to Utah we ate a delicious lunch.
*On our flight to Utah, we ate a delicious lunch.*

1. Oh how can I win against such impossible odds?
2. Before three o'clock that afternoon a light rainfall began.
3. When the children saw the rainbow they began to talk excitedly of a pot of gold.
4. Surprised Oliver gazed in amazement at the people gathered to congratulate him.
5. Repaired the bicycle will last for several years.
6. Goodness no one could lift this rock without help.
7. To win a prize a person must throw all the rings over the peg.
8. Until the first of the year I will be living at the same address.
9. For many days and nights the small craft was lost at sea.
10. Even though Lynn had studied for the exam she thought the questions were difficult.

**Exercise 2** **Using Commas with Parenthetical Expressions.** In the following sentences, add commas as needed to set off the parenthetical expressions.

**EXAMPLE:** Their garden however was untouched by the storm.
*Their garden, however, was untouched by the storm.*

1. Wait Ron and Hugh until the elevator doors open.
2. We nevertheless appreciated your help during the campaign.
3. Travel in this helium-filled balloon is not without hazards of course.
4. Write a one-page essay on the meaning of liberty Lois.
5. Maxine did succeed therefore in raising her grade.
6. Don't feed peanuts to the giraffe Elaine.
7. The truth in fact is just the opposite.
8. The praying mantis on the other hand kills many harmful insects.
9. Please Vic tell me which fork is used for salad.
10. This table I think should be placed near the door.

## 26.2 Commas That Set Off Nonessential Elements • Practice 1

**Commas with Nonessential Expressions**   Essential material cannot be left out without changing the meaning of the sentence. Nonessential material, on the other hand, can be left out. Use commas to set off nonessential expressions.

| Essential Expressions | Nonessential Expressions |
|---|---|
| The speaker from the State Department made several good points. | The speaker, a representative from the State Department, made many good points. |
| The woman speaking on foreign policy is my aunt. | The woman, speaking on foreign policy, advocated a freeze on nuclear weapons. |
| Someone whom I had never met spoke to me by name. | Mr. Hayes, whom I had never met, spoke to me by name. |

▷ **Exercise 1**   **Recognizing Essential and Nonessential Expressions.**   Decide whether the underlined expression in each sentence is essential or nonessential. On the line after each sentence, identify the expression with an *E* (for essential) or an *N* (for nonessential).

**EXAMPLE:** Billy Waters the six year old next door plays in the yard.   ___N___

1. *Sing Down the Moon* which is about a Navaho girl was written by Scott O'Dell. _____
2. Someone that I met at your party once lived in Ireland. _____
3. Alana whose father is an archaeologist has traveled to Egypt. _____
4. Adam a friend of mine from camp will be visiting me next week. _____
5. Mrs. Parsons is the teacher whom most of us have for science. _____
6. The man who won the state lottery gave most of his money to charity. _____
7. Jeff noticed a car leaving the scene of the accident. _____
8. The police keeping well out of sight followed the suspect for two miles. _____
9. The captain of the basketball team who is also an A student won a full scholarship. _____
10. The student who won the scholarship is my brother. _____

▷ **Exercise 2**   **Using Commas with Nonessential Expressions.**   Rewrite each sentence you labeled *N* in Exercise 1, adding commas where they are needed.

**EXAMPLE:**   *Billy Waters, the six year old next door, plays in the yard.*

1. _____
2. _____
3. _____
4. _____
5. _____

# 26.2  Commas That Set Off Nonessential Elements • Practice 2

▶ **Exercise 1**  **Using Commas with Nonessential Expressions.**  Read each of the following sentences carefully to determine whether the underlined expression is essential or nonessential. If the material is essential, write *E* on the line. If it is nonessential, write *N*. Then add a comma or commas as needed.

**EXAMPLE:**  Lee Taylor who lives in Miami is visiting us. _____

   *Lee Taylor, who lives in Miami, is visiting us.*    *N*

1. The fan cheering loudest is my mother. _____
2. I have invited the Gordon brothers who live next door. _____
3. Lauren Edwards my cousin is visiting me. _____
4. The cousin who has been visiting me is going home. _____
5. I enjoyed reading the mystery stories written by Agatha Christie. _____
6. Did you see the boy running down the street? _____
7. Edna St. Vincent Millay the well-known poet wrote "Renascence" when she was only

   nineteen. _____
8. The Sierra Club was founded in 1892 by the explorer, naturalist, and writer

   John Muir. _____
9. In 1890, Congress influenced by John Muir established the first national parks in the United

   States. _____
10. In 1908, Muir Woods National Monument a redwood forest near San Francisco was named in his

   honor. _____

▶ **Writing Application**  **Using Commas to Set Off Added Elements.**  Write five sentences of your own. Include in each of your sentences one of the following items. Use commas where they are needed to set off added elements.

**EXAMPLE:**  an introductory phrase

   *During the last week of May, it was announced that we had won the contest.*

1. An introductory clause

   _____

   _____

2. a common expression as a parenthetical expression

   _____

   _____

3. a nonessential adjective clause

   _____

   _____

4. a person's name used in direct address

   _____

   _____

5. a nonessential appositive

   _____

   _____

# 26.2 Special Uses of the Comma • Practice 1

**Commas with Dates and Geographical Names**   When a date is made up of two or more parts, use a comma after each item except in the case of a month followed by a day. When a geographical name is made up of two or more parts, use a comma after each item.

| Dates | Geographical Names |
|---|---|
| Thursday, March 30, 1985, was opening night. The play opened on Thursday, March 30. He left in July 1985 (*or* July, 1985). | Cleveland, Ohio, is the home of the Browns football team. Alice visited London, England, on her vacation. |

**Other Uses of the Comma**   Use a comma after each item in an address made up of two or more parts. Use a comma after the salutation in a personal letter and after the closing in all letters. With numbers of more than three digits, use a comma after every third digit, counting from the right. Use commas to set off a direct quotation from the rest of a sentence.

*In Addresses:* Paula now lives at 17026 East Main Street, Dover, Delaware 19901.
*In Letters:* Dear Aunt Sue,      Yours truly,
*With Numbers:* 3,097      1,398,201
*With Quotes:* "I hope," Brenda said, "that we will be back in an hour."

▷ **Exercise 1**   **Using Commas with Dates and Geographical Names.**   Add commas where they are needed in these sentences. One sentence needs no commas.

**EXAMPLE:** On Tuesday April 7 my parents will celebrate their fifteenth wedding anniversary.
*On Tuesday, April 7, my parents will celebrate their fifteenth wedding anniversary.*

1. That company is opening a new office in Rome Italy.

2. Scout meetings will resume on Monday September 28 at 7:00 P.M.

3. On June 14 2001 my sister will be sixteen.

4. My grandfather retired in December 1984.

5. We visited the Pilgrim Monument at Provincetown Massachusetts.

▷ **Exercise 2**   **Using Commas in Other Situations.**   Add commas where they are needed in each item.

**EXAMPLE:** The caller asked politely "May I please speak with Marc?"
*The caller asked politely, "May I please speak with Marc?"*

1. "The answer to the first question" said Phil "is on page 1237."

2. To date, record sales have raised $9500280 for charity.

3. Please mail this to Donna Harris 328 Maple Street Branford Connecticut 06405.

4. Dear Cousin Betty Your cousin Harriet

5. "Do you think" Bert asked "that you can come with us?"

## 26.2 Special Uses of the Comma • Practice 2

▶ **Exercise 1** **Using Commas with Dates and Geographical Names.** In each of the following sentences, add commas where they are needed.

**EXAMPLE:** Their destination was Austin Texas.
*Their destination was Austin, Texas.*

1. We will be visiting Annapolis Maryland on May 20.

2. On July 20 1969 astronauts landed on the moon for the first time.

3. Anna expects her grandparents to arrive Friday April 3.

4. After traveling to Bryce Canyon Utah Karen drove to Canyonlands National Park Utah where she took pictures of the sandstone formations.

5. On October 17 1781 General Cornwallis surrendered in Yorktown Virginia.

▶ **Exercise 2** **Using Commas in Other Situations.** Commas have been left out of the following items. Add commas where they are needed.

**EXAMPLE:** "My sister is studying to be a chemist" he said.
*"My sister is studying to be a chemist," he said.*

1. Beth answered dreamily "What was the question?"

2. My dear Jason              Affectionately

                                                Susan

3. She said "Our new telephone number is (312) 555-0476."

4. "Coal is just one of many sources of energy" responded Chris.

5. This huge igloo is made of 3500 blocks of ice.

6. He told them "The serial number is 103 22 411."

7. Address the letter to Diane Freemont 104 Fairview Drive Richmond Virginia 23227.

8. The teacher said "You will find it on page 1324."

9. "I am eager" said Nan "to meet the new exchange student."

10. Mr. Frederick Clifford
    1490 Apple Orchard Street
    Covington Kentucky 41011

▶ **Writing Application** **Using Commas in Special Situations.** Write five sentences of your own, each including one of the following items. Use commas where they are needed to set off material.

**EXAMPLE:** a page number in a book
      <u>The information you need is on page 1,142.</u>

1. the name of a city and a state

   _____

2. a direct quotation

   _____

3. the number 15423672

   _____

4. a date consisting of a month, day, and a year

   _____

5. an address consisting of a name, street, town or city, state, and ZIP code

   _____

**Semicolons • Practice 1**

**Semicolons Used to Join Independent Clauses**  Use a semicolon to join independent clauses that are not already joined by the conjunctions *and, or, nor, for, but, so,* or *yet.*

| INDEPENDENT CLAUSES |
|---|
| Pam felt confident going into the test; she had studied very hard. |
| Put your napkin on your lap; don't tuck it into your shirt. |

**Semicolons Used to Avoid Confusion**  Consider the use of a semicolon to avoid confusion when items in a series already contain commas.

| TO AVOID CONFUSION |
|---|
| Beth Meyers, a freshman at Penn State; Hugh Gibbons, a high-school senior; and Fran Kirby, a secretary, were contestants on the game show. |
| Some of the most popular selections at the concert were "Hey, Jude," a Beatles hit; "People Will Say We're in Love," a song from the musical *Oklahoma;* and "Pomp and Circumstance," a march by Edward Elgar. |

▶ **Exercise 1**  **Using Semicolons to Join Independent Clauses.**  Rewrite each pair of sentences below as a compound sentence in which two independent clauses are joined by a semicolon.

**EXAMPLE:**  Kim is eight years older than her brothers. She often baby-sits for them.
_____Kim is eight years older than her brothers; she often baby-sits for them._____

1. Gradually the water evaporates. The salt forms crystals.

   _____

2. Most of my friends will go to public high school. A few will go away to boarding school.

   _____

3. Their new home is beautiful. No one would guess it was once a barn.

   _____

4. Jeremy is an excellent soccer player. His brother prefers baseball.

   _____

5. Pat can help you with that problem. She is a terrific math student.

   _____

▶ **Exercise 2**  **Using Semicolons to Avoid Confusion.**  Circle any comma in these sentences that should be a semicolon.

**EXAMPLE:**  We ordered soup, which was cold(,) roast beef, which was overcooked(,) and salad.

1. Alana, who lives in the next apartment, Louise, who is in my homeroom, and Marcia, whom I have known since kindergarten, are my best friends.

2. The waitress announced, "Our soups today are New England clam chowder, which is made with clams, potatoes, and cream, minestrone, a hearty Italian vegetable soup, and mulligatawny, a meat soup with curry seasoning."

3. On our trip across the country, my favorite cities were Boston, Massachusetts, Cincinnati, Ohio, and Portland, Oregon.

## 26.3 Semicolons • Practice 2

▶ **Exercise 1**    **Using Semicolons to Join Independent Clauses.**    Semicolons have been left out of the following sentences. Insert semicolons where they are required.

**EXAMPLE:** Becky is fascinated by sharks however, she has not yet met one close up.
*Becky is fascinated by sharks; however, she has not yet met one close up.*

1. Some cheeses are made from cow's milk others are made from goat's milk.

2. They decided not to go shopping instead, they went walking in the park.

3. This glass lens is concave the other is convex.

4. Ten goldfish swam in the pond their scales glinted in the sun.

5. This home used to be a one-room schoolhouse it was built over a century ago.

▶ **Exercise 2**    **Using Semicolons to Avoid Confusion.**    Add semicolons where they should be used in the following sentences.

**EXAMPLE:** They received cards from Honolulu, Hawaii Phoenix, Arizona and Seattle, Washington.
*They received cards from Honolulu, Hawaii; Phoenix, Arizona; and Seattle, Washington.*

1. We were served onion soup topped with melted cheese homemade rye bread, covered with butter and fruit salad, made with six different kinds of fresh fruit.

2. The little girl was wearing a yellow raincoat, which was made of shiny vinyl a matching hat, which was tied neatly under her chin and red boots, which reached to her knees.

3. In less than a year, William had expanded the family to include a large woolly dog with a huge appetite two skinny, stray cats with unfriendly dispositions and a pair of cooing, fluttering pigeons.

4. The music was performed by Fred, who played the flute Samantha, who played the clarinet and Ella, who played the saxophone.

5. Richard, my cousin Donna, the girl next door and Liz, my best friend, went to the concert with me.

▶ **Writing Application**    **Using Semicolons in Your Own Writing.**    Write two different sentences for each of the following items.

1. Use a semicolon to join two closely related, independent clauses.

_____

_____

_____

_____

2. Use a semicolon to separate a series of items already containing several commas.

_____

_____

_____

_____

# 26.3 Colons • Practice 1

**The Colon as an Introductory Device**   Use a colon before a list of items following an independent clause. A colon should not be used directly after a verb or preposition.

| Incorrect | Correct |
|---|---|
| The six New England states are: Maine, Vermont, New Hampshire, Rhode Island, Massachusetts, and Connecticut. | New England consists of six states: Maine, Vermont, New Hampshire, Rhode Island, Massachusetts, and Connecticut. |

**The Colon in Special Situations**   Use a colon in a number of special writing situations.

| SPECIAL USES OF THE COLON | |
|---|---|
| Expressions of Time | 9:45 A.M.      8:30 P.M. |
| Salutations in Business Letters | Dear Ms. Hines:     Dear Sir: |
| Labels Signaling Important Ideas | Warning: Dangerous electrical equipment |
| | Caution: May cause drowsiness |

▶ **Exercise 1**   **Using Colons to Introduce Lists of Items.**   Insert colons where they are needed in the following sentences.

**EXAMPLE:** The basic unit consists of three rooms a living room, bedroom, and kitchen.
*The basic unit consists of three rooms: a living room, bedroom, and kitchen.*

1. The ingredients needed to make brownies are as follows butter, brown sugar, an egg, vanilla, baking powder, flour, and salt.

2. Four team sports are popular in U.S. schools basketball, baseball, football, and soccer.

3. The day after Thanksgiving is a holiday in these states Florida, Maine, Minnesota, Nebraska, and Washington.

4. Four states border Mexico California, Arizona, New Mexico, and Texas.

5. Campers should bring the following items sheets, blankets, and towels.

▶ **Exercise 2**   **Using Colons in Special Situations.**   Insert colons where they are needed in the following items.

**EXAMPLE:** The next flight for Los Angeles leaves at 405.
*The next flight for Los Angeles leaves at 4:05.*

1. Warning Keep this medicine out of reach of children.

2. The feature starts at 7 10.

3. Dear Dr. Morgan

4. Caution Slippery when wet

5. Dear Sir or Madam

## 26.3  Colons • Practice 2

▶ **Exercise 1**  **Using Colons to Introduce Lists of Items.**  Colons have been left out of each of the following sentences. Insert colons where needed.

**EXAMPLE:**  The movie starred my favorite actors Paul Newman, Robert Redford, and Katherine Ross.
*The movie starred my favorite actors: Paul Newman, Robert Redford, and Katherine Ross.*

1. This company produces paper pulp used for the following products paper plates, party hats, streamers, and confetti.
2. The apartment consisted of many spacious rooms three bedrooms, an eat-in kitchen, two baths, and a living room.
3. Maryanne chose three poets to study Dickinson, Frost, and Sandburg.
4. A reliable medical encyclopedia should include certain information descriptions of major diseases, lists of their symptoms, and advice about when to consult a physician.
5. In this wallet are my life's savings six dollar bills, eight quarters, and two nickels.
6. We wanted to buy a home in the country to have these benefits room to expand, space to enjoy outdoor activities, and land for a vegetable garden.
7. Their birthdays were all in the summer June 30, July 15, and August 12.
8. Zack arrived at the beach with these items a picnic basket, a rubber raft, and towels.
9. Indications of extreme stress may include the following rapid pulse, accelerated breathing, dizziness, or fatigue.
10. I will visit three countries Japan, China, and India.

▶ **Exercise 2**  **Using Colons in Special Situations.**  Add the colon missing in each of the following items.

**EXAMPLE:**  700 A.M.      *7:00 A.M.*

1. 630 P.M.
2. Caution Falling rocks
3. Dear Mmes. Jordon and Farnsworth
4. Gentlemen
5. Warning The Surgeon General has determined that cigarette smoking is dangerous to your health.

▶ **Writing Application**  **Using Colons in Your Own Writing.**  Follow the instructions that are given below to write sentences of your own. Use colons as needed.

**EXAMPLE:**  Write a salutation for a business letter.
           *Dear Miss Rivera:*

1. Write a sentence containing a numeral that gives the time of day.

   _____

2. Write a list of items following an independent clause.

   _____

3. Write a sentence containing a list that does not require a colon.

   _____

4. Write a label followed by an important idea.

   _____

# 26.4 Quotation Marks with Direct Quotations
## • Practice 1

**Direct and Indirect Quotations**  A direct quotation represents a person's exact speech or thoughts and is enclosed in quotation marks (" "). An indirect quotation reports the general meaning of what a person said or thought and does not require quotation marks.

| Direct Quotations | Indirect Quotations |
|---|---|
| "I'll be ready in a minute," said Alicia. | Alicia said that she would be ready in a minute. |
| "I'll try one more time," Jeff thought. | Jeff thought he would try one more time. |

**Direct Quotations with Introductory, Concluding, and Interrupting Expressions**
Expressions such as *he said, she explained,* or *they answered* generally accompany quotations. These expressions can introduce, conclude, or interrupt the quoted material.

| Rule | Example |
|---|---|
| Use a comma after an introductory expression. | Ms. Ligeros said, "Open your books to page 143." |
| Use a comma, question mark, or exclamation mark after a quotation followed by a concluding expression. | "I'm all ready to go," said Peter. "Does anyone need more time?" Mr. Ames asked. "I can't believe it!" Mother exclaimed. |
| Use a comma before and after an interrupting expression. | "Most abbreviations," explained Ms. Lampwick, "are inappropriate in formal writing." |

▶ **Exercise 1**  **Distinguishing Between Direct and Indirect Quotations.**  Place quotation marks around each direct quotation in the sentences below. If the sentence contains an indirect quotation, write *I* in the blank.

**EXAMPLE:**  What a great idea! John exclaimed. _____
            *"What a great idea!" John exclaimed.* _____

1. Ms. Sharpe asked the class where the Mandan Indians lived. _____

2. We'll be ready for them, Coach Hawkins said to the reporters. _____

3. Gail hoped that the meeting would end early. _____

4. Is there a difference between a camel and a dromedary? asked Elaine. _____

5. Try to remember where you put the key, Paula urged him. _____

▶ **Exercise 2**  **Punctuating Direct Quotations.**  Place quotation marks, commas, and other punctuation marks where they are needed.

**EXAMPLE:**  A cliché explained Mr. Thomas is a worn-out metaphor.
            *"A cliché," explained Mr. Thomas, "is a worn-out metaphor."*

1. Have you guessed the riddle yet the Hatter asked

2. No I give up said Alice What's the answer

3. I haven't the slightest idea said the Hatter

4. I think you might do something better with the time said Alice than wasting it on riddles that have no answers

5. If you knew time as well as I do said the Hatter you wouldn't talk about wasting it

# Quotation Marks with Direct Quotations
## • Practice 2

▶ **Exercise 1** **Distinguishing Between Direct and Indirect Quotations.** Read each of the following sentences carefully to determine whether it contains a direct quotation that requires quotation marks or an indirect quotation. If the sentence contains a direct quotation, write *D* next to it. If it contains an indirect quotation, write *I*.

**EXAMPLE:** She hoped that she would be chosen. ___*I*___

1. I guess I've lost my watch again, Chris moaned. _____

2. Termites have caused extensive damage to the house, explained the inspector. _____

3. Bill wondered if he should try out for the track team. _____

4. She said that each person was responsible for his or her own actions. _____

5. Let's leave now, suggested Barbara. _____

6. I wondered why all my pens had disappeared. _____

7. Carol thought that school would be canceled because of the snow. _____

8. This situation is intolerable, Mike declared with a frown. _____

9. All day, I hoped that someone else would wash the dinner dishes tonight. _____

10. No one is listening to the stereo, Mother said. _____

▶ **Exercise 2** **Using Direct Quotations with Introductory, Concluding, and Interrupting Expressions.** The following direct quotations have not been correctly punctuated or capitalized. Make the necessary corrections.

**EXAMPLE:** Where are the ski poles he asked.
         *"Where are the ski poles?" he asked.*

1. Why would you throw out these blue jeans asked Milly don't you know they're an important part of my wardrobe

2. I guess it's time said Laverne to return to work

3. Here laughed Lauren are the missing keys

4. Otters are among the most playful animals Glenn explained

5. Stop the guard yelled this is private property

6. The secretary smiled icily and said you can't see her without an appointment

7. I can't decide whether to order the clams or the scallops said Shirley which is better

8. A lion Edna stated does not make a good pet

9. Delphene moaned I can't walk another mile without stopping to rest

10. The pen I borrowed from you leaked all over my shirt complained Arthur

# Quotation Marks with Other Punctuation
## • Practice 1

**Quotation Marks with Other Punctuation Marks**   Always place a comma or a period inside the final quotation mark. Place a question mark or exclamation mark inside the final quotation mark if the end mark is part of the quotation. Place a question mark or exclamation mark outside the final quotation mark if the end mark is part of the entire sentence, not part of the quotation.

| OTHER PUNCTUATION MARKS | |
|---|---|
| **Commas and Periods** | "I think," said Miss Hill, "that you might be right." |
| **Question Marks and Exclamation Marks** | "Where is the meeting?" Nancy asked.<br>Who said, "A fool and his money are soon parted"? |

**Quotation Marks for Dialogue**   When writing dialogue, begin a new paragraph with each change of speaker.

| DIALOGUE |
|---|
| "Tell us a story," said the March Hare. He stared intently and moved closer. "Yes, please do!" said Alice. |

▶ **Exercise 1**   **Punctuating Direct Quotations.**   In each sentence, one or two punctuation marks are missing. Add them correctly to the sentences.

**EXAMPLE:**   "What is your favorite sport" Karen asked Paul.
              "What is your favorite sport?" Karen asked Paul.

1.  Stephen asked "Did you get the last problem right"

2.  "When you see Elena" Michelle said "tell her we all miss her."

3.  "What a beautiful sunset" exclaimed Ralph.

4.  "I agree" said the judge, "that this is a somewhat unusual case"

5.  "I don't believe it" the winning contestant cried.

6.  Who was it who said "A penny saved is a penny earned"

7.  "I'm going to the store now" he said. "Do you need anything"

8.  We were surprised when she asked "May I join you"

9.  "Please open your test booklets to page 3" the teacher said

10. "I will pick you up after school" Mother said.

▶ **Exercise 2**   **Paragraphing Dialogue.**   Circle the words that should be indented to start new paragraphs.

   "Take some more tea," the March Hare said to Alice. "I've had nothing yet," Alice replied in an offended tone, "so I can't take more." "You mean you can't take *less*," said the Hatter. "It's very easy to take more than nothing."

—adapted from *Alice's Adventures in Wonderland*
by Lewis Carroll

# 26.4 Quotation Marks with Other Punctuation
## • Practice 2

▶ **Exercise 1**  **Using End Marks with Direct Quotations.**  End marks have been left out of the following sentences. Read each sentence and decide if the missing punctuation goes inside or outside the quotation marks. Add the missing end marks in the correct locations.

**EXAMPLE:**  He asked the lifeguard, "When can we swim"
He asked the lifeguard, "When can we swim?"

1.  The director told us, "Do not run near the pool"

2.  Karen shrieked, "We won the game"

3.  Didn't you hear him say, "Tomorrow is a holiday"

4.  Mona thought, "Shouldn't a lifeguard be on duty"

5.  The small child cried, "I want that bear"

6.  Did the park attendant say, "Please place your rubbish in the containers"

7.  I was shocked to hear him say, "I won't answer you"

8.  When did I last say, "That's a really tough job"

9.  Angrily, he shouted, "You don't know anything about it"

10.  Rosa asked, "Has the position been filled yet"

▶ **Exercise 2**  **Using Quotation Marks with Dialogue.**  The following selection is an example of dialogue. However, it is missing some punctuation marks and indentations. Read the selection carefully and decide where punctuation marks and indentations are required. Then copy the paragraphs in the space provided, making the necessary changes. You should have four paragraphs when you finish.

What exclaimed Andrea, pointing at a strange-looking object lying on the sand, is that? Don't you know? asked Marty. That's an empty horseshoe crab shell. I've never seen anything like it said Andrea. Are horseshoe crabs good to eat? No, they aren't replied Marty. Perhaps that's why they aren't an endangered species. In fact, these peculiar creatures have been in existence since the days of the dinosaurs.

_____

_____

_____

_____

_____

_____

_____

_____

_____

_____

**26.4** # Quotation Marks or Underlining • Practice 1

**Underlining**  Underline the titles of long written works, magazines, newspapers, movies, radio and television series, long musical compositions, and other works of art. Also underline the names of individual air, sea, space, and land craft.

| WORKS THAT ARE UNDERLINED | |
|---|---|
| *Book:* The Sea Around Us | *Movie:* Amadeus |
| *Magazine:* Sky and Telescope | *Newspaper:* The New York Herald Tribune |
| *Musical Work:* New World Symphony | *Aircraft:* the Concorde |

**Quotation Marks**  Use quotation marks around the titles of short written works, titles of episodes in a series, songs, and parts of long musical compositions.

| WORKS WITH QUOTATION MARKS |
|---|
| *Short Story:* "The Ransom of Red Chief" |
| *Short Poem:* "Two Tramps in Mud Time" |
| *Song:* "We Are the World" |
| *Chapter:* "A Mad Tea Party" from Alice's Adventures in Wonderland |
| *Part of a Long Musical Work:* "Hallelujah Chorus" from The Messiah |
| *Episode in a Series:* "Possum" from Five Mile Creek |

▷ **Exercise 1**  **Punctuating Different Types of Works.**  Use underlining or quotation marks with the works in the sentences below.

**EXAMPLE:**  Poe's poem The Raven brought him sudden fame.
*Poe's poem "The Raven" brought him sudden fame.*

1. The soloist sang Shubert's Ave Maria.
2. The poem of Carl Sandburg's that I like best is Fog.
3. The drama club is putting on Our Town this spring.
4. The book Silent Spring made many aware of the danger of insecticides.
5. I enjoyed James Thurber's story The Night the Bed Fell.
6. Aunt Susan gave me a subscription to National History Magazine.
7. Judy Garland sang Somewhere Over the Rainbow in The Wizard of Oz.
8. Michelangelo's statue David is world-famous.
9. Mark Twain included The Raft Passage in the earliest draft of The Adventures of Huckleberry Finn.
10. When the Titanic sank, many lives were lost at sea.

▷ **Exercise 2**  **Choosing the Correct Form.**  Circle the correct form from the choices below.

**EXAMPLE:**  America the Beautiful or ("America the Beautiful")

1. Edwin Arlington Robinson's short poem "Richard Cory" or Richard Cory
2. Shakespeare's play "Julius Caesar" or Julius Caesar
3. An article in the Atlantic or the "Atlantic"
4. I bought a copy of Robert Frost's Collected Poems or "Collected Poems"
5. O. Henry's story "The Gift of the Magi" or The Gift of the Magi

# 26.4 **Quotation Marks or Underlining • Practice 2**

> **Exercise 1** **Underlining Titles and Names.** Underline the title or name that requires underlining.

**EXAMPLE:** Enid Bagnold's novel <u>National Velvet</u> has been a classic for years.

1. Many of the articles in Science Weekly Magazine can be understood by people with little scientific knowledge.
2. In 1847 Henry Wadsworth Longfellow's long narrative poem Evangeline was published.
3. Olivia Newton-John and John Travolta starred in Grease.
4. Their drama club will be presenting the play The Dark at the Top of the Stairs.
5. Each week the children looked forward to watching the television series The Wonderful World of Nature.
6. In 1976 Viking I landed on Mars.
7. I am reading Rumer Godden's novel An Episode of Sparrows.
8. The Hudson River was named for Henry Hudson who explored it in the Half Moon.
9. When we lived in Virginia, we had subscriptions to the magazines News World and Modern Life.
10. John Singleton Copely, a famous American artist, painted Watson and the Shark.

> **Exercise 2** **Using Quotation Marks with Titles.** Each sentence contains a title that needs quotation marks. Some sentences also contain titles that need underlining. Add the quotation marks or underlining.

**EXAMPLE:** Her favorite patriotic song was Katharine Lee Bates' America the Beautiful.
> *Her favorite patriotic song was Katharine Lee Bates' "America the Beautiful."*

1. If mysteries interest you, read Chapter 4, Some Who Escaped, in the book The Bermuda Triangle.
2. Jim used an article, The Lee Boyhood Home, from the magazine Colonial Homes as a source for his paper on General Robert E. Lee.
3. Paula, a collector of old songs, played School Days for us.
4. My favorite selection from the Peer Gynt Suite, Edvard Grieg's orchestral work, is In the Hall of the Mountain King.
5. Bob read Weekender Sloop, an article in World of Sailing magazine, and then built his own craft.

> **Writing Application** **Using Underlining and Quotation Marks.** Write five sentences of your own, each including one of the following items. Be sure to punctuate and capitalize correctly.

**EXAMPLE:** the title of a short story
> *Shirley Jackson's "Charles" reminds me of my own little brother.*

1. a song title

_____

2. the title of a short poem

_____

3. the title of a book and one of its chapters

_____

4. a movie title

_____

5. the name of a magazine

_____

**26.5** **Hyphens** • **Practice 1**

**Hyphens for Numbers**   Use a hyphen when writing out the numbers twenty-one through ninety-nine and when writing fractions that are used as adjectives.

| NUMBERS AND FRACTIONS |
| --- |
| thirty-two    eighty-eight    a two-thirds majority |

**Hyphens for Word Parts and Compound Words**   Use a hyphen after a prefix that is followed by a proper noun or adjective. Use a hyphen after some prefixes and the suffix *-elect*. Use a hyphen to connect two or more nouns used as one word, unless a dictionary gives a different spelling. Use a hyphen to connect a compound modifier before a noun. Do not use a hyphen when a compound modifier includes a word ending in -ly.

| OTHER USES OF THE HYPHEN | | |
| --- | --- | --- |
| **With Prefixes** | **With Compound Nouns** | **With Compound Modifiers** |
| anti-Soviet | son-in-law | wind-borne seeds |
| ex-mayor | secretary-treasurer | five-room apartment |
| senator-elect | great-aunt | silk-lined coat |

**Rules for Dividing Words at the End of a Line**   Divide words only between syllables. Do not leave a single letter alone on a line. Do not divide proper nouns or proper adjectives. Divide a hyphenated word only after the hyphen.

| **Correct** | | **Incorrect** | |
| --- | --- | --- | --- |
| com-pound | change-able | stud-y | Hol-land |
| help-ful | self-portrait | help-ed | self-por-trait |

▶ **Exercise 1**   **Using Hyphens.**   Place hyphens where they are needed.

**EXAMPLE:**   The Secret Service guards all ex Presidents.
*The Secret Service guards all ex-Presidents.*

1. A two thirds vote is required to change the club rules.

2. My brother in law is running for the school board.

3. Door to door selling is a hard way to make a living.

4. A five pound roast should cook in about an hour and a half.

5. The company's sales are at an all time high.

6. Alaska was the forty ninth state.

7. A well paved road connected the capital to the seaport.

8. Athens and Sparta were rival city states of ancient Greece.

9. Ninety nine senators voted.

10. Self reliance is an admirable quality.

▶ **Exercise 2**   **Hyphenating Words.**   Rewrite each word in syllables that can be divided at the end of a line. Draw a vertical line between the syllables. Circle words that cannot be divided.

**EXAMPLES:** progress ____pro|gress____

among ____(among)____

1. England _____

2. enough _____

3. complete _____

4. handbook _____

5. slipped _____

6. rhythm _____

7. reject _____

8. athlete _____

9. gracious _____

10. Shakespeare _____

## 26.5 Hyphens • Practice 2

**Exercise 1** Using Hyphens with Numbers. Read the following sentences carefully to decide where hyphens are needed. If words in a sentence need a hyphen, add the hyphen. If a sentence does not have any missing hyphens, write *correct* next to it.

**EXAMPLE:** Three fourths of the students attended the game. ___correct___

1. Stephanie started her own business at the age of thirty three. _____
2. One third of the apartments are rented. _____
3. Our class has to read eighty five pages in this book by next Friday. _____
4. To be frank, your paper consists of one fifth fact and four fifths fiction. _____
5. There were more than one hundred kinds of ice cream flavors. _____
6. This drink is made up of two thirds citrus juice and one third water. _____
7. One eighth of the student body attended the concert last night. _____
8. Uncle George moved to San Diego when he was twenty one. _____
9. A nine tenths majority has voted to pass the amendment. _____
10. Twenty two students attended the science seminar. _____

**Exercise 2** Using Hyphens with Word Parts and Compound Words. Look at the following items and decide where hyphens are needed. If an item is correct as it is, write *correct*. If an item does need hyphenation, rewrite the item to make it correct.

**EXAMPLE:** an old fashioned story ___*an old-fashioned story*___

1. a pre Columbian civilization _____
2. a mid April deadline _____
3. a well known speaker _____
4. a North American river _____
5. a senator elect _____
6. a self improvement course _____
7. an all important decision _____
8. a daughter in law _____
9. three four year olds _____
10. a carefully prepared report _____

**Exercise 3** Using Hyphens to Divide Words. If a word can be divided at the end of a line, write the part of the word that would appear at the end of the first line. If the word cannot be divided, write the complete word.

**EXAMPLE:** Anthony ___*Anthony*___

1. dirty _____
2. fight _____
3. better _____
4. Spanish _____
5. icicle _____

6. well-deserved _____
7. payment _____
8. stretch _____
9. abolish _____
10. restless _____

**26.5** # Apostrophes • **Practice 1**

**Apostrophes with Possessive Nouns**   Use the following rules to form the possessive case of nouns.

| FORMING POSSESSIVE NOUNS | |
| --- | --- |
| **Rules** | **Examples** |
| Add an apostrophe and *-s* to show the possessive case of most singular nouns. | a dog's life, the girl's sweater |
| Add just an apostrophe to show the possessive case of plural nouns ending in *-s* or *-es*. | a girls' school, actors' roles |
| Add an apostrophe and *-s* to show the possessive case of plural nouns not ending in *-s*. | the people's choice, women's doubles |

**Apostrophes with Pronouns**   Use an apostrophe and *-s* with indefinite pronouns to show possession. Do not use an apostrophe with possessive personal pronouns.

| POSSESSIVE FORMS OF PRONOUNS | | |
| --- | --- | --- |
| **Indefinite** | | **Personal** |
| someone's | one another's | my, mine, our, ours |
| everybody's | one's | you, yours |
| anyone's | each other's | his, her, hers, its, their, theirs |

▶ **Exercise 1**   **Writing Possessive Forms.**   Write the possessive form in the space provided.

**EXAMPLE:**  the clothes of the men _____*the men's clothes*_____

1. a budget of a city _____
2. the royalties of the authors _____
3. the roots of the plants _____
4. the hole of the mice _____
5. the tires of the car _____
6. the cage of the lovebirds _____
7. the toys of the children _____
8. the smell of strawberries _____
9. the foliage of the trees _____
10. suits for women _____

▶ **Exercise 2**   **Using Apostrophes Correctly with Pronouns.**   Underline the correct pronoun in each set of parentheses.

**EXAMPLE:**  The clock had only one of (it's, <u>its</u>) hands.

1. Is this picnic basket (our's, ours)?
2. The fish seem happy in (their, they're) new tank.
3. Each tool has (it's, its) own special place in the cupboard.
4. Is the red bike yours or (her's, hers)?
5. That must be (someone else's, someone elses') notebook.

# 26.5 The Apostrophe • Practice 2

> **Exercise 1** **Using Apostrophes to Form Possessives of Nouns.** The first ten of the following nouns are singular. The last ten are plural. Write the correct possessive form for each word in the appropriate column below.

**EXAMPLE:** friend

|  | *Singular* |  | *Plural* |
|---|---|---|---|
|  | *friend's* |  | _____ |

| 1. boss | 6. Gus | 11. mice | 16. calves |
|---|---|---|---|
| 2. piano | 7. wheel | 12. homes | 17. oaks |
| 3. stove | 8. bass | 13. authors | 18. cars |
| 4. butter | 9. chimney | 14. women | 19. children |
| 5. wind | 10. mouse | 15. sweaters | 20. keys |

|        *Singular* |        *Plural* |
|---|---|
| _____ | _____ |
| _____ | _____ |
| _____ | _____ |
| _____ | _____ |
| _____ | _____ |
| _____ | _____ |
| _____ | _____ |
| _____ | _____ |
| _____ | _____ |
| _____ | _____ |

> **Exercise 2** **Using Apostrophes with Pronouns.** In each of the following sentences, fill in the blank or blanks with the possessive forms of appropriate indefinite pronouns or personal pronouns.

**EXAMPLE:** They borrowed _____*each other's*_____ jackets.

1. _____ is the red bicycle and _____ is the blue one.

2. _____ voice is unique.

3. Mr. Stanton told _____ class to bring _____ books daily.

4. Try not to listen to just _____ advice.

5. _____ baseball glove may not fit you.

6. The injured bird had lost _____ sense of direction.

7. We counted _____ vote before we wrote _____ new secretary's name on the board.

8. _____ opinion would be welcome.

9. _____ sister and _____ brother are playing tennis tonight.

10. _____ was a good idea, but _____ was even better.

**26.5** # Apostrophes • **Practice 1**

**Apostrophes with Contractions**   Use an apostrophe in a contraction to indicate the position of a missing letter or letters.

| CONTRACTIONS WITH VERBS | | |
|---|---|---|
| Verb + *not* | isn't (is not)<br>won't (will not) | aren't (are not)<br>weren't (were not) |
| Pronouns + the Verb *will* | I'll (I will)<br>he'll (he will) | we'll (we will)<br>they'll (they will) |
| Pronoun or Noun + the Verb *be* | I'm (I am)<br>it's (it is) | they're (they are)<br>Jack's (Jack is) |
| Pronoun or Noun + the Verb *would* | you'd (you would)<br>she'd (she would) | we'd (we would)<br>Terry'd (Terry would) |

**Special Uses of the Apostrophe**   Use an apostrophe and -*s* to form the plurals of numbers, symbols, letters, and words used to name themselves.

| SPECIAL USES OF THE APOSTROPHE | | | |
|---|---|---|---|
| three 6's | too many !'s | dot your i's | too many *and*'s |

▶ **Exercise 1**   **Using Contractions Correctly.**   Make contractions from the words in parentheses and fill them in where they belong.

**EXAMPLE:** We ___*won't*___ be ready for another hour, at least. (will not)

1.  After the show, _____ planning to stop for a pizza. (we are)
2.  _____ amazing how well that child can play the violin. (It is)
3.  _____ have won the race if she hadn't stumbled. (She would)
4.  Paul's dad _____ work in an office. (does not)
5.  Do you think _____ remember to bring his records? (he will)
6.  We _____ have enough time to finish the project today. (do not)
7.  _____ saving his money for a new bike. (Mike is)
8.  _____ help with the dishes if you would let us. (We would)
9.  _____ call you as soon as I get home. (I will)
10. This _____ hurt a bit. (will not)

▶ **Exercise 2**   **Using Apostrophes Correctly.**   Write the contraction or plural called for in each numbered item.

**EXAMPLE:** The plural of *t* ___*t's*___     are + not ___*aren't*___

1.  will + not _____
2.  plural of ? _____
3.  Jim + is _____
4.  plural of 7 _____
5.  plural of *if* _____
6.  they + would _____
7.  it + is _____
8.  who + will _____
9.  was + not _____
10. does + not _____

## 26.5 Apostrophes • Practice 2

▶ **Exercise 1**   **Using Apostrophes with Contractions.**   Each of the following sentences contains one or more word groups that can be written as contractions. In the space provided, write each of these word groups as a contraction.

**EXAMPLE:** They are leaving at five. _____*They're*_____

1. Who would want a car that cannot go more than ten miles without breaking
   down? _____

2. I was not listening and did not hear your question. _____

3. Who will pick out Lee's birthday present? _____

4. Who is going to the dance? _____

5. Connie is feeling much better, and she will be released from the hospital
   tomorrow. _____

6. We will appoint one representative who will attend every meeting. _____

7. Where is the book that was on the top shelf? _____

8. Were you not about to say something? _____

9. We did not see Krista's picture in the school yearbook. _____

10. We could not decide whether we would go to the movies or just stay home. _____

▶ **Writing Application**   **Using Apostrophes in Your Own Writing.**   Write ten sentences of your own according to the instructions in each of the following items.

**EXAMPLE:** Use the possessive form of the word *kitten.*
   _____*The kitten's paws were very soft.*_____

1. Use the possessive form of the word *apartments.*

   _____

2. Use the contraction for *they will.*

   _____

3. Use the possessive form of the indefinite pronoun *someone.*

   _____

4. Use the possessive form of the word *children.*

   _____

5. Use the possessive form of the word *glass.*

   _____

6. Use the contraction for *you would.*

   _____

7. Use the plural form of the letter *d.*

   _____

8. Use the possessive personal pronoun *their.*

   _____

9. Use the plural form of the number *6.*

   _____

10. Use the possessive form of the word *actress.*

   _____

# (27) Capitals for Sentences and the Word *I*
## • Practice 1

**Sentences**  Capitalize the first word in declarative, interrogative, imperative, and exclamatory sentences.

| CAPITALS TO BEGIN SENTENCES |
|---|
| *Declarative:* The museum is open to the public daily.<br>*Interrogative:* Have you seen the most recent exhibit?<br>*Imperative:* Be sure to go before it closes.<br>*Exclamatory:* How beautiful the portraits are! |

**The Word *I***  Always capitalize the word *I*.

| CAPITALIZING *I* |
|---|
| I was sorry to be late.<br>The museum closed before I got there. |

> **Exercise 1**  **Using Capitals for Sentences and the Word *I*.**  Underline the word or words that should be capitalized in each sentence.

**EXAMPLE:** the teacher asked if i had finished my rough draft.

1. sometimes i like to spend time alone.
2. did you remember to invite Ilona?
3. how much i hoped we would win!
4. please tell Jen i was asking about her.
5. we arranged to meet Jordy at the Community House.
6. how surprised i was to see Mandy there!
7. let me show you the sweater i made.
8. i hope you can join us.
9. several of the art projects were made of papier-mâché.
10. when will i see you again?

> **Exercise 2**  **Using Capitalized Words.**  Complete each sentence by adding an appropriate capitalized word.

**EXAMPLE:** This summer _____*I*_____ am going to camp for six weeks.

1. _____ will the pizza be delivered?
2. _____ students will enter the contest?
3. _____ Martin teaches industrial arts at the high school.
4. Peggy knows that _____ am going to the party.
5. _____ your help, we wouldn't have finished in time.
6. _____ time does the movie begin?
7. What do you think _____ should write about?
8. _____ dwarfs lived in the cottage where Snow White stayed.
9. _____ day Dad jogs before breakfast.
10. If you need anything, _____ will be happy to help.

# 27  Capitals for Sentences and the Word *I*
## • Practice 2

▶ **Exercise 1**  **Using Capitals to Begin Sentences.**  Copy the following items, adding the missing capitals.

**EXAMPLE:**  why did you choose this restaurant?
_____*Why did you choose this restaurant?*_____

1.  what an interesting plot that was!

   _____

2.  sit up and listen carefully.

   _____

3.  would you mind if we ask one more question before you leave?

   _____

4.  which way should we turn? right? left?

   _____

5.  show me the blueprint for your new home.

   _____

6.  if anyone can change your opinion, he can.

   _____

7.  why not? they owe you a favor.

   _____

8.  today clothing fashions are determined by the individual.

   _____

9.  my mother and father would like both of you to stay for dinner.

   _____

10.  wow! these fireworks are spectacular!

   _____

▶ **Exercise 2**  **Capitalizing the Word *I*.**  Copy the following sentences, adding the missing capitals.

**EXAMPLE:**  she and i have never been friends.
_____*She and I have never been friends.*_____

1.  i began to wonder what i should do next.

   _____

2.  the child smiling into the camera is i.

   _____

3.  i think i am going to be a little late.

   _____

4.  he said i would be the candidate.

   _____

5.  after that experience, i'll never swim there again.

   _____

**27** # Capitals for Proper Nouns (Names, Places)
## • Practice 1

**Names of People**   Capitalize each part of a person's full name.

| PERSONS' NAMES |
| --- |
| Anthony James Palmer   Anthony J. Palmer   A. J. Palmer |

**Geographical Places**   Capitalize geographical names.

| GEOGRAPHICAL NAMES | |
| --- | --- |
| *Streets:* State Street | *Mountains:* the Alps, Mount Rainier |
| *Towns, Cities:* Dover, Toronto | *Sections:* the Midwest |
| *Counties:* Fairfield County | *Islands:* Bermuda, Sardinia |
| *States, Provinces:* Ohio, Manitoba | *Scenic Spots:* the Everglades |
| *Nations:* Italy, Guatemala | *Rivers, Falls:* Thames, Niagara Falls |
| *Continents:* Africa, Asia | *Lakes, Bays:* Lake Erie, Chesapeake Bay |
| *Deserts:* Sahara | *Seas, Oceans:* Dead Sea, Pacific Ocean |

▶ **Exercise 1**   **Using Capitals for People's Names.**   Underline each word that should be capitalized in the sentences below.

**EXAMPLE:**  The first speaker was julio rodriguez.

1. The envelope was addressed to janice lawson.

2. Have you told jason, nancy, and ben what time to come?

3. joe and elberta went for a walk through the park.

4. Whenever I see elaine, she is with paula.

5. frank's full name is franklin xavier cambridge jones.

6. I would like to read more books by scott o'dell.

7. claire f. rose will be speaking at the high school tonight.

8. alex's best friend likes to be called j. c.

9. As soon as I met linda richmond, I knew we would be friends.

10. frank zappa named his children moonunit and dwiesel.

▶ **Exercise 2**   **Using Capitals for Geographical Names.**   Underline the geographical names that should be capitalized in the sentences below.

**EXAMPLE:**  The Parkers moved from their apartment on lyman place to a house on vernon avenue.

1. The city of cleveland lies on the shore of lake erie.

2. The capital of yugoslavia is belgrade.

3. The yellow sea separates south korea from china.

4. The city of chicago is in cook county, illinois.

5. We spent our vacation at white bear lake near st. paul, minnesota.

6. The cities of san francisco and oakland are on opposite sides of san francisco bay.

7. The allegheny and monongahela rivers join to form the ohio river at pittsburgh.

8. The mohave desert is in california, southeast of the sierra nevada mountains.

9. Their new address is 721 west main street, canton, ohio.

10. The whole family enjoyed the visit to mount rushmore in south dakota.

# 27 Capitals for Proper Nouns (Names, Places)
## • Practice 2

**▶Exercise 1**  **Using Capitals for Names.**  Each of the following sentences contains one or more names that need to be capitalized. Rewrite the names, adding the missing capitals.

**EXAMPLE:** Many unusual ingredients show up in the omelets chris makes. ____*Chris*____

1. Our whole class has just finished reading a book by paul zindel. _____

2. I guessed correctly that jamie left the water in the sink and that pete forgot to lock the door. _____

3. The scholarship awards were presented by anthony r. hughes. _____

4. We asked marcia to bring the pizza and jim to bring a tossed salad. _____

5. This newly built wing of the library will be dedicated to p. l. martinez. _____

**▶Exercise 2**  **Using Capitals for Geographical Names.**  Add the missing capitals to each geographical place name.

**EXAMPLE:** The capital of austria is vienna. ____*Austria, Vienna*____

1. We drove to mount rainier national park. _____

2. My favorite postcard shows the grand canyon. _____

3. The canary islands are west of africa in the atlantic ocean. _____

4. I watched a program about the everglades. _____

5. The iris is the state flower of tennessee. _____

6. We hope to visit australia and new zealand. _____

7. The matterhorn is one of the mountains in the alps. _____

8. Tracy lives in van nuys, orange county, california. _____

9. They are staying near lake winnipeg in manitoba. _____

10. The white sands desert resembles snowy hills. _____

**27** **Capitals for Proper Nouns • Practice 1**

**Other Proper Nouns**   Capitalize the names of specific events and periods of time. Capitalize the names of various organizations, government bodies, political parties, races, and nationalities, as well as the languages spoken by different groups. Capitalize references to religions, deities, and religious scriptures. Capitalize the names of other special places and items.

---

**OTHER PROPER NOUNS**

*Specific Events and Times:* Monday, Labor Day, September, World War I, the Gettysburg Address
*Specific Groups:* Boy Scouts of America, Penn State University, Wentworth Industries, the Supreme Court, Chinese
*Religious References:* Lord, the Torah, Islam, Passover
*Other Special Places and Items:* the Washington Monument, Venus, National Book Award, the Mayflower, Sunglory Raisin Bran

---

▶ **Exercise 1**   **Capitalizing Other Proper Nouns.**   Underline the words in each sentence that should begin with a capital letter.

**EXAMPLE:** Our family got a <u>primo</u> computer for <u>christmas</u>.

1. My sister will enter the university of minnesota in september.

2. The report said that the democrats will open a walk-in office in the new ellicott building.

3. The President awarded him a purple heart for his service in world war II.

4. Tryouts for the pickle players will be held the first saturday in march.

5. The bible, torah, and koran were on display at the museum.

6. The parent-teacher association will hold its open house on october 10.

7. Did astronauts on the space shuttle *columbia* drink tropical brand orange juice?

8. In high school, I will study either french or spanish.

9. The rose bowl parade is televised every new year's day.

10. George Washington fought on the side of the british in the french and indian war.

▶ **Exercise 2**   **Using Capitals for Proper Nouns.**   Write a proper noun for each common noun given below. Use capital letters where they are needed.

**EXAMPLE:** a celestial body _____Uranus_____

1. a specific event _____

2. a rock group _____

3. a cereal _____

4. a business _____

5. a month _____

6. a car _____

7. a monument _____

8. a language _____

9. a religion _____

10. a club _____

# 27 Capitals for Proper Nouns • Practice 2

▶ **Exercise 1** **Capitalizing Proper Nouns.** Each of the following sentences contains one or more proper nouns that need to be capitalized. Rewrite the proper nouns, adding the missing capital letters.

**EXAMPLE:** Jane Addams won the nobel peace prize in 1931. ___*Nobel Peace Prize*___

1. Next saturday, I plan to visit the century building. _____

2. The professor explained that islam requires its followers to fast during the holy month of ramadan. _____

3. In 1917, the british issued the balfour declaration, a statement of their policy on the middle east. _____

4. During the renaissance, many forms of art flourished. _____

5. The caldecott medal is awarded annually for an illustrated children's book. _____

6. Mark, who knows both portuguese and spanish, said that the two languages are quite different from each other. _____

7. Jeff water-skied when he attended the university of hawaii. _____

8. The bill of rights is an essential part of the constitution of the united states. _____

9. This year our class will learn about the platforms of the two major political parties—the republicans and the democrats. _____

10. Stella's youngest brother just joined the little league, and his team will be playing the first friday in may. _____

11. Lucy interviewed one of the first men to work for the tennessee valley authority. _____

12. As an employee of general automotive, Sal was well informed about new developments in car safety. _____

13. We stood quietly inside the lincoln memorial. _____

14. Every easter, we enjoy watching the easter parade on television. _____

15. Last year, my parents celebrated new year's eve by going for a ride on the staten island ferry. _____

16. Napoleon was defeated by the english at the battle of waterloo. _____

17. The highest court in our nation is the supreme court. _____

18. I prefer grainway's rice krispettes to any other cereal. _____

19. The last star in the handle of the little dipper is polaris. _____

20. Next, ben gave a clear description of grant's tomb. _____

▶ **Writing Application** **Using Capitals for Proper Nouns.** Write ten sentences of your own, each containing a proper noun or nouns of the kind indicated in the following items. Be sure to capitalize correctly.

**EXAMPLE:** a holiday ___*Thanksgiving is Jack's favorite holiday.*___

1. an award

_____

2. a trademark

_____

3. a day of the week and a month

_____

**27** # Capitals for Proper Adjectives • Practice 1

**Proper Adjectives**   Capitalize most proper adjectives and brand names used as adjectives.

| Proper Adjectives | Brand Names as Adjectives |
|---|---|
| Mexican food | Grande taco shells |
| Italian leather | Softies tissues |

▶ **Exercise 1**   **Forming Proper Adjectives.**   Rewrite each phrase below so that a proper adjective modifies a noun.

**EXAMPLE:** An emperor of Rome ___*a Roman emperor*___

1.  the clothes from America _____
2.  geese from Canada _____
3.  the pyramids in Egypt _____
4.  a senator from Massachusetts _____
5.  tea bags made by Blakely _____
6.  winters in Minnesota _____
7.  traditions of the Jews _____
8.  cars made by Strategem _____
9.  a camera made in Japan _____
10.  a playwright from England _____

▶ **Exercise 2**   **Using Capitals for Proper Adjectives.**   Write a proper adjective or brand name to modify each noun below. Be sure to capitalize it correctly.

**EXAMPLE:** ___*Pureglow*___ soap

1.  _____ tea
2.  _____ cars
3.  _____ play
4.  _____ cameras
5.  _____ sausage
6.  _____ running shoes
7.  _____ flag
8.  _____ city
9.  _____ toothpaste
10.  _____ restaurant

# 27 Capitals for Proper Adjectives • Practice 2

▶ **Exercise 1** **Using Capitals for Proper Adjectives.** Write a meaningful proper adjective to complete each of the following phrases. Be sure to capitalize the phrases correctly.

**EXAMPLE:** ___*French*___ fashions

1. _____ shampoo
2. _____ meatballs
3. _____ imports
4. _____ designer
5. _____ bread
6. _____ margarine
7. _____ music
8. _____ television
9. _____ potatoes
10. _____ cameras

▶ **Writing Application** **Using Capitals for Proper Adjectives.** Pretend that you have just finished shopping for groceries. Write a brief paragraph describing the contents of your shopping cart. Use at least five proper adjectives to describe the products that you have purchased, including at least three brand names.

_____

_____

_____

_____

_____

_____

_____

_____

_____

_____

# ㉗ Capitals for Titles of People • Practice 1

**Social and Professional Titles**   Capitalize the title of a person when the title is followed by the person's name or when it is used in direct address.

| TITLES OF PEOPLE |
| --- |
| *Social:* Mister, Madame, Miss, Sir |
| *Business:* Doctor, Professor, Chairman |
| *Religious:* Reverend, Father, Rabbi, Sister |
| *Military:* Sergeant, Corporal, General |
| *Government:* Ambassador, Governor, Senator |

**Titles for Family Relationships**   Capitalize titles showing family relationships when the title is used with the person's name or in direct address. The title may also be capitalized when it refers to a specific person, except when the title comes after a possessive noun or pronoun.

| TITLES FOR FAMILY RELATIONSHIPS | |
| --- | --- |
| **With Capitals** | **Without Capitals** |
| Oh, Aunt Rose, we had a great vacation! | Our aunt listened to the tales of our travels. |
| I told Mother the whole story. | I told my mother the whole story. |

▷ **Exercise 1**   **Using Capitals for Social and Professional Titles.**   Underline any title in the sentences below that should be capitalized. Rewrite the title correctly. If a sentence is correct as written, write *C* on the line.

**EXAMPLE:**   You have a three o'clock appointment with doctor Lyons.   _____*Doctor*_____

1. Have you decided how you will vote, senator? _____
2. The movie is about the adventures of a young private. _____
3. Next week, father Hawkins will preach on humility. _____
4. That course is usually taught by professor Maloney. _____
5. The wedding took place before both a minister and a rabbi. _____
6. My aunt once met sir Laurence Olivier. _____
7. May I ask, madame, where you got that hat? _____
8. The committee will meet tonight to select a new chairman. _____
9. The jury asked judge Harriman to explain the testimony. _____
10. The students asked sister Joan for new art supplies. _____

▷ **Exercise 2**   **Using Capitals for Family Titles.**   Most of the following sentences contain words with errors in capitalization. Rewrite the words, correcting the errors. If a sentence is correct, label it *C.*

**EXAMPLE:**   Terry's Dad is a police detective.   _____*dad*_____

1. We were thrilled to hear about uncle Jack's promotion. _____
2. Will your father let us use his tools? _____
3. Please try some of aunt Mary's famous lasagna. _____
4. Can't I please go to the movies, mom? _____
5. The children call their grandfather papa Walter. _____

# 27 Capitals for Titles of People • Practice 2

▶ **Exercise 1** **Using Capitals for Social and Professional Titles.** Each of the following sentences contains either a title before a name or a title used in direct address. Rewrite each title, adding the missing capital.

**EXAMPLE:** The young recruit saluted sergeant Benjamin. ___*Sergeant*___

1. We asked captain Miller to speak to us. _____

2. During the meeting, ambassador Bede spoke twice. _____

3. Ask professor Smedley when the papers are due. _____

4. During the war, Jim became lieutenant Harding. _____

5. At three o'clock sister Helen led the children outdoors. _____

6. The men have been pushed to the breaking point, colonel. _____

7. Our lawyer, attorney Black, explained the contract to us. _____

8. Quick, nurse, take this sample to the laboratory. _____

9. The cartoonist criticized the foreign policy of president Johnson. _____

10. Please, governor, tell us whether you intend to run again. _____

▶ **Exercise 2** **Using Capitals for Family Titles.** If a title in a sentence lacks a capital or if a title has been incorrectly capitalized, rewrite the title, correcting the error. If the sentence is correct, write *correct*.

**EXAMPLE:** My sister and I wear the same size. ___*correct*___

1. Are we having meat loaf again, dad? _____

2. Paul's Uncle gave us free swimming lessons. _____

3. The children begged Grandfather Davis to come along. _____

4. Naturally, uncle Glen wanted to show my brothers and me his new ranch. _____

5. My Mother is always willing to listen to me. _____

6. Last winter our Aunt was vacationing in the Alps. _____

7. They finally decided that Mother McKee was not guilty. _____

8. I told you, cousin Angela, that everyone liked the fudge. _____

9. Why not ask your brother to lend you his bicycle? _____

10. I'm sorry, son, but you will not be allowed to go. _____

▶ **Writing Application** **Using Capitals for Titles of People.** Write five sentences, each including an example of the title described.

**EXAMPLE:** a government title used before a name. ___*Representative Rachel Taylor spoke to our class.*___

1. a military title

_____

2. a family member's title used in direct address

_____

3. a social title used before a name

_____

4. a business title used before a name

_____

5. a family member's title used after a possessive

_____

# Capitals for Titles of Things • Practice 1

**Written Works and Works of Art**   Capitalize the first word and all other important words in the titles of books, periodicals, poems, stories, plays, paintings, and other words of art.

| TITLES OF WORKS |
| --- |
| *Books: The Loneliness of the Long Distance Runner*<br>*Periodicals: Penny Power*<br>*Poems: "The Song of Hiawatha"*<br>*Stories: "The Pit and the Pendulum"*<br>*Plays: The Miracle Worker*<br>*Paintings: The Night Watch*<br>*Sculpture: The Thinker*<br>*Musical Works: "Ode to Joy"* |

**School Courses**   Capitalize the title of a course when the course is a language or when the course is followed by a number.

| SCHOOL COURSES | |
| --- | --- |
| **With Capitals** | **Without Capitals** |
| Algebra II | algebra |
| Science 201 | science |
| German | |

▶ **Exercise 1**   **Using Capitals for Titles of Works.**   Rewrite each title below using capital letters where they are needed. Use underlining and quotation marks as shown.

**EXAMPLE:** the last of the mohicans     *The Last of the Mohicans*

1. popular pets magazine _____
2. "a day's wait" _____
3. Mr. Smith Goes to Washington _____
4. the rise of silas lapham _____
5. moonlight sonata _____
6. "the wreck of the hesperus" _____
7. "the secret life of walter mitty" _____
8. great expectations _____
9. "the star-spangled banner" _____
10. a midsummer night's dream _____

▶ **Exercise 2**   **Using Capitals for Courses.**   Some of the sentences below use correct capitalization and some do not. Correct any error in capitalization, on the lines at the right. Label each correct sentence *C*.

**EXAMPLE:** Tom's math course is algebra I.     *Algebra I*

1. My sister is majoring in biology with a minor in russian. _____
2. I have signed up for ceramics as my art course. _____
3. In civics 2A, we keep an editorial scrapbook. _____
4. Joanna will be taking Chemistry in her junior year. _____
5. One of the new offerings is a course in French civilization. _____

Name _____  Date _____

## 27  Capitals for Titles of Things • Practice 2

**Exercise 1**  **Using Capitals for Written Works and Works of Art.**  Rewrite each of the following titles, adding the missing capitals. Use underlining and quotation marks as shown.

**EXAMPLE:** "of missing persons"  _____"Of Missing Persons"_____

1. the heart is a lonely hunter _____
2. fashion illustrated _____
3. "the monkey's paw" _____
4. joy in the morning _____
5. head of a woman _____
6. the gold of the gods _____
7. the man who came to dinner _____
8. "to a field mouse" _____
9. road and car _____
10. "to a waterfowl" _____

**Exercise 2**  **Using Capitals for Courses.**  In each of the following sentences, choose the correctly written course title from the choices in parentheses and write it in the blank space.

**EXAMPLE:** Lisa is a student in my ____algebra____ class. (algebra, Algebra)

1. While studying _____, I became interested in politics. (civics I, Civics I)
2. Few people in _____ understood their assignments. (physics, Physics)
3. After Pat finished her first year of _____, she decided to study an easier language. (russian, Russian)
4. Next year Bert and I will be taking _____. (geometry, Geometry)
5. In _____ we are studying the conjugation of verbs. (spanish, Spanish)

**Writing Application**  **Using Capitals for Titles of Things.**  Write five sentences, each including the kind of title described in the item.

**EXAMPLE:** a sculpture (underlined)

   _Rodin's The Thinker is one of the most famous sculptures in the world._

1. a poem (in quotation marks)

_____

2. a language course

_____

3. a painting (underlined)

_____

4. a math course

_____

5. a book (underlined)

_____

Name _____     Date _____

 **27** # Capitals in Letters • Practice 1

**Parts of Letters**   Capitalize the first word and all nouns in letter salutations, and the first word in letter closings.

| Salutations | Closings |
|---|---|
| Dear Aunt Edith, | Your loving niece, |
| Dear Sir: | Yours truly, |
| My dear Friend, | Your old pal, |

▷ **Exercise 1**   **Using Capitals for Parts of Letters.**   Rewrite each of the following letter parts, adding the missing capitals.

**EXAMPLE:** dear uncle phil,    _Dear Uncle Phil,_

1. my dear miss walker, _____
2. affectionately, _____
3. very truly yours, _____
4. my dear old friend, _____
5. dear sir or madam: _____
6. your loving grandson, _____
7. with warmest regards, _____
8. dear sue and amy, _____
9. dear uncle al, _____
10. your classmate, _____

▷ **Exercise 2**   **Using Capitals in Letters.**   Write a short letter of one paragraph inviting a friend to visit you. Write your address and the date in the space provided in the upper right hand corner, and use capital letters where they are needed throughout your letter.

_____
_____
_____

_____
_____
_____
_____
_____
_____
_____
_____

## 27 Capitals in Letters • Practice 2

▶ **Exercise 1** Using Capitals for Salutations and Closings in Letters. Rewrite each of the following letter parts, adding the missing capitals.

**EXAMPLE:** dear uncle bill, _____*Dear Uncle Bill,*_____

1. my dear kevin, _____
2. dearest friends, _____
3. dear gwen and brenda, _____
4. affectionately yours, _____
5. yours truly, _____

▶ **Writing Application** Using Capitals in Letters. Write a short letter of one paragraph thanking a relative for a gift. Be sure to capitalize correctly throughout the letter.

_____

_____

_____

_____

_____

_____

_____

_____

_____

_____

_____

_____

_____

_____

# Diagraming Basic Sentence Parts

**Subjects and Verbs**   In a sentence diagram, the subject and verb are placed on a horizontal line, separated by a vertical line. The subject is on the left and the verb is on the right.

| SUBJECT AND VERB |
| --- |
| *Roger is dancing.* |
| Roger \| is dancing |

**Adjectives, Adverbs, and Conjunctions**   An adjective is placed on a slanted line directly below the noun or pronoun it describes. Adverbs are placed on slanted lines directly under the verbs, adjectives, or adverbs they modify. Conjunctions are placed on dotted lines drawn between the words they connect.

| ADDING ADJECTIVES AND ADVERBS | ADDING CONJUNCTIONS |
| --- | --- |
| *The tall, dark stranger entered very quietly.* | The lost *and* lonely boy cried softly. |

▶ **Exercise 1**   **Diagraming Sentences.**   Diagram each sentence. Refer to the examples for any help you need.

1. The old and battered steam kettle whistled loudly.

2. That tiny woodpecker hammers constantly.

▶ **Exercise 2**   **More Work with Diagraming.**   Diagram the following sentences.

1. Battered but victorious, the frigate sailed away.

2. The sleek horse jumped smoothly and effortlessly.

# Diagraming Basic Sentence Parts

▶ **Exercise 1**   **Diagraming Subjects and Verbs.**   Each of the following sentences contains a subject and a verb. Diagram each sentence.

1. Judy wrote.

2. Snow was falling.

3. Ann Frederick has departed.

▶ **Exercise 2**   **Diagraming Sentences with Modifiers and Conjunctions.**   Diagram each sentence.

1. The large truck moved slowly.

2. A strong and dangerous storm approached.

3. The elderly man walked surprisingly fast.

# Diagraming Basic Sentence Parts

**Compound Subjects and Verbs**   Each part of a compound subject is diagramed on a separate horizontal line, and the conjunction that connects them is placed on a dotted vertical line. Compound verbs are diagramed in a similar way.

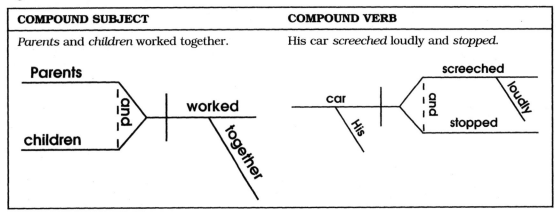

**Orders**   Orders are diagramed with the understood subject *you* placed in the regular subject position, but in parentheses.

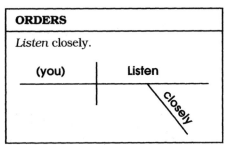

▷ **Exercise 1**   **Diagraming Compound Subjects and Verbs.**   Diagram each sentence below.

1. The tulips and the daffodils bloomed very early.

2. Mark blocked well and tackled brilliantly.

▷ **Exercise 2**   **Diagraming Orders.**   Diagram each sentence below.

1. Come here.

2. Turn very slowly.

# Diagraming Basic Sentence Parts

▷ **Exercise 1** **Diagraming Compound Subjects and Compound Verbs.** Diagram the following sentences.

1. Bricks and mortar were used.

2. Susan walks often but jogs infrequently.

3. Some yellow marigolds and three beautiful pink roses were blooming.

▷ **Exercise 2** **Diagraming Orders.** Diagram the following sentences, placing the understood subjects correctly.

1. Work quickly.

2. Speak softly.

3. Draw especially freely.

# Diagraming Basic Sentence Parts

**Complements**   The three kinds of complements—direct objects, indirect objects, and subject complements—are diagramed in different ways. A direct object is placed on the same horizontal line as the subject and the verb. It follows the verb and is separated from it by a vertical line. An indirect object is placed on a short horizontal line extending from a slanted line directly below the verb. Subject complements follow linking verbs and are placed on the same line as the subject verb. They are placed after the verb and separated from it by a slanted line that points to the subject.

**Exercise 1**   **Diagraming Direct Objects and Indirect Objects.**   Diagram these sentences.

1.  I sent Uncle Jim a birthday card.


2.  Mary gave him some help.


**Exercise 2**   **Diagraming Subject Complements.**   Diagram these sentences.

1.  That pool looks very deep.


2.  Bob is the class speaker.

# Diagraming Basic Sentence Parts

▶ **Exercise 1**   **Diagraming Direct Objects and Indirect Objects.**   Diagram the following sentences.

1. The ushers opened the doors.

2. Frank sold them the house.

3. She showed us many valuable coins.

▶ **Exercise 2**   **Diagraming Subject Complements.**   Diagram the following sentences.

1. Peter is an excellent student.

2. The cellar is damp.

3. The room is now a dull color.

# Diagraming Prepositional Phrases and Appositives

**Prepositional Phrases**    Place a prepositional phrase used as an *adjective* directly under the noun it modifies. Place a prepositional phrase used as an *adverb* under the verb it modifies.

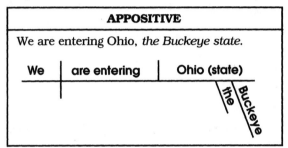

| ADJECTIVE PHRASE | ADVERBIAL PHRASE |
|---|---|
| The photographs *on the wall* are lovely. | We drove *into the city*. |

**Appositives**    Place an appositive in parentheses next to the noun or pronoun it renames. Any words that modify the appositive should be placed below it.

| APPOSITIVE |
|---|
| We are entering Ohio, *the Buckeye state*. |

▷ **Exercise 1**    **Diagraming Prepositional Phrases.**    Diagram each sentence below.

1. The leopard swam across the broad river.

2. We picked the red roses in our garden.

▷ **Exercise 2**    **Diagraming Appositive Phrases.**    Diagram each of these sentences.

1. The house down the street, an old colonial, was sold recently.

2. Hannibal, the famous general, fought against Rome.

# Diagraming Prepositional Phrases and Appositives

▶ **Exercise 1**  **Diagraming Prepositional Phrases.**   Each of the following sentences contains one prepositional phrase. Diagram the sentences.

1. This is a valley of extraordinary beauty.

2. The ship in the harbor is very large.

3. This is the beginning of the longest trail.

▶ **Exercise 2**  **Diagraming Appositive Phrases.**   Diagram these sentences, each having an appositive phrase.

1. Betty, a lawyer of the firm, will arrive today.

2. Michael showed me a picture of Pikes Peak, a mountain in Colorado.

3. You can take the *Congressional*, a train to Washington, D.C.

# Diagraming Clauses

**Compound Sentences**   A compound sentence consists of two or more independent clauses which are diagramed on separate horizontal lines. The clauses are joined at the verbs with a dotted line in the shape of a step, and the conjunction is placed on the horizontal part of the step.

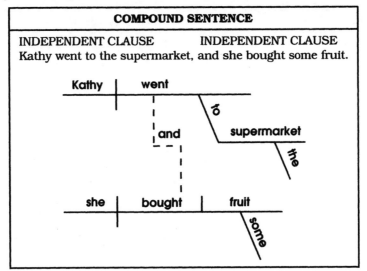

▷ **Exercise 1**   **Diagraming Compound Sentences.**   Diagram each compound sentence.

1.  Mom went to her office, and she worked for nine hours.

2.  Bill washed his face, and then he went to bed.

# Diagraming Clauses

**Complex Sentences** An adjective clause in a complex sentence is diagramed on a separate line under the independent clause. A dotted line connects the clauses. An adverb clause in a complex sentence is also diagramed on a separate line under the independent clause, and a dotted line connects the clause.

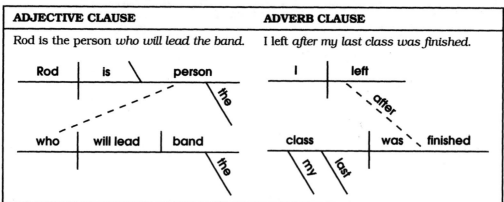

▶**Exercise 1** **Diagraming Complex Sentences.** Diagram each complex sentence.

1. I have a map which shows all the trails on this mountain.

2. We washed the dishes after supper was over.

# Diagraming Clauses

▶ **Exercise 1**  **Diagraming Compound Sentences.**  Diagram each of the following compound sentences.

1. Fortunately, the fever passed and his condition improved.

2. Ed collects stamps; many of them are quite valuable.

3. The George Washington Bridge is a suspension bridge; it contains two levels for automobile traffic.

▶ **Exercise 2**  **Diagraming Subordinate Clauses.**  Each of the following complex sentences contains either an adjective clause or an adverb clause. Diagram each sentence.

1. Gulls, which have distinctive calls, often fly along the beach.

2. If you hurry to the platform, you will catch the express train.

3. There is the flower that you admired.

# Answers

## 14.1   Nouns (Page 1)
### Exercise 1   Identifying Nouns
1. summer, lake
2. month, birthday
3. birds, winter
4. brother, speech
5. dog, puppies
6. park, ducks
7. light, window
8. teacher, classroom
9. cat, fireplace
10. man, honesty

### Exercise 2   Using Nouns in Sentences
Sample nouns are given.
1. tree
2. Chicago, hours
3. Mrs. Hall, house
4. bicycle
5. brother, record
6. flowers, garden
7. theater
8. patience
9. Nancy, zoo
10. weather, month

## 14.1   Nouns (Page 2)
### Practice 2
### Exercise 1   Classifying Nouns

| People | Places | Things |
|--------|--------|--------|
| teacher | theater | pillow |
| sister | hotel | happiness |
| counselor | beach | lungs |
| | | tulip |
| | | beauty |
| | | string bean |
| | | map |
| | | giraffe |
| | | sadness |
| | | bald eagle |
| | | growth |
| | | magazine |
| | | carelessness |
| | | success |

### Writing Application
Sample sentences are given.
1. My aunt and my uncle came to visit.
2. This is the tree that I climbed.
3. I can see his willingness to win.
4. Her bicycle is brand new.
5. I have not visited Chicago or Boston.

## 14.1   Collective and Compound Nouns (Page 3)
### Practice 1
### Exercise 1   Identifying Collective Nouns
1. crowd
2. army
3. club
4. family
5. herd
6. orchestra
7. class
8. committee
9. navy
10. group

### Exercise 2   Identifying Compound Nouns
1. backyard
2. great-grandfather
3. high school
4. doorknob
5. racehorse
6. self-control
7. lifeguards
8. light-years
9. landing-craft
10. bedroom

## 14.1   Collective and Compound Nouns (Page 4)
### Practice 2
### Exercise 1   Recognizing Collective Nouns
1. family
2. jury
3. squad
4. crew
5. assembly

### Exercise 2   Identifying Compound Nouns
1. water holes
2. dining room, swimming pool
3. typewriter, father-in-law
4. wolf spider, horned beetle, praying mantis
5. football, basketball

### Exercise 3   Finding the Correct Form of Compound Nouns
1. postmaster
2. sideline
3. son-in-law
4. baseball
5. fireplace

## 14.1   Common and Proper Nouns (Page 5)
### Practice 1
### Exercise 1   Identifying Common and Proper Nouns
1. play, (Shakespeare)
2. (Drama Club), president
3. family, (Miami)
4. house, (Elm Street)
5. father, (Colorado)
6. dog, (Max)
7. (Statue of Liberty)
8. holiday, (Thanksgiving)
9. brother, (Rocky Mountains)
10. pictures, (Niagara Falls)

### Exercise 2   Using Proper Nouns in Sentences
Sample proper nouns are given.
1. Anne Smith
2. Michael Jackson
3. Tiger Woods
4. Phoenix
5. Vine Street

6. Pike's Peak
7. Albany
8. Gandhi
9. Macy's
10. Ned Harris

## 14.1 Common and Proper Nouns (Page 6)
### Practice 2
### Exercise 1 Identifying Common and Proper Nouns
Sample nouns are given.
1. C—Main Street
2. P—car
3. P—city
4. C—Ulysses S. Grant
5. P—writer
6. P—dog
7. C—"Maria"
8. C—Rudy Guiliani
9. P—athlete
10. C—Hudson

### Writing Application
Sample sentences are given.

1. The band will rehearse today.
2. She went shopping with her mother-in-law.
3. Each day, he and his wife take a bus through the Lincoln Tunnel.
4. The post office is closed on legal holidays.
5. The airport is only five miles from here.

## 14.2 Pronouns and Antecedents (Page 7)
### Practice 1
### Exercise 1 Identifying Pronouns and Antecedents

1. (explorers), their
2. (Bill), his
3. (Bob), you
4. (skater), his
5. (woman), her
6. (actors), their
7. (deer), their
8. (Martha), yours
9. (astronaut), his
10. (sheepdog), its

### Exercise 2 Using Personal Pronouns
Sample personal pronouns are given.
1. his
2. my
3. her
4. its
5. their

## 14.2 Pronouns and Antecedents (Page 8)
### Practice 2
### Exercise 1 Recognizing Antecedents
1. Ted
2. treasurer
3. apples

4. boys
5. Baking
6. rattlesnake
7. Maria
8. boys
9. steamboat
10. policeman

### Exercise 2 Identifying Personal Pronouns
1. We—first
2. your—second
3. its—third
4. mine—first
5. she—third
6. him—third
7. they—third
8. I—first
9. their—third
10. he—third

## 14.2 Demonstrative and Interrogative Pronouns (Page 9)
### Practice 1
### Exercise 1 Distinguishing Between Demonstrative and Interrogative Pronouns
1. interrogative
2. demonstrative
3. demonstrative
4. interrogative
5. interrogative
6. demonstrative
7. interrogative
8. interrogative
9. demonstrative
10. demonstrative

### Exercise 2 Adding Demonstrative and Interrogative Pronouns to Sentences
Samples are given.
1. What
2. What
3. that
4. those
5. What
6. These
7. That
8. whom
9. that
10. Which

## 14.2 Demonstrative and Interrogative Pronouns (Page 10)
### Practice 2
### Exercise 1 Recognizing Demonstrative Pronouns
1. This
2. This
3. That
4. these
5. This
6. these
7. those
8. These
9. that
10. Those

### Exercise 2 Recognizing Interrogative Pronouns
1. whom
2. Whose
3. Which
4. Who
5. What

6. Who
7. What
8. Which
9. whom
10. Which

## 14.2 Indefinite Pronouns (Page 11)
### Practice 1
**Exercise 1    Identifying Indefinite Pronouns**
1. everybody
2. neither
3. none
4. somebody
5. each
6. several
7. something
8. most
9. little
10. nothing

**Exercise 2    Using Pronouns in Sentences**
Samples are given.
1. Several
2. everything
3. All
4. each
5. anyone
6. Both
7. many
8. little
9. most
10. Neither

## 14.2 Indefinite Pronouns (Page 12)
### Practice 2
**Exercise 1    Recognizing Indefinite Pronouns**
1. few
2. everyone
3. many
4. neither, both
5. everyone
6. both
7. most
8. none
9. most
10. all

### Writing Application
Sample sentences are given.
1. These are the results of the election.
2. I bought a baseball and a football. These were the most appealing sale items.
3. Which of the trails looks rocky?
4. Who is going to the party?
5. Both of the swimmers did well in the race.

## 15.1 Action Verbs (Page 13)
### Practice 1
**Exercise 1    Recognizing Visible and Mental Actions**

1. expect
2. decided
3. carried
4. scored
5. walked

6. remembered
7. barked
8. worry
9. flew
10. wrote

**Exercise 2    Adding Action Verbs to Sentences**
Samples are given.
1. lived
2. understand
3. hopped
4. played
5. cooked
6. hope
7. wonder
8. built
9. played
10. hiked

## 15.1 Action Verbs (Page 14)
### Practice 2
**Exercise 1    Identifying Kinds of Action Verbs**
1. visible
2. mental
3. visible
4. visible
5. mental
6. visible
7. visible
8. visible
9. mental
10. mental

**Exercise 2    Recognizing Action Verbs**
1. placed
2. sprinkled
3. takes
4. baked
5. waved
6. cut
7. struck
8. occupied
9. bought
10. plugged

### Writing Application
Sample sentences are given.
1. Dad sings in the shower
2. I ride my bike to school.
3. She plants bulbs in the spring.
4. He is going to tell us a story.
5. Don't touch the cactus.
6. I like to watch basketball games.
7. Sue swims two miles every day.
8. I want to read that book.
9. Mom drives us to school every day.
10. The teacher will ask if you finished your homework.

## 15.2 Linking Verbs (Page 15)
### Practice 1
**Exercise 1    Identifying Forms of the Linking Verb *Be***

1. flowers    must have been    sunflowers

2. I (am) president.

3. Thursday (is) birthday.

4. tennis (must be) difficult.

5. painting (was) "The Starry Night"

6. you (should have been) happy

7. problem (may have been) shyness

8. woman (will be) governor

9. Steve (will be) pirate

10. shirt (might be) perfect

**Exercise 2   Recognizing Other Linking Verbs**

1. answer (appears) incorrect

2. sisters (remained) friends

3. pudding (tastes) sweet

4. lettuce (stayed) fresh

5. you (look) handsome

## 15.2  Linking Verbs (Page 16)
**Practice 2**
**Exercise 1   Recognizing Forms of the Linking Verb Be**
Verbs are underlined; linked words are circled.

1. (book) will be (When the Legends Die)

2. (jewel) is (amethyst)

3. (keys) have been (rusty)

4. (colors) are (turquoise) , (tan)

5. (Judy) was (star)

6. (Carlos Cruz) might be (mayor)

7. (play) was
(You're a Good Man, Charlie Brown)

8. (She) should have been (happy)

9. (snowflakes) are (hexagons)

10. (I) am (hungry)

**Exercise 2   Identifying Other Linking Verbs**
Verbs are underlined; linked words are circled.

1. (David) appears (hungry) , (tired)

2. (answer) seemed (wrong)

3. (comics) remained (partners)

4. (beach) looks (inviting)

5. (voices) sound (shrill) , (scratchy)

6. (pie) smells (delicious)

7. (quartz) looks (colorless)

8. (Mary Ann) became (lawyer)

9. (house) stayed (empty)

10. (fabric) feels (rough)

## 15.2  Linking Verbs (Page 17)
**Practice 1**
**Exercise 1   Distinguishing Between Linking Verbs and Action Verbs**
1. felt, *LV*
2. felt, *AV*
3. turns, *LV*
4. tasted, *AV*
5. looked, *AV*
6. looked, *LV*
7. sounded, *AV*
8. smells, *LV*
9. grow, *LV*
10. sounds, *LV*

**Exercise 2   Using Verbs in Sentences**
Sample verbs are given.
1. became, *LV*
2. turned, *AV*
3. smell, *LV*
4. grow, *LV*
5. became, *LV*
6. stayed, *AV*
7. sound, *LV*
8. appear, *LV*
9. tasted, *LV*
10. seem, *LV*

## 15.2  Linking Verbs (Page 18)
**Practice 2**
**Exercise 1   Distinguishing Between Linking Verbs and Action Verbs**
1. sounded, *AV*
2. turned, *LV*
3. seems, *LV*
4. grows, *AV*
5. appears, *AV*
6. tastes, *LV*
7. stayed, *AV*
8. became, *LV*
9. looks, *LV*
10. turned, *LV*

**Writing Application**
Sample sentences are given.

1. After Bush, Clinton became president.

2. The meat was salty.

3. The witnesses remained calm.

4. Their voices sound different on the recording.

5. The stars look bright.

6. The children appear to be happy.

7. The wind felt chilly.

8. His beard grew very long.

9. The meal smells wonderful.

10. The leaves turned colorful before they fell from the trees.

## 15.3 Helping Verbs (Page 19)
### Practice 1
**Exercise 1   Identifying Helping Verbs**

1. should (leave)
2. will be (attending)
3. is (laughing)
4. did (eat)
5. do (remember)
6. will be (coming)
7. has (risen)
8. are (competing)
9. have (heard)
10. may (arrive)

**Exercise 2   Adding Helping Verbs to Sentences**
Sample helping verbs are given.
1. should have
2. did, have
3. was
4. would have
5. could have

## 15.3 Helping Verbs (Page 20)
### Practice 2
**Exercise 1   Supplying Helping Verbs**
Sample helping verbs are given.
1. will
2. has been
3. will have
4. has
5. should have
6. has
7. would
8. did
9. has
10. should have

**Exercise 2   Finding Helping Verbs**
1. were sent

2. have planted
3. should have been taken
4. has been doing
5. should have taken
6. have chosen
7. have remembered
8. had planned
9. could have reached
10. does remember

## 16.1   Adjectives (Page 21)
### Practice 1
**Exercise 1   Recognizing Adjectives and the Words They Modify**

1. sleek, gray, (horse)
2. This, fine, (novel)
3. long, narrow, (column)
4. every, qualified, (person)
5. four, large, (sandwiches)
6. one, special, (wish)
7. powerful, efficient, (vehicle)
8. little, (snow), no, (temperatures)
9. (I), proud, happy
10. great, (flocks), large, (birds)

**Exercise 2   Using Adjectives in Sentences**
Sample adjectives are given.
1. red, five
2. small, calm
3. hairy, dusty
4. blue, pink
5. summer
6. glass, paper
7. six
8. heavy
9. some, new
10. delicious

## 16.1   Adjectives (Page 22)
### Practice 2
**Exercise 1   Recognizing Adjectives and the Words They Modify**
Modified words are circled.

1. loud, shrill, (whistle)
2. (She), beautiful, graceful
3. (desert), smooth, white
4. noisy, crowded, (intersection)
5. Tall, slim, (he)
6. (They), unhappy

7. small, round, hairy, (animal)

8. some, (change), more, (money)

9. third, fourth, (years), swimming (records)

10. That, (man), several, (tickets)

## Exercise 2   Recognizing Adjectives

For a brief moment, the bright sun peeked through the dark clouds. Shivering and uncomfortable, Terence looked up. "Could this cruel winter be coming to an end?" he wondered. As the icy wind blew, Terence held his old green coat closed tightly around his thin body.

## Exercise 3   Adding Adjectives to Sentences

Sample adjectives are given.
1. Brad was tired and hungry after the football game.
2. The fast ball was hit by the talented batter.
3. The young child had a bad cold.
4. Ripe and sweet, the red apples were ready to be picked.
5. The enormous dog played with the happy young child.
6. The noisy geese flew over the little green house.
7. The old peeling barn needed some fresh red paint.
8. Carla, strong and determined, pulled the pesky weeds.
9. Janet wanted a new dress for the birthday party.
10. Duncan helped the red-haired girl get onto the black horse.

## 16.1   Articles; Nouns Used as Adjectives (Page 23)

### Practice 1

### Exercise 1   Distinguishing Between Definite and Indefinite Articles
1. an
2. the
3. an
4. an
5. a
6. an
7. a
8. the
9. an
10. the

### Exercise 2   Recognizing Nouns Used as Adjectives

1. tax (collector)

2. golf (course)

3. dog (warden)

4. police (department)

5. town (hall)

## 16.1   Articles; Nouns Used as Adjectives (Page 24)

### Practice 2

### Exercise 1   Distinguishing Between Definite and Indefinite Articles
1. the
2. An
3. a/a
4. The
5. an/a
6. an
7. The/a
8. An/the
9. the/the
10. an/the

### Exercise 2   Identifying Nouns Used as Adjectives

Modified nouns are circled.

1. newspaper (reporter)

2. tennis (racket)

3. light (bulb)

4. battle (conditions)

5. eye (doctor)

6. desk (lamp)

7. room (service)

8. television (news)

9. stone (walls)

10. highway (sign)

## 16.1   Proper Adjectives and Compound Adjectives (Page 25)

### Practice 1

### Exercise 1   Identifying Proper Adjectives and Compound Adjectives
1. proper
2. compound
3. compound
4. proper
5. compound
6. proper
7. compound
8. compound
9. proper
10. compound

### Exercise 2   Using Proper and Compound Adjectives in Sentences

Sample proper and compound adjectives are given.
1. Roman
2. roadside
3. baseball
4. French
5. overcome

## 16.1 Proper Adjectives and Compound Adjectives (Page 26)
**Practice 2**
### Exercise 1 Recognizing Proper Adjectives
Modified nouns are circled.

1. Mozart, symphonies
2. Austrian, costumes
3. Easter, holiday
4. Swiss watch
5. Lincoln memorial
6. French fable
7. Elizabethan England
8. Los Angeles smog
9. American frontier
10. Mayan pyramids

### Exercise 2 Recognizing Compound Adjectives
Modified nouns are circled.

1. better-qualified candidate
2. farsighted person
3. short-handed goals
4. hometown crowd
5. know-it-all attitude
6. thirty-five textbooks
7. bluish-green dress
8. heartbreaking news
9. hit-and-run driver
10. shell-like covering

## 16.1 Possessive Adjectives (Page 27)
**Practice 1**
### Exercise 1 Identifying Possessive Adjectives
Antecedents are circled.

1. we our dog
2. explorers their tent
3. I my training
4. crow its young
5. I my parents
6. Sarah her wallet

7. Bill his class
8. general his men
9. they their costumes
10. You your suggestions

### Exercise 2 Using Possessive Adjectives in Sentences
Sample possessive adjectives are given. Antecedents are circled.

1. his, Bill
2. its, duck
3. our, We
4. its, house
5. her, Carol
6. their, boys
7. his, George
8. your, you
9. my, I
10. its, dog

## 16.1 Possessive Adjectives (Page 28)
**Practice 2**
### Exercise 1 Identifying Possessive Adjectives

| | Possessive Adjective | Noun Modified | Antecedent |
|---|---|---|---|
| 1. | her | father | Leslie |
| 2. | his | sunglasses | lifeguard |
| 3. | its | leaves | maple |
| 4. | their | appointment | astronauts |
| 5. | her | responsibilities | Andrea |
| 6. | his | backpack | Les |
| 7. | her | cat | Andrea |
| 8. | their | cabin | Andersons |
| 9. | his | room | Homer |
| 10. | its | tires | car |

### Exercise 2 Using Possessive Adjectives
Sample possessive adjectives are given.
1. your
2. her
3. his
4. her
5. his

## 16.1 Demonstrative and Interrogative Adjectives (Page 29)
**Practice 1**
### Exercise 1 Recognizing Demonstrative Pronouns and Adjectives
Pronouns and adjectives are circled.

1. these , pronoun
2. this , adjective

3. ( these ) , adjective

4. ( this ) , pronoun

5. ( this ) , adjective

6. ( these ) , pronoun

7. ( these ) , adjective

8. ( this ) , adjective

9. ( that ) , pronoun

10. ( that ) , adjective

**Exercise 2  Identifying Interrogative Pronouns and Adjectives**

Pronouns and adjectives are circled.

1. ( which ) , way

2. ( what ) , kind

3. ( whose ) , hairdryer

4. ( which ) , novel

5. ( what ) , pronoun

6. ( which ) , test

7. ( whose ) , play

8. ( what ) , vegetable

9. ( which ) , pronoun

10. ( what ) , pronoun

**16.1  Demonstrative and Interrogative Adjectives (Page 30)**
**Practice 2**
**Exercise 1  Recognizing Demonstrative Adjectives**
Pronouns and adjectives are underlined.
  1. Those, bracelets
  2. that, pronoun
  3. this, tunnel
  4. that, novel
  5. those, pronoun
**Exercise 2  Recognizing Interrogative Adjectives**
Pronouns and adjectives are underlined.
  1. Which, blouse
  2. What, pronoun
  3. Whose, mother
  4. Which, pronoun
  5. What, kind
**Writing Application**
Sample sentences are given. Modified words are underlined.

  1. What day are you leaving?

2. Her dress is a pretty color.

3. That bike is too expensive.

4. Our house is on the corner lot.

5. Would you read these books?

6. Which car is he driving?

7. I can't wait to see their movie.

8. This journal travels with me everywhere.

9. Do you know his name?

10. My sister is studying medicine.

**16.2  Adverbs (Page 31)**
**Practice 1**
**Exercise 1  Recognizing Adverbs That Modify Verbs**
Adverbs are underlined.
  1. rapidly, In what manner?
  2. reluctantly, In what manner?
  3. barely, To what extent?
  4. completely, To what extent?
  5. seldom, When?
  6. frequently, When?
  7. Slowly, In what manner?
  8. outside, Where?
  9. clumsily, In what manner?
  10. really, To what extent?
**Exercise 2  Adding Adverbs to Modify Verbs**
Sample adverbs are given.
  1. slowly
  2. often
  3. immediately
  4. monthly
  5. almost
  6. outside
  7. never
  8. brightly
  9. daily
  10. carefully

**16.2  Adverbs (Page 32)**
**Practice 2**
**Exercise 1  Identifying How Adverbs Modify Verbs**

| Where? | When? | In What Manner? | To What Extent? |
| --- | --- | --- | --- |
| nearby | eventually | mechanically | nearly |
| | finally | cautiously | scarcely |
| | yesterday | happily | |
| | now | | |

**Exercise 2  Using Adverbs**
Sample adverbs are given.
  1. kindly
  2. extremely
  3. very
  4. immediately
  5. here
  6. quite

7. overly
8. suspiciously
9. excitedly
10. Everywhere
11. later
12. nearby
13. soon
14. generously
15. now

## 16.2 Adverbs (Page 33)
### Practice 1
### Exercise 1 Recognizing the Words Adverbs Modify
Circled words are modified words.

1. (close) , adjective
2. (sorry) , adjective
3. (high) , adverb
4. (strong) , adjective
5. (quietly) , adverb
6. (noisy) , adjective
7. (softly) , adverb
8. (ever) , adverb
9. (often) , adverb
10. (afraid) , adjective

### Exercise 2 Using Adverbs in Sentences
Sample adverbs are given.

1. very
2. quite
3. entirely
4. not
5. extremely
6. too
7. rather
8. more
9. rather
10. relatively

## 16.2 Adverbs (Page 34)
### Practice 2
### Exercise 1 Recognizing Adverbs That Modify Adjectives
Adverbs are underlined. Adjectives are listed.

1. unusually, pleasant
2. very, loud
3. too, short
4. extremely, upset
5. seriously, ill
6. quite, tart
7. absolutely, still
8. thoroughly, adept
9. almost, right
10. not, sad

### Exercise 2 Recognizing Adverbs That Modify Other Adverbs
Adverbs that modify are underlined.

1. too, slowly
2. Almost, happily
3. unusually, well
4. quite, easily
5. less, loudly
6. rather, suddenly
7. slightly, late
8. entirely, too
9. more, slowly
10. relatively, soon

## 16.2 Adverbs Used in Sentences (Page 35)
### Practice 1
### Exercise 1 Distinguishing Between Adverbs and Adjectives
1. adjective
2. adverb
3. adjective
4. adverb
5. adverb
6. adverb
7. adjective
8. adjective
9. adverb
10. adjective

### Exercise 2 Using Adverbs and Adjectives in Sentences
Sample adjectives and adverbs are given.

1. poorly
2. first
3. quickly
4. smooth
5. regularly
6. occasionally
7. careful
8. easily
9. beautiful
10. always

## 16.2 Adverbs Used in Sentences (Page 36)
### Practice 2
### Exercise 1 Locating Adverbs in Sentences
Modified words are circled.

1. (sailed) slowly
2. seldom (approached)
3. (had) deliberately (told)

4. rather (sad)

5. rather vaguely (explained)

6. Cautiously, (edged)

7. (has) almost (completed)

8. often (teases)

9. totally (stopped)

10. efficiently (produce)

## Exercise 2  Distinguishing Between Adverbs and Adjectives
1. adjective
2. adjective
3. adverb
4. adjective
5. adjective
6. adverb
7. adjective
8. adjective
9. adverb
10. adverb

## 17.1  Prepositions (Page 37)
### Practice 1
### Exercise 1  Identifying Prepositions
1. above
2. across
3. beneath
4. during
5. under
6. inside
7. over
8. within
9. before
10. underneath

### Exercise 2  Using Prepositions in Sentences
Sample prepositions are given.
1. instead of
2. out of
3. behind
4. in front of
5. during
6. opposite
7. on account of
8. inside
9. beyond
10. by means of

## 17.1  Prepositions (Page 38)
### Practice 2
### Exercise 1  Recognizing Prepositions
Prepositions are underlined. Sample sentences are given.
1. outside The ticket holders waited patiently inside the theater.
2. beside A new dining room was built next to the old one.
3. under The telephone book is on the table.
4. along She placed the flower pots on the windowsill.
5. through How did you get out of the traffic jam?

6. during The stamp show begins before winter vacation.
7. across A housing development has been built along the river.
8. near Let's pick the strawberries beyond the fence.
9. around The doctor's office is on the corner.
10. Opposite Behind the old statue, you will see the library.

### Exercise 2  Recognizing Compound Prepositions
Prepositions are underlined. Sample sentences are given.
1. in back of The broken lawnmover is behind the barn.
2. In front of Near the entrance is a large warning notice.
3. next to The new highway passes below the foothills.
4. In addition to Along with the application, you must include a reference.
5. ahead of A very slow bus was next to our car.

## 17.2  Prepositions Used in Sentences (Page 39)
### Practice 1
### Exercise 1  Identifying Prepositional Phrases
Prepositions are underlined. Objects are circled.

1. next to (table)

2. in place of (Martha)

3. in (time)

4. around (corner)

5. until (tomorrow)

6. within (hour)

7. because of (pitching)

8. toward (door)

9. since (meeting)

10. outside (window)

### Exercise 2  Distinguishing Between Prepositions and Adverbs
1. preposition
2. adverb
3. adverb
4. preposition
5. preposition
6. adverb
7. adverb
8. preposition
9. preposition
10. adverb

## 17.2  Prepositions Used in Sentences (Page 40)
### Practice 2
### Exercise 1  Identifying Prepositional Phrases
Prepositions are underlined; objects are circled.

1. in (village)

2. by means of (Platte River)

3. of (Old South)

4. In (morning)

5. in (attic)

6. Behind (door)

7. into (sun)

8. Between (us)

9. on top of (donkey)

10. in front of (grandstand)

### Exercise 2   Distinguishing Between Prepositions and Adverbs

Prepositional phrases are underlined.
1. *about her army experiences;* about—adverb
2. before—adverb; *before breakfast*
3. *underneath the bridge;* underneath—adverb
4. along—adverb; *along the creek*
5. near—adverb; *Near the old library*

### Writing Application

Sample sentences are given. Prepositions are underlined; objects of prepositions are in parentheses.
1. The gull circled above the (water).
2. We were tired after the (game).
3. I sat down beside the (tree).
4. He met me during the halftime (show).
5. The girl you saw is from (Sweden).

### 18.1   Conjunctions (Page 41)
### Practice 1
### Exercise 1   Identifying Conjunctions

Conjunctions are underlined.
1. but, coordinating
2. neither, nor, correlative
3. or, coordinating
4. both, and, correlative
5. yet, coordinating
6. but, coordinating
7. whether, or, correlative
8. neither, nor, correlative
9. not only, but also, correlative
10. and, coordinating

### Exercise 2   Using Conjunctions in Sentences

Sample conjunctions are given.
1. but
2. neither, nor
3. and
4. or
5. Either, or
6. Both, and
7. yet
8. for
9. or
10. whether, or

### 18.1   Conjunctions (Page 42)
### Practice 2
### Exercise 1   Recognizing Coordinating Conjunctions

Coordinating conjunctions are in circles; words connected by conjunctions are underlined.
1. Andrew (and) Jane live far apart.

2. I have to take my medicine before breakfast (or) before dinner.

3. What is the connection between lightning (and) thunder?

4. My family is looking for a large (yet) inexpensive house.

5. I will be late getting home, (for) I have to make several stops.

6. Wind (and) rain lashed the Florida coastline.

7. I would like to bake cookies, (but) I am missing a few ingredients.

8. In the morning (and) in the evening, traffic backs up at this light.

9. The dancer was thin (but) strong.

10. You have a choice of cotton, wool, (or) polyester.

### Exercise 2   Recognizing Correlative Conjunctions

Correlative conjunctions are in parentheses; words connected by conjunctions are underlined.
1. She will pay her tuition (either) by check (or) by money order.

2. (Both) Anne (and) Barbara volunteered to decorate the hall.

3. I will (either) buy (or) make her birthday card.

4. (Not only) were the rebels short on men, (but) they were (also) short on supplies.

5. She asked (whether) football (or) baseball was my favorite sport.

6. (Neither) flowers (nor) candy seems an appropriate gift.
7. The girls invited (both) Manuel (and) Pat to the dance.

8. (Not only) will they attend, (but) they will (also) bring five guests.

9. We expect them (either) in the evening (or) in the early morning hours.

10. That afternoon Robert was (neither) swimming (nor) diving.

### Exercise 3   Writing Sentences Using Conjunctions
Sample sentences are given.
1. Either one or both of us will come.
2. I wonder whether you or I will be there.
3. Not only did we miss the bus, but we also left the tickets home.
4. Yesterday, Jane and I volunteered.
5. Neither Hank nor Tony arrived on time.

## 18.2   Interjections (Page 43)
### Practice 1
### Exercise 1   Using Interjections
Sample interjections are given.
1. Oh
2. Tsk
3. Uh
4. Gee
5. Ouch
6. Wow
7. Uh
8. Gee
9. Ouch
10. Aw

### Exercise 2   Adding Interjections to Sentences
Sample interjections are given.
1. uh
2. Ouch!
3. Oh,
4. Man!
5. Darn!
6. Wow!
7. Goodness!
8. Whew!
9. Aw!
10. Oh!

## 18.2   Interjections (Page 44)
### Practice 2
### Exercise 1   Recognizing Interjections
Sample interjections are given.
1. Gee! I'm so glad you're here!
2. Oh, you're never ready on time.
3. Ow! Does that sting.
4. Uh, I don't know what to say.
5. Wow, I can't believe you said that.

### Writing Application
Sample sentences are given.
1. Whew! That was a workout!
2. Shucks, I missed again.
3. Well, don't you look lovely!
4. Ouch! That dish is hot!
5. Oh, I didn't know you called him, too.

## 19.1   The Basic Sentence (Page 45)
### Practice 1
### Exercise 1   Identifying Subjects and Verbs
The subject is underlined once and the verb twice.
1. Shakespeare, wrote
2. we, saw
3. Bob, sang
4. dog, looks
5. Doves, flew
6. they, are skating
7. building, was destroyed
8. quarterback, is being tackled
9. visitor, delayed
10. salad, was made

### Exercise 2   Recognizing Sentences
1. sentence
2. sentence
3. incomplete
4. incomplete
5. sentence
6. incomplete
7. sentence
8. incomplete
9. incomplete
10. sentence

## 19.1   The Basic Sentence (Page 46)
### Practice 2
### Exercise 1   Recognizing Subjects and Verbs
The subject is underlined once and the verb twice.
1. school, offers
2. eagle, soared
3. hammer, disappeared
4. We, visited
5. sunburn, caused
6. Parthenon, is being eroded
7. train, chugged
8. Rossini, wrote
9. ribbon, comes
10. farmhouse, is built

### Exercise 2   Recognizing Sentences
Sample sentences are given. Subjects are underlined once and verbs twice.
1. sentence
2. The pastry shop in town will be closed tomorrow.
3. The new coach of the basketball team comes from Ohio State.
4. He stood at the top of the stairs.
5. The girl in the yellow dress is my sister.
6. She knew that catuses grew in the desert.
7. Two visitors from Hartford came to my father's workplace.
8. Between you and me, I can say that things are going to get better.
9. The children decided to stay in the park.
10. sentence

## 19.2 Complete Subjects and Predicates (Page 47)

### Practice 1

**Exercise 1   Identifying Complete Subjects and Predicates**

Complete subjects are underlined once and complete predicates twice.

1. We are learning about careers in forestry.
2. Roger's room was filled with miniature soldiers.
3. The dentist worked in his office all day.
4. Bill created crossword puzzles for the newspaper.
5. The temperature hit 100°F on that July day.
6. We were given a tour of the museum.
7. The elephants in the circus are well trained.
8. You will find our house on Main Street.
9. The aquarium was filled with fish.
10. My favorite restaurant is going to close.

**Exercise 2   Adding Parts to Sentences**

Sample sentence parts are given.
1. was built over a century ago.
2. Pieces of driftwood
3. made their nest in the birdhouse.
4. surged through the crowd.
5. One marathon runner
6. The injured player
7. was standing outside my door.
8. played in the backyard.
9. The speaker
10. walked slowly down the street.

## 19.2   Complete Subjects and Predicates (Page 48)

### Practice 2

**Exercise 1   Recognizing Complete Subjects and Predicates**

Subjects are underlined once and verbs twice. A vertical line is drawn between the complete subject and complete predicate.

1. A tall stranger | appeared on the stage.
2. This painting by Velázquez | is extremely valuable.
3. The ship's watertight doors | close automatically.
4. The smiling governor | shook hands with all her guests.
5. Fire | spread through the entire forest.
6. The people in the stands and on the field | applauded loudly.
7. Our newly elected mayor | took the oath of office.
8. This small engraving | is a masterpiece of its type.
9. Costa Brava | is an area of seaside resorts in Spain.
10. The fresh vegetables | cooked rapidly in the wok.

### Writing Application

**Developing Complete Subjects and Predicates**

Sample sentences are given.
1. The first story begins on page 2.
2. That overgrown path leads to the abandoned house.

3. The overcrowded bus rumbled through the narrow streets.
4. Each of the girls is taking riding lessons.
5. My sister eventually decided to join us for lunch.

## 19.3   Compound Subjects and Compound Verbs (Page 49)

### Practice 1

**Exercise 1   Identifying Compound Subjects**

Compound subjects are underlined.
1. house, barn
2. lemons, limes, oranges
3. sister, I
4. Paintings, sculpture
5. mother, father
6. jewelry, pottery
7. cows, horses
8. lightning, thunder, rains
9. July, August
10. Washington, Oregon

**Exercise 2   Recognizing Compound Verbs**

Compound verbs are listed.
1. will run, will pass
2. sat, read
3. rose, shone
4. ate, drank
5. wrote, took
6. coached, played
7. mowed, pruned, cleaned
8. will go, buy
9. twisted, turned
10. will be surprised, may be pleased

## 19.3   Compound Subjects and Compound Verbs (Page 50)

### Practice 2

**Exercise 1   Recognizing Compound Subjects**

Subjects are underlined.
1. Lou and Tony are working at the supermarket.
2. During the storm, the teacher and the class waited under an awning.
3. A bus or train can be used to reach the museum.
4. Austria and Hungary were once united.
5. Lettuce, tomatoes, and cucumbers are the chief ingredients in his salad.

**Exercise 2   Recognizing Compound Verbs.**

Verbs are underlined.
1. Arnie walks or takes the bus to school.
2. Dad planted a Japanese maple twenty years ago and has cherished it ever since.
3. My friends often go to the movies and have a pizza afterward.
4. The architect surveyed the land, asked questions, and began to draw her plans.
5. Later, Lucy washed her hair and settled down with a book.

**Exercise 3   Recognizing Compound Subjects and Compound Verbs**

Compound subjects and compound verbs are listed.
1. bricks, artifacts—compound subject
2. began, continued—compound verb
3. Lisa, Sandy—compound subject; draw, paint—compound verb
4. picked, made—compound verb
5. Peanuts, pretzels, popcorn—compound subject
6. Rodgers, Hammerstein—compound subject; wrote, worked—compound verb

7. escaped, slithered—compound verb
8. Haiti, Martinique—compound subject
9. trembled, shook, collapsed—compound verb
10. livestock, foods—compound subject

### 19.4   Hard-to-Find Subjects (Page 51)
**Practice 1**
**Exercise 1   Finding the Subject in Orders and Directions**

Arrows are put where the understood subject *you* belongs in the sentence. Subjects other than *you* are underlined.

1. After turning onto Main Street, ↑ drive for one mile. (you)
2. Team, ↑ watch carefully. (you)
3. Bob always turns off the television.
4. Class, ↑ look at the board. (you)
5. When riding your bicycle in traffic, ↑ be careful. (you)
6. ↑ Don't feed the animals in that cage. (you)
7. Carol, ↑ please give me your homework. (you)
8. The warm breezes were a sign of spring.
9. After breakfast, ↑ feed the dog. (you)
10. Mark, ↑ please stop talking. (you)

**Exercise 2   Finding Subjects in Sentences.**

1. They are showing what movie today.
2. The doctor is arriving when.
3. Whose exhibit won first prize.
4. He does keep the flour where.
5. We are having what for dinner.
6. You did see Carol at the party.
7. You can finish the homework assignment tonight.
8. The park is in which direction.
9. The play will begin when.
10. The jury has reached a verdict.

### 19.4   Hard-to-Find Subjects (Page 52)
**Practice 2**
**Exercise 1   Recognizing the Subjects That Give Orders or Directions**

Subjects are listed.

1. (You)
2. (you)
3. You
4. (You)
5. (you)
6. blanket
7. (you)
8. (You)
9. dictionary
10. (you)

**Exercise 2   Finding the Subjects in Questions**

Subjects are underlined.

1. Where is the encyclopedia?
2. Have they visited the town hall yet?
3. Which rooms will be redecorated?
4. Whose science project finally won?
5. Are blueberries in season now?
6. What will you do with these packages?
7. Who planned last year's picnic?
8. How should I draw the solid bars on this graph?
9. Have the judges reached a decision?
10. When will we read Poe's short stories?

### 19.4   Sentences Beginning with *There* or *Here* (Page 53)
**Practice 1**
**Exercise 1   Identifying Subjects in Sentences Beginning with *There* or *Here***

Subjects are listed.

1. ducks
2. recipe
3. principal
4. upsets
5. storm
6. picture
7. flowers
8. father
9. civilization
10. flights

**Exercise 2   Writing Sentences Beginning with *There* or *Here***

Sample sentences are given.

1. There will be no baseball game today.
2. Here is an interesting career to pursue.
3. There go three deer across the river.
4. Here are the balloons for the party.
5. There is the oldest house in town.
6. Here is my favorite book.
7. There is my dog.
8. Here is my parents' farm.
9. Here comes the sun.
10. There is Joe's mother.

### 19.4   Subjects in Sentences Beginning with *There* or *Here* (Page 54)
**Practice 2**
**Exercise 1   Finding the Subjects in Sentences Beginning with *There* or *Here***

Subjects are underlined.

1. Here comes the express bus now.
2. There was another phone call for you an hour ago.
3. There have been three strikes in less than five years.
4. Here is some strawberry shortcake for dessert.
5. There goes the last train to the city.
6. There is an exciting new play on Broadway.
7. Here are the tickets to the hockey game.
8. There in the valley are the Mayan ruins.
9. There, smiling proudly, stands the winner of the ribbon.
10. Here is the money for your haircut.

**Writing Application**
**Writing Sentences with Subjects in Various Positions**

Sample sentences are given. Subjects are underlined.

1. Are you surprised by my grades?
2. Here are the books with the best illustrations.
3. Which topic are you going to choose?
4. Choose either the blue dress or the white dress. (You)
5. There are only twenty-four hours in a day.

### 19.5   Direct Objects (Page 55)
**Practice 1**
**Exercise 1   Identifying Direct Objects**

Verbs are underlined. Direct objects are listed.

1. dug, hole
2. painted, murals
3. deposited, savings

4. will watch, eclipse
5. blew, hat
6. orbits, Earth
7. made, necklace
8. read, newspaper
9. washed, clothes
10. opened, account

### Exercise 2   Recognizing Compound Direct Objects
1. clothes, lunch
2. books, articles
3. toast, cereal
4. French, Spanish
5. gold, jewels
6. car, dog
7. towels, umbrella, cooler
8. touchdown, point
9. mountains, deserts
10. corn, potatoes

## 19.5   Direct Objects (Page 56)
### Practice 2
### Exercise 1   Recognizing Direct Objects
Direct objects are underlined.
1. The visitor rang the bell twice.
2. Beethoven wrote only one opera.
3. She ate spaghetti for lunch.
4. My mother reads at least two books a month.
5. Phillis Wheatley wrote poetry about her life as a slave.
6. This morning Father skipped breakfast.
7. This tree produces hazelnuts.
8. She wrote original music for the show.
9. The steamer blew its whistle during the storm.
10. The kitchen clock uses only batteries.

### Exercise 2   Recognizing Compound Direct Objects
Nouns or pronouns that make up each direct object are listed.
1. Toronto, Ottawa
2. him, me
3. breads, cookies, cakes
4. biology, chemistry
5. Bill, her
6. *The Pearl, Death Be Not Proud*
7. vaccination, checkup
8. ice cream, fruit, pie
9. Colombia, Panama
10. praise, rewards

## 19.5   Distinguishing Direct Objects (Page 57)
### Practice 1
### Exercise 1   Distinguishing Direct Objects, Adverbs, and Objects of Prepositions
Objects are listed, adverbs are underlined once, and prepositional phrases are underlined twice.
1. keys, in the car
2. pebble, into the pond
3. quickly, down the field
4. wells, in the ocean floor
5. Jupiter, with my telescope
6. effortlessly, into the air
7. insects
8. chairs, tables for the classrooms

9. safely, on the runway
10. in your seat

### Exercise 2   Using Direct Objects in Sentences
Sample sentences are given. Direct objects are underlined.
1. We watched an alligator slither into the stream.
2. Bill and I have formed a new club at school.
3. The animals drank water from the pond.
4. I bought a radio on the trip.
5. They saw dark clouds on the horizon.
6. Jack threw the football to Mary.
7. Sue gave a flower to Juan.
8. Ron ate a hamburger.
9. Jane read the book several times.
10. Zack gave a present to Zeke.

## 19.5   Distinguishing Direct Objects (Page 58)
### Practice 2
### Exercise 1   Distinguishing Direct Objects, Adverbs, and Objects of Prepositions
Objects are underlined. Adverbs or prepositional phrases are circled.
1. She touched the rabbit (in the cage) .
2. I asked my father (often) (about the surprise) .
3. Merri put the stamp (on the letter) .
4. Richard reminded Al (repeatedly) (about the rehearsal) .
5. He took his daughter (with him) (to England) .
6. Winifred watched the falling snowflakes (outside her window) .
7. The children (gleefully) built a snowman (in front) (of the house) .
8. The family (quickly) harvested the vegetables (from their backyard garden.)
9. Wanda simmered the meat (gently) (in her large stewpot) .
10. Don (imaginatively) added oregano (to the bread dough) .

### Exercise 2   Using Direct Objects, Adverbs, and Objects of Prepositions
Samples are given.
1. obstacles
2. quickly
3. zoo
4. axe
5. Gary Paulsen
6. thoroughly
7. forest

8. extremely
9. sweater
10. pollution
11. details
12. book
13. enthusiastically
14. bread
15. regularly

## 19.5  Direct Objects in Questions (Page 59)
### Practice 1
### Exercise 1  Identifying Direct Objects in Questions
1. instructions
2. lawn
3. song
4. novel
5. What
6. Whom
7. trail
8. What
9. bicycle
10. items

### Exercise 2  Writing Questions with Direct Objects
Samples are given. Direct objects are underlined.
1. What are you cooking for lunch?
2. Which birds did you see at the bird feeder?
3. What Christmas carols are we singing in the pageant?
4. Whom did Dad see at the football game?
5. Which poem did Margaret write?
6. Whose house are you touring this weekend?
7. Which dress is Mom wearing for the wedding?
8. What language are you studying in school?
9. Whose guitar did you borrow?
10. Which team did Stan join?

## 19.5  Direct Objects in Questions (Page 60)
### Practice 2
### Exercise 1  Finding Direct Objects in Questions
Direct objects are underlined.
1. Whom did your sister invite to the party?
2. Which coat will you wear tonight?
3. What will you do with the twenty dollars?
4. What shall I buy?
5. Which groups will they audition for the dance?
6. Whom has Julie chosen as co-captain?
7. Whose radio did they borrow yesterday?
8. What effect did the aspirin have on the pain?
9. Which windows did the sonic boom break?
10. Which story will she read to us this evening?

### Writing Application
### Writing Sentences with Direct Objects
Sample sentences are given.
1. My brother borrowed my bike.
2. Whose lawn have they mowed?
3. Tom threw the frisbee effortlessly.
4. The children flew their kites over the houses.
5. Samantha played tennis exceptionally in every match.

## 19.5  Indirect Objects (Page 61)
### Practice 1
### Exercise 1  Recognizing Indirect Objects
Indirect objects are circled.

1. (me)

2. (team)

3. (Mom)

4. (father)

5. (brother) , (me)

6. (young)

7. (Howard)

8. (him)

9. (aunt) , (uncle)

10. (us)

### Exercise 2  Using Indirect Objects in Sentences
Sample sentences are given.
1. I will tell you the answer to the question.
2. Did you send your mother and father a postcard?
3. We offered her a ride home.
4. Susan bought them a present.
5. Karl showed his brother and sister new skates.
6. Wendy poured her horse some water.
7. Elvis gave his friends record albums.
8. Lois gave her partner some advice.
9. Ken bought his uncle a watch and his aunt a necklace.
10. We left the waiter and the waitress a tip.

## 19.5  Indirect Objects (Page 62)
### Practice 2
### Exercise 1  Recognizing Indirect Objects
Indirect objects are underlined.
1. Yesterday Mother bought me a new dress.
2. After two meetings, we finally gave our club a name.
3. Senator Lawton gave Mary the award.
4. Can he really get the boys tickets for the game?
5. I can show you the stamp album now.
6. Our teacher sent the principal an invitation.
7. I will draw her a map of directions to the restaurant.
8. The President sent Congress an important message.
9. Can you lend me a dollar?
10. The entire class wrote our representative a letter.

### Exercise 2  Recognizing Compound Indirect Objects
1. Rafael, Maria
2. Jimmy, her
3. mother, father
4. doctor, nurse
5. flower, plant
6. Brian, Matthew
7. Max, Gail
8. Willy, Jeff
9. Mark, John
10. Ellie, Sue

## 19.5  Distinguishing Indirect Objects (Page 63)
### Practice 1
### Exercise 1  Distinguishing Between Indirect Objects and Objects of Prepositions
1. indirect object
2. object of preposition
3. object of preposition
4. indirect object

5. indirect object
6. object of preposition
7. object of preposition
8. indirect object
9. object of preposition
10. indirect object

**Exercise 2   Writing Sentences with Indirect Objects and Objects of Prepositions**

Sample sentences are given.
1. The rock star gave his autograph to me.
2. I cooked myself a gourmet meal.
3. Richard brought his parents a beautiful bouquet.
4. Let's give three cheers for Mr. Keith.
5. The manager offered a job to me for the summer.
6. Bill left Sheila a message at the office.
7. After working so hard, Carol prepared herself a special treat.
8. My grandmother sent two tickets for the opera to me.
9. I made myself a delicious sandwich.
10. She sent a year's subscription to *Time* to us.

## 19.5   Distinguishing Indirect Objects (Page 64)
### Practice 2
**Exercise 1   Distinguishing Between Indirect Objects and Objects of Prepositions**

Indirect objects are underlined. Objects of a preposition are circled.

1. The boys will show <u>us</u> the lake.

2. I found the keys for (them).

3. Every Saturday Pete makes pizza for his

   (family).

4. Certainly, I will tell <u>her</u> the answer.

5. I gave my ring to my younger (sister).

6. Have you given the instructions to (them) yet?

7. She promised <u>him</u> another chance.

8. They are preparing a picnic basket for

   (themselves).

9. Why don't you buy <u>Amy</u> a soda?

10. Terry happily delivered the package to (them).

### Writing Application
**Writing Sentences with Indirect Objects**

Sample sentences are given.
1. Their grandmother gave them a present.
2. Meg showed her father and mother her loose tooth.
3. I gave her the message.
4. We showed the girls where we used to live.
5. She hasn't told Mom or Dad what happened yesterday.

## 19.5   Subject Complements (Page 65)
### Practice 1
**Exercise 1   Identifying Predicate Nouns and Pronouns**
1. capital

2. test
3. trees
4. center
5. country
6. she
7. beasts
8. best-seller
9. player
10. bird

**Exercise 2   Recognizing Predicate Adjectives**
1. perfect
2. powerful
3. familiar
4. full
5. quiet

## 19.5   Subject Complements (Page 66)
### Practice 2
**Exercise 1   Recognizing Predicate Nouns and Pronouns**

Predicate nouns or pronouns are underlined.
1. The losers will be <u>they</u>.
2. *The City Boy* is the <u>title</u> of a book by Herman Wouk.
3. This should be the correct <u>address</u>.
4. The capital of Turkey is <u>Ankara</u>.
5. In Greek mythology, Athena was the <u>goddess</u> of wisdom.
6. One plant with supposedly magical powers is the <u>mandrake</u>.
7. A little knowledge is a dangerous <u>thing</u>.
8. The Amazon has always been the most famous <u>river</u> in South America.
9. <u>Lichens</u> are primitive <u>plants</u>.
10. The name of those fruit <u>flies</u> is <u>drosophila</u>.

**Exercise 2   Recognizing Predicate Adjectives**

Predicate adjectives are underlined.
1. The new recipe for chili looks <u>interesting</u>.
2. St. Stephen's Cathedral in Vienna is absolutely <u>majestic</u>.
3. The <u>sky</u> became <u>dark</u> before the storm.
4. Of all the girls, <u>she</u> is the most <u>athletic</u>.
5. Because of the weather, the flight will be <u>hazardous</u>.
6. After winning, he was <u>dizzy</u> with excitement.
7. The sound from that <u>speaker</u> seems <u>tinny</u>.
8. The valley is particularly <u>peaceful</u> in the spring.
9. That roast duck smells <u>delicious</u>.
10. The climate there is unusually <u>mild</u> all year round.

## 19.5   Compound Subject Complements (Page 67)
### Practice 1
**Exercise 1   Identifying Compound Subject Complements**
1. sunny, calm
2. Florida, Jamaica
3. cool, refreshing
4. soft, luxurious
5. fresh, crisp
6. Ralph, Dawn
7. Charlotte, I
8. tangy, delicious
9. fun, rewarding
10. Renoir, Van Gogh

**Exercise 2   Writing Sentences with Compound Subject Complements**

Sample compound subject complements are given.
1. red, white, and blue
2. squirrels, chipmunks, and skunks
3. enjoyable and instructive
4. Hard Times and Oliver Twist
5. long and dusty
6. strong and fragrant
7. lonely and afraid
8. Connors and Winfield
9. hot and zesty
10. sleek and powerful

## 19.5   Compound Subject Complements (Page 68)
**Practice 2**

**Exercise 1   Recognizing Compound Subject Complements**

Each part of the subject complement is underlined.
1. After the ice storm, the path was smooth and slick.
2. That woman is both a talented musician and a lyricist.
3. The main course is either beef or veal.
4. Two Spanish cities on the sea are Barcelona and Cádiz.
5. This time the desert appeared vast and treacherous.
6. The saxophonists in the band are Luis and she.
7. The colors of the banner will be orange, green, and purple.
8. The trip up the coast was neither smooth nor scenic.
9. Over the years, the statue has turned old and gray.
10. Lincoln was a fine writer and storyteller.

**Writing Application**

**Writing Sentences with Subject Complements**

Sample sentences are given.
1. The two best cheerleaders are Amy and Jill.
2. Those cupcakes look delicious.
3. That dog is a German Shepard.
4. The roads were wet and slippery.
5. The best musicians in the jazz ensemble are she and he.

## 20.1   Prepositional Phrases (Adjective) (Page 69)
**Practice 1**

**Exercise 1   Recognizing Adjective Phrases**

Adjective phrases are underlined and modified words are listed.
1. of orange juice, pitcher
2. about the fox and the grapes, fable
3. of beauty, thing
4. about my summer vacation, essay
5. about Emily Dickinson, play
6. with the flat tire, bicycle
7. of yarn, ball
8. beside the garage, tree
9. from New Orleans, boy, beside me, seat
10. of this country, capital

**Exercise 2   Adding Adjective Phrases to Sentences**

Sample adjective phrases are given.
1. of my dog
2. with blue feathers
3. of tennis

4. with orange stripes
5. for the circus
6. about ancient Egypt
7. of England
8. to the newspaper
9. of cocoa
10. to the riddle

## 20.1   Prepositional Phrases (Adjective) (Page 70)
**Practice 1**

**Exercise 1   Identifying Adjective Phrases**

Adjective phrases are underlined and arrows point from them to modified words.
1. He drank a whole quart of milk.
2. My aunt is the president of the charity.
3. Grandfather told a story about Maine.
4. The stamp on that envelope is extremely rare.
5. The city of Damascus is several thousand years old.
6. A visitor from Italy showed slides of Rome and Florence.
7. Is this the road to the exhibit?
8. The box of nails in the cellar spilled all over.
9. The dot in the center of the map is Lake Zaragosa.
10. The room in the back of the house is mine.
11. Please place this bowl of fruit on the table.
12. The flowers by the window are called dahlias.
13. The cat with the long fur is my favorite one.
14. The calendar on the wall has photographs by Ansel Adams.
15. The photograph of Half Dome is one of his most famous ones.

**Exercise 2   Using Adjective Phrases**

Sample adjective phrases are given.
1. with a puzzled look
2. in the pet-store window
3. in front of Keith's house
4. with loud voices

5. With happy expressions
6. on the back fender
7. with her eyes closed
8. for the show
9. from school
10. of your friend
11. in blue pants
12. from Canada
13. of cereal
14. behind the school
15. with large backpacks

## 20.1 Prepositional Phrases (Adverb) (Page 71)
### Practice 1
### Exercise 1 Recognizing Adverb Phrases
Modified words are listed; adverb phrases are underlined.
1. upset, about her long homework assignment
2. retreated, down the valley
3. ran, in a panic
4. stopped, in front of the net
5. late, for work
6. optimistic, about our chances
7. flew, from Detroit; flew, to Miami
8. acknowledged, with a broad smile
9. rumbled, across the sky
10. answer, in a moment

### Exercise 2 Writing Sentences with Adverb Phrases
Sample sentences are given.
1. In the past, life was simpler.
2. We returned home at sunset.
3. The caravan moved across the desert.
4. Many creatures live under the sea.
5. The senator was pleased with the election results.
6. We are leaving in the morning.
7. I am going shopping after school.
8. We sailed down the river.
9. The runner collapsed close to the finish line.
10. We drove over the bridge.

## 20.1 Prepositional Phrases (Adverb) (Page 72)
### Practice 2
### Exercise 1 Identifying Adverb Phrases
Modified words are listed; adverb phrases are underlined.
1. winds through the forest
2. early with her science report
3. At dawn prepared for the rescue attempt
4. happy with her new job
5. At the hotel learned about the delay
6. late for the test run
7. In a well-prepared speech explained
8. piled near the station wagon
9. From the doctor's office drove to the library
10. happy about our victory

### Writing Application
### Writing Sentences with Prepositional Phrases
Sample sentences are given. Phrases are underlined and arrows are drawn from them to the words modified.

1. The baby naps in the afternoon.

2. The coat on the hanger just came back from the cleaner.

3. The dancer in the white shoes is my sister.

4. Our teacher will talk to the museum director before our tour.

5. The horses are grazing near cool water.

## 20.1 Appositives in Phrases (Page 73)
### Practice 1
### Exercise 1 Recognizing Appositives
Appositives are circled, and the words they rename are underlined.

1. artist, Picasso
2. coach, Mr. Sawyer
3. state, Alaska
4. mountain, Pike's Peak
5. play, Death of a Salesman
6. poet, Walt Whitman
7. artist, Winslow Homer
8. capital, Austin
9. restaurant, Smiley's
10. composers, Chopin , Mozart

### Exercise 2 Identifying Appositive Phrases
Phrases are underlined and the words they explain are circled.

1. Thomas Jefferson , our third President
2. Washington, D.C. , the nation's capital
3. " Star-Spangled Banner ", our national anthem
4. animals , the lynx, the bobcat
5. Jenny , the class speaker
6. horse , a dappled mare
7. Audie Murphy , a real war hero
8. Ulysses Grant , commander of the Union armies
9. Thursday , the day after tomorrow
10. trees , a red maple, a Douglas fir

## 20.1 Appositives in Phrases (Page 74)
### Practice 2
### Exercise 1 Identifying Appositives and Appositive Phrases

Appositives or phrases are underlined and arrows point from them to words they rename.

1. The singer Marilyn Horne has a magnificent mezzo-soprano voice.

2. He owns just one car, a Packard.

3. Her home, an old Victorian mansion, was destroyed in the fire.

4. Stephen Crane's poem  A Learned Man is among my favorites.

5. Houston, a city of opportunity, has attracted many newcomers.

6. The composer Mozart wrote many pieces while still a child.

7. Her shoes, brown and white Indian moccasins, were handmade.

8. We were introduced to the leading man a tall, strange, scowling person.

9. The desserts—chocolate pudding, peach pie, and fruit salad —are all delicious.

10. The English writer Virginia Woolf had a sister who was a respected painter.

### Writing Application
### Writing Sentences with Appositives

Sample sentences are given.
1. Chicago, my favorite city, is on Lake Michigan.
2. The Rolling Stones, an exciting group, played here on their last tour.
3. Niagara Falls, a beautiful sight, is where they went on their honeymoon.
4. John Bauer, the coach, joined the basketball players on the court.
5. Okra, a green vegetable, is not often served.

## 20.1 Participles (Page 75)
### Practice 1
### Exercise 1 Identifying Present and Past Participles

Participles are underlined and the words they modify are circled.

1. expanding   (community)

2. polished   (surface)

3. laughing   (I)

4. known   (liar)

5. convicted   (criminal)

6. roasted   (chestnuts)

7. sunken   (treasure)

8. defeated   (army)

9. whistling   (sound)

10. restored   (barn)

### Exercise 2 Writing Sentences with Participles

Sample sentences are given. Participles are underlined.
1. I enjoy eating toasted marshmallows.
2. These two families have a running feud.
3. He had a worried look on his face.
4. The cage contained two roaring lions.
5. They left a written record of their adventures.
6. The singing birds made a joyful noise.
7. The dented fender will have to be repaired.
8. She had a surprised look on her face.
9. The falling snow covered the tracks.
10. We found a lost kitten.

## 20.1 Participles (Page 76)
### Practice 2
### Exercise 1 Identifying Present and Past Participles

Participles are underlined, and arrows are drawn from them to modified words.

1. The burning logs were soon only embers.

2. The detective examined the marked bill.

3. What is the asking price for this vase?

4. The sheriff said the outlaw is a daring fugitive.

5. The broken lamp can be repaired.

6. This is a frightening turn of events.

7. The spoiled cheese has turned green.

8. The pitcher was applauded by the cheering crowd.

9. Charlotte, a growing city, offers a rich past as well.

10. After the tournament she became a well-known athlete.

11. Josie believes in the power of the written word.

12. Did you see the skater's amazing leaps?

13. A well-trained dog can be a big help to a family.

14. As a growing child, Alicia needs her vitamins.

15. Exhausted, the runner barely made it to the finish line.

## Exercise 2   Using Participles
Sample participles are given.
1. smiling
2. Puzzled
3. sparkling
4. twinkling
5. Falling
6. galloping
7. dried
8. disturbing
9. planned
10. painted
11. Alarmed
12. cheering
13. disappointed
14. unopened
15. frozen

## 20.1   Participles in Phrases (Page 77)
### Practice 1
### Exercise 1   Identifying Participial Phrases
Phrases are underlined and the words modified are circled.

1. (coin) , buried in the sand.

2. (ruins) , untouched for centuries

3. (explorer) , exhausted by his journey

4. (chick) , separated from its parents

5. (Grand Canyon) , known for its spectacular vistas

6. (castle) , shrouded in mystery

7. (soldiers) , marching with heavy packs

8. (grass) , glistening with dew

9. (The Three Musketeers) , written by Alexandre Dumas

10. (fire engines) , speeding through the city

### Exercise 2   Writing Sentences with Participial Phrases
Sample participial phrases are given.
1. Looking ahead ten years
2. playing the symphony to perfection
3. Looking for a bargain
4. barking furiously
5. rising from the forest
6. floating lazily overhead
7. Working all night
8. painted by a local artist
9. feeling sick that morning
10. Swimming along the coral reef

## 20.1   Participles in Phrases (Page 78)
### Practice 2
### Exercise 1   Recognizing Participial Phrases
Phrases are underlined and arrows are drawn to modified words.

1. The girl smiling shyly is my cousin from Florida.

2. Troubled by the news, Glenn phoned his parents.

3. Mrs. Grant, waiting for the right moment, whisked the fly out the window.

4. He found the ring hidden in a trunk.

5. Gliding swiftly, the canoe approached the rapids.

6. The *Twentieth Century Limited*, redecorated for the occasion, began its last run.

7. Noted for its mountains, Banff National Park is a popular resort.

8. I spoke to the runner, holding his side in pain.

9. Greeting the guests, the mayor shook dozens of hands.

10. The ancient mammals, frozen for centuries in ice, were well preserved.

### Writing Application
### Writing Sentences with Participial Phrases
Samples are given. Phrases are underlined and arrows point to modified words.

1. Shivering in the cold air, we looked about for shelter.

2. Across the table sat the quarterback, examining the contract closely.

3. In the middle of the field sat June, holding a colorful bouquet of flowers.

4. Entering the room, the professor said nothing, but looked exhausted.

5. Responding to the question, George gave a brief summary of Nick's position.

## 20.2   Adjective Clauses (Page 79)
### Practice 1
### Exercise 1   Identifying Adjective Clauses
1. when Prohibition was the law
2. which I highly recommend to you

3. that you saw in the museum
4. which is an evergreen forest
5. to whom you gave your tickets
6. which will be used for weather forecasting
7. since we last met
8. whose work we are reading
9. which we will see tonight
10. that you saw at the zoo

**Exercise 2   Using Adjective Clauses in Sentences**

Sample adjective clauses are given.
1. that you are singing
2. who made that table
3. who signed the Emancipation Proclamation
4. when knighthood was in flower
5. which will be easy to follow
6. who wrote *Julius Caesar*
7. which is located in Illinois
8. who invented the electric light bulb
9. that are millions of light-years away
10. that we face

**20.2   Adjective Clauses (Page 80)**

**Practice 2**

**Exercise 1   Identifying Adjective Clauses**

Adjective clauses are underlined.
1. He is the pitcher whom we saw the last time.
2. *Kabloona*, which describes a Frenchman living among the Eskimos, was written by Gontran De Poncins.
3. A *tsunami* is a huge wave that is caused by an earthquake or volcanic eruption.
4. Is this the teacher who also makes silver jewelry?
5. In her talk, the ambassador described Luxembourg, which has changed greatly.
6. The man whom you want lives across the street and three houses down.
7. A movie that I will never forget is *Zorba the Greek*.
8. The house where she lived is now a historic site.
9. This is the travel agent who offers trips to China.
10. The girl whose pen I used is my sister Elizabeth's best friend.

**Writing Application**

**Writing Sentences with Adjective Clauses**

Sample sentences are given. Adjective clauses are underlined.
1. Eddie, who always forgets his baseball glove, always borrows mine.
2. I got a nice letter from the friend whom I visited recently.
3. Harold, whose main job was filing applications, was promoted yesterday.
4. The movie that George and I saw was *My Father Is a Hero* with Jet Li.
5. The watch that costs fifty dollars was dropped at the bus stop.

**20.2   Adverb Clauses (Page 81)**

**Practice 1**

**Exercise 1   Recognizing Adverb Clauses**

Adverb clauses are underlined; modified words are circled.
1. (drive)  after I finish lunch
2. (arrive)  Although we set out early

3. (served)  Before James Madison became President
4. (different)  If the South had won the Civil War
5. (faced)  When Charles de Gaulle became president of France
6. (better)  than most other politicians
7. (changed)  while you were gone
8. (sad)  because we have to say "good-bye"
9. (graduate)  until she passes this course
10. (has grown)  since you left

**Exercise 2   Identifying Adverb Clauses and the Words They Modify**

Adverb clauses are underlined; modified words are circled.
1. (delicious) , because it has so many spices
2. (defended) , until the last man was dead
3. (can catch) , if we hurry
4. (more) , than the other teachers did
5. (will tell) , since you insist
6. (was) , when Andrew Jackson became president
7. (happy) , if you choose him for your team
8. (entered) , after the Roman Empire fell
9. (should visit) , while we're in Virginia
10. (carefully) , so that the project would be done correctly

**20.2   Adverb Clauses (Page 82)**

**Practice 2**

**Exercise 1   Identifying Adverb Clauses**

Adverb clauses are underlined.
1. If the book is delivered in time, I will use it for my report.
2. Mike writes to his aunt at least twice a month even though she seldom answers.
3. I will return whenever you need me.
4. Grandma ran for mayor when the incumbent retired.
5. When Fred Astaire started his career, he danced with his sister Adele.
6. Our prinicipal is busier than I have ever seen her.
7. A storm developed after we reached the turnpike.
8. Winston Churchill was better read than were most of the other world leaders of his time.
9. They drove to the park although it was nearby.

10. Fortunately, my brother runs faster <u>than I do</u>.

**Writing Application**

**Using Adverb Clauses in Sentences**

Sample sentences are given. Adverb clauses are underlined.

1. <u>Because Bob was late to the show</u>, he missed part of the first act.
2. <u>Although the lookout saw the danger</u>, the ship still struck the iceberg.
3. <u>After they picked two bushels of blueberries</u>, they fell asleep.
4. <u>When the traffic light suddenly flashed red</u>, we tried to stop the car.
5. <u>If you want to see the play</u>, why don't you write away for tickets?

## 20.2 Classifying Sentences by Structure (Page 83)

**Practice 1**

**Exercise 1 Recognizing Simple Sentences**

Subjects are underlined, and verbs are circled.

1. Barbara, (was)
2. we, (brought)
3. Vikings, (settled)
4. Joyce, Darlene (went)
5. house, (rattled), (shook)
6. Sarah, (built), (put)
7. we, (hiked)
8. Tim, I, (waved), (shouted)
9. aunt uncle, (have retired)
10. you, (are)

**Exercise 2 Distinguishing Between Simple and Compound Sentences**

1. simple
2. compound
3. compound
4. simple
5. simple
6. simple
7. compound
8. compound
9. simple
10. compound

## 20.2 Classifying Sentences by Structure (Page 84)

**Practice 2**

**Exercise 1 Recognizing Simple Sentences**

Subjects are underlined once and verbs twice.

1. <u>Rick</u> and <u>I</u> <u>caught</u> trout under the bridge.
2. The <u>trail</u> <u>left</u> the forest and <u>wound</u> its way up the steep mountain.
3. According to the Bible, <u>Ichabod</u> <u>was born</u> at the hour of the capture of the Ark.

4. <u>Spinach</u>, <u>kale</u>, <u>beans</u>, and <u>peas</u> <u>are</u> all relatively inexpensive.
5. The empty <u>wagon</u> <u>struck</u> the fence and then <u>crashed</u> into the tree.

**Exercise 2 Recognizing Compound Sentences**

Subjects are underlined once and verbs twice.

1. <u>James</u> <u>must remember</u> to bring the lantern, or <u>we</u> <u>will have</u> no light in the cabin.
2. The <u>capital</u> of Louisiana <u>is</u> Baton Rouge; other important <u>cities</u> <u>are</u> Shreveport, Lake Charles, and New Orleans.
3. The southern <u>magnolia</u> <u>has</u> huge white flowers; the northern <u>variety</u> <u>has</u> smaller, somewhat pinkish flowers.
4. <u>She</u> <u>is</u> interested in space exploration, so <u>she</u> <u>reads</u> every article and book on the subject.
5. The night <u>sky</u> <u>was</u> clear, but <u>we</u> <u>did</u> not <u>see</u> a single shooting star.

## 20.2 Classifying Sentences by Structure (Page 85)

**Practice**

**Exercise 1 Recognizing Complex Sentences**

Subjects are underlined once and verbs twice. Clauses are circled.

1. <u>I</u> <u>cleaned up</u>, (that you made)
2. <u>car</u>, <u>stopped</u>, (which had run smoothly all day)
3. <u>someone</u> <u>stole</u>, (while I was watching the parade)
4. <u>we</u> <u>will be</u>, (if our school wins)
5. <u>soldiers</u>, <u>were famished</u>, (who had not eaten all day)

**Exercise 2 Distinguishing Between Complex and Compound-Complex Sentences**

1. complex
2. compound-complex
3. compound-complex
4. complex
5. compound-complex

## 20.2 Classifying Sentences by Structure (Page 86)

**Practice 2**

**Exercise 1 Recognizing Complex Sentences**

Subjects are underlined once and verbs twice. Clauses are in parentheses.

1. The main <u>road</u> <u>was closed</u> (after the <u>bridge</u> <u>collapsed</u>.)
2. The <u>actress</u> (whom <u>I</u> <u>admire</u> the most) <u>is</u> Carol Burnett.
3. <u>We</u> <u>continued</u> our vacation trip (when the dense <u>fog</u> <u>lifted</u>.)

4. (If you are not happy with their work,) you can wallpaper the room yourself.

5. The cactus will grow (if you do not overwater it.)

## Exercise 2 Recognizing Compound-Complex Sentences

Subjects are underlined once and verbs twice. Clauses are in parentheses.

1. (If she can pack quickly) she can leave with me, but I must leave exactly in an hour.

2. The roads were closed (after the storm struck,) and they are still dangerous now.

3. (After we fell asleep,) raccoons invaded our campsite, but we awoke and chased them away.

4. I will help you (if I can,) yet I know little about making jelly.

5. Sarah called home (because she was late for dinner,) but no one answered.

## Exercise 3 Identifying the Structure of Sentences

1. simple
2. complex
3. complex
4. compound
5. simple
6. complex
7. compound
8. complex
9. simple
10. compound-complex

## 21.1 The Four Functions of Sentences (Page 87)
### Practice 1
### Exercise 1 Recognizing the Four Types of Sentences

1. imperative
2. interrogative
3. exclamatory
4. declarative
5. declarative
6. interrogative
7. declarative
8. imperative
9. interrogative
10. declarative

### Exercise 2 Writing the Four Types of Sentences

Sample sentences are given.
1. I watched a snake slither up the tree.
2. You're kidding me!
3. Who was our second president?
4. Be quiet now!
5. Plant the bulbs five inches apart.

## 21.1 The Four Functions of Sentences (Page 88)
### Practice 2
### Exercise 1 Identifying the Four Types of Sentences

1. declarative .
2. imperative . or !
3. interrogative ?
4. imperative ! or .
5. interrogative ?
6. declarative .
7. declarative .
8. imperative . or !
9. exclamatory !
10. interrogative ?

## Writing Application
## Writing Sentences with Different Uses

Sample sentences are given.
1. Who won the contest?
2. How delighted we were!
3. Emily Dickinson was a nineteenth-century U.S. poet.
4. Finish cleaning your room before you go outside.
5. Trenton is the capital of New Jersey.

## 21.2 Shortening Sentences That Are Too Long (Page 89)
### Practice 1
### Exercise 1 Shortening Rambling Compound Sentences

Sample sentences are given.
1. Daniel hurriedly packed his books, and he quickly put on his coat. He raced down the stairs, for he was meeting his friend Charles after school. They were going shopping for computer games, and they wanted to get to the store at least an hour before it closed.

2. Emily knew she could spend the afternoon chatting with her friend, Alexandra, or she could help her mother weed the garden and tend the plants. Instead, she chose to spend the time alone in her room, for she wanted to write in her diary.

### Exercise 2 Shortening Complicated Complex Sentences

Sample sentences are given.
1. Anita was getting ready to leave for school when Helen called to tell her not to forget her American history project. The project was due on the teacher's desk the first thing in the morning, even though history class didn't meet until later that afternoon.

2. My cousin, who attends college in Massachusetts, is studying chemistry. He wants to work in a laboratory which is filled with interesting equipment that he can use to perform ingenious experiments. He hopes his experiments will lead to improvements in our daily lives.

## 21.2 Shortening Sentences That Are Too Long (Page 90)
### Practice 2
### Exercise 1 Shortening Rambling Compound Sentences

Sample sentences are given.
1. Joyce wished to enter medical school, so she joined a premedical society at college. In addition, she worked as a volunteer in an emergency room at the university hospital. She also worked every other Saturday in a convalescent home for elderly people.

2. A shirt begins as yarn of one of more colors. Then it is woven into a roll of fabric, and next it is sent to a factory. There it is cut and sewn, and finally it is shipped with other manufactured shirts to a clothing store.

3. The canyon was narrow and winding, and at the bottom a stream trickled over greenish rocks. On either side of the stream, the walls of the canyon thrust up hundreds of feet toward the racing clouds. Some parts of the cliffs had crumbled into the river, and other parts were pocked with caves carved out by the wind and storms.

### Exercise 2 Shortening Complicated Complex Sentences

Sample sentences are given.
1. Although we crossed the Mojave Desert late in the

afternoon, we could hardly stand the extreme heat. Unfortunately, we did not have air conditioning in the car, which would have allowed us to close the windows. Instead, we suffered the fiery blasts that blew in as we drank water from our cooler and sped east.

2. The old movie that I love most is *Shane* with Alan Ladd as Shane. Shane is a farmhand with a mysterious past who tries to give up his life as a gunfighter until he becomes involved in a conflict between farmers and a cruel rancher. The conflict is settled when Shane decides to risk his life and fight again to save the family he loves.

3. Even though more carpooling would improve traffic conditions, it alone would not cut down on the congestion that clogs the highways and creates smog. One reason not everyone can commute with other people is that they often have very different work schedules.

## 21.3 Using Different Sentence Openers (Page 91)
### Practice 1
### Exercise 1  Using Different Sentence Openers
Sample sentences are given.
1. Before he went to sleep, Andrew listened to music.
2. Enthusiastic, the tennis player looked for an opponent.
3. Under some shady trees, we had a picnic.
4. Feeling tired, the hikers sat down to rest.
5. Although it may be too cool to go swimming, you should bring your bathing suit.
6. Since he is a qualified leader, Ira was asked to head the committee.
7. Repeatedly, he asked the stewardess when the plane was due to land.
8. Satisfied, the customer left the store with a heavy parcel.
9. Seeing his master approach, the dog ran to greet him.
10. Generously, Carol offered to share her lunch with her friend.

### Exercise 2  Varying Sentence Openers Within a Passage
Sample sentences are given.
1. Even though he was unsuccessful in business, Samuel Adams was quite successful in politics.
2. Fearless, this organizer helped to form the Sons of Liberty in 1765.
3. To protest British trade policies, he helped plan the Boston Tea Party.
4. When he served as a delegate to the Continental Congress, he urged the colonies to move towards independence.
5. Proudly, Adams signed the Declaration of Independence.

## 21.3 Using Different Sentence Openers (Page 92)
### Practice 2
### Exercise 1  Using Different Sentence Openers
Sample sentences are given.
1. Just after his store was robbed, Mr. Wu called the police.
2. Curious, the chimpanzee explored the house.
3. At exactly midnight, the doorbell rang.
4. During the intense heat spell this summer, their air-conditioning system failed to operate.
5. To become a veterinarian, Clara attended school for five more years.

### Writing Application
### Varying Sentence Openers
Sample sentences are given.
1. The game was tied as it headed into the bottom of the ninth.
2. Taking careful aim, the pitcher delivered a curve ball, and the first batter singled.
3. Because of a wild pitch, the first batter then moved to second base.
4. Next, the second batter took a ball, and the man on base stole third.
5. The pitcher then struck out the second batter.
6. After only four pitches, the third batter walked.
7. The fourth batter, with a powerful swing, hit a long fly ball.
8. Though the sun was in his eyes, the right fielder caught the ball.
9. The man on third base was tagged out trying to reach home.
10. As the excitement grew, the game entered the tenth.

## 21.3 Improving Short Sentences (Page 93)
### Practice 1
### Exercise 1  Adding Details to Short Sentences
Sample sentences are given.
1. At noon, the airplane landed according to schedule.
2. The most famous scientist in the field of astronomy spoke to them.
3. Katherine read them a story full of mystery and adventure.

### Exercise 2  Combining Short Sentences
Sample sentences are given.
1. Speaking frankly, he said he opposed the plan.
2. Bruce understands the procedure, but he still makes mistakes.
3. When she heard the startling news, she rushed to the telephone.

## 21.3 Improving Short Sentences (Page 94)
### Practice 2
### Exercise 1  Adding Details to Short Sentences
Sample sentences are given.
1. The ragged couch in the playroom needs to be re-covered by a professional.
2. Blue and green carnations placed on the night stand brightened the hospital room.
3. Using all his patience and wisdom, Dad could not start the old truck's engine after it overheated.

### Exercise 2  Combining Short Sentences
Sample sentences are given.
1. She began her career as a laboratory technician at Huntington General Hospital.
2. Clint admired my poster collection, and he offered to buy five posters.
3. At the shore we bodysurfed and played volleyball in the afternoon.
4. When the company changed its package design, sales increased sharply.
5. Because our television's reception was poor, we added a cable adapter.

## 21.4 Correcting Sentence Fragments (Page 95)
### Practice 1
### Exercise 1  Recognizing Sentence Fragments
1. fragment
2. sentence
3. fragment

4. fragment
5. fragment
6. sentence
7. sentence
8. fragment
9. fragment
10. fragment

## Exercise 2 Identifying Sentence Fragments

Sentences are underlined once; fragments are underlined twice.

1. I couldn't see the house in the fog.
2. With all its colors flying
3. In the last chapter of the book
4. Since September, I have grown five inches.
5. Since I started school this fall
6. If he could have one wish
7. She couldn't understand the strange language.
8. We talked.
9. Beyond the little village
10. Will take many years

## 21.4 Correcting Sentence Fragments (Page 96)

### Practice 2

### Exercise 1 Recognizing Sentence Fragments

Sample sentences are given.

1. F Laverne had an accident near the new traffic light.
2. F We saw a car jumping the curb and hitting the sign.
3. S
4. F Unfortunately, we tried all day to contact them but were not successful.
5. F Mrs. Corvera was selected to translate since she speaks Spanish so well.
6. F The roof of the old auditorium collapsed with the weight of the snow.
7. S
8. F A child was rescued when he was discovered at the bottom of the well.
9. F At last, I finished my shopping for the holidays.
10. F They will lose their reservations unless they answer by tomorrow.
11. F Did you see the bicycle in front of the store?
12. F The governor standing on the new platform is my dad.
13. F The man suffering from the heat was rushed to a hospital.
14. S
15. F Our teacher was surprised that we completed the project in an hour.

## 21.4 Correcting Fragments (Phrases, Clauses) (Page 97)

### Practice 1

### Exercise 1 Identifying Phrase Fragments and Clause Fragments

1. phrase fragment
2. clause fragment
3. clause fragment
4. clause fragment
5. sentence
6. phrase fragment
7. sentence
8. clause fragment
9. phrase fragment
10. sentence

## Exercise 2 Correcting Fragments

Sample sentences are given.

1. We heard strange noises during the night.
2. I have tickets for the show which opened last week on Broadway.
3. After the rodeo had ended, we talked to one of the riders.
4. When I reach the age of twenty-five, I want to have my own business.
6. On July 4, 1776, our country became independent.
8. Bill's ancestors, who arrived from Ireland many years ago, settled in Boston.
9. Sitting by the window, Nancy watched the traffic on the streets below.

## 21.4 Correcting Fragments (Phrases, Clauses) (Page 98)

### Practice 2

### Exercise 1 Changing Phrase Fragments into Sentences

Sample sentences are given.

1. They talk on the telephone for hours.
2. It's hard to think clearly with all this noise.
3. Nancy drank a cup of coffee before studying to avoid getting tired.
4. It's important to be on time to class because we have a test today.
5. I gathered all the shells found on the beach.
6. On weeknights, Jim is usually waiting at school by the gym for his ride home.
7. I find that when I can't sleep at night, drinking cold milk helps.
8. On last night's news, Stuart saw the imminent hurricane warnings.
9. My father usually reads the newspaper at breakfast.
10. My little brother rushed home after being stung by a bee.

### Exercise 2 Changing Clause Fragments into Sentences

Sample sentences are given.

1. If you write to me soon, I will be sure to answer.
2. Is there anyone who knows the combination to the lock?
3. I don't believe the story that he told us.
4. That is the intruder whom they described to the police.
5. Although she doesn't speak French too well, the Parisians welcomed her and her fellow exchange students warmly.

## 21.4 Correcting Run-ons (Page 99)

### Practice 1

### Exercise 1 Identifying Run-ons

1. run-on
2. run-on
3. run-on
4. run-on
5. sentence
6. run-on
7. sentence
8. run-on
9. run-on
10. run-on

### Exercise 2 Recognizing Run-ons

2. Hawaii is located in the Pacific, it is famous for magnificent beaches and lush, tropical foliage.
3. The Vikings established a kingdom in Russia, they were courageous seafarers.
7. I am reading an interesting novel, it was written by Willa Cather.

8. We are organizing a large Labor Day Parade this one will be the biggest in years.
10. Watch the news tonight I think you will see something very unusual.

## 21.4 Correcting Run-ons (Page 100)
### Practice 2
### Exercise 1    Recognizing Run-ons
1. RO
2. RO
3. S
4. RO
5. RO
6. S
7. RO
8. RO
9. S
10. RO

### Exercise 2    Recognizing Run-ons
1. All jackets, sweaters, and coats in the store are on sale the discounts are up to fifty percent. NP
2. Let's shop early, you know I need a new jacket for the winter. C
3. I've always wanted to get a red jacket with fur trim, of course the fur would have to be fake. C
4. How about you what kind of jacket would you like to get? NP
5. After we shop, we can eat lunch, let's try that new restaurant on Fourth. C
6. The restaurant serves pizza, chicken, and salads, I've heard the salads are very good. C
7. Later we can go to the art museum there's a new photography exhibit. NP
8. Who's your favorite photographer I like Dorothea Lange. NP
9. I have two free passes to the art museum, that's a savings of about ten dollars. C
10. If it's cold enough, we can wear our new jackets we'll be the best-dressed pair there! NP

## 21.4 Correcting Run-ons (Page 101)
### Practice 1
### Exercise 1    Identifying Run-ons
1. S
2. R
3. R
4. R
5. R
6. S
7. R
8. S
9. R
10. S

### Exercise 2    Correcting Run-ons
Sample sentences are given.
2. We expected the senator to arrive tonight; she just returned from Africa.
3. Franklin Roosevelt became President in 1933, and he served until 1945.
4. Where are we going? When will we arrive?
5. I like cereal for breakfast, but my brother likes eggs and toast.
7. A team is only as good as its players, and we have the best.
9. Here is the package you ordered. It was delivered this morning.

## 21.4 Correcting Run-ons (Page 102)
### Practice 2
### Exercise 1    Correcting Run-ons
Sample sentences are given.
1. I had a terrible day at school. I lost my lunch and stained my shirt with dye during science.
2. An old saying says that a new broom sweeps clean; our new coach may thus make a lot of changes.
3. Do you know who the last President of the United States was to serve two full terms? President George Bush served only one term.
4. Nancy love humorous poems; her favorites are Carroll's "Jabberwocky" and Nash's "The Panther."
5. Finish your homework. Then clean your desk.
6. My mother and aunt collect porcelain, but my brother and I collect coins.
7. Histamines cause itching, so some people take antihistamines for relief.
8. Benito Juarez is a national hero in Mexico. He helped defeat the French and drive them from his land.
9. Crops are damaged by a variety of pests, but spraying them with special insecticides sometimes helps.
10. A silver jubilee celebrates an event that occurred twenty-five years before. Queen Elizabeth II celebrated her silver jubilee in 1977.

## 21.4 Recognizing Misplaced Modifiers (Page 103)
### Practice 1
### Exercise 1    Recognizing Misplaced Modifiers
Misplaced modifiers are underlined.
1. walking home
2. sitting on the dock
3. lying in the sun
4. riding his horse in front of them
5. on astronomy
6. about Gandhi
7. working all day
8. with a sunroof
9. looking through the binoculars
10. shopping in the bazaar

### Exercise 2    Identifying Misplaced Modifiers
1. C
2. MM
3. MM
4. MM
5. MM
6. MM
7. MM
8. C
9. C
10. MM
11. MM
12. MM
13. C
14. MM
15. MM

## 21.4 Recognizing Misplaced Modifiers (Page 104)
### Practice 2
### Exercise 1    Recognizing Misplaced Modifiers
1. MM
2. MM
3. MM
4. C
5. MM

6. MM
7. C
8. MM
9. C
10. MM

**Exercise 2   Recognizing Misplaced Modifiers**
1. Walking up the driveway
2. near the house
3. the week before
4. wearing a white coat
5. Shivering a bit
6. Wearing a pair of open sandals
7. Barking loudly
8. Running from the side of the house to greet her
9. Slightly frightened
10. Coming from behind the tree

## 21.4   Correcting Misplaced Modifiers (Page 105)
**Practice 1**
**Exercise 1   Recognizing Misplaced Modifiers**
1. with the green ribbon
2. chattering in the tree
3. with the silver buttons
4. cruising rapidly through space
5. set in Ireland
6. with a stethoscope
7. blowing his whistle
8. with a zip-out lining
9. after school ended
10. writing diligently

**Exercise 2   Correcting Misplaced Modifiers**
Sample sentences are given.
1. I went with the green ribbon to the checkout counter at the bargain store.
2. We listened to two squirrels chattering in the tree.
3. Sally put on her coat with the silver buttons before she reached the door.
4. Cruising rapidly through space, the rocket left Earth far behind.
5. When I finished dinner, I watched the television program set in Ireland.
6. Carefully listening with a stethoscope, the doctor examined the boy.
7. Blowing his whistle, the policeman began to chase the thief.
8. For his birthday, he received a jacket with a zip-out lining from his father.
9. After school ended, Carol visited Bryce Canyon, which is located in Utah.
10. Writing diligently, the author finished the book in six months.

## 21.4   Correcting Misplaced Modifiers (Page 106)
**Practice 2**
**Exercise 1   Correcting Misplaced Modifiers**
Samples are given. The original misplaced modifier is underlined, and an arrow points from the modifier to the word it modifies.

1. The dress that she wanted had already been purchased.

2. Reaching the park, I found my aunt waiting on a bench.

3. At the bazaar, Uncle Ron bought a hat with a green feather.

4. I read the story with the surprise ending when I got home.

5. Told to move along, the crowd increased its hissing.

6. The famous actor whom everyone hoped to see arrived late.

7. Walking rather slowly toward the station, I almost missed the train.

8. Tudor Castle, built in 1512, was destroyed by a terrible fire.

9. I received from my mother a new television with remote controls.

10. After a long chase the soldiers finally caught the man who was spying on them.

## 21.4   Double Negatives (Page 107)
**Practice 1**
**Exercise 1   Correcting Double Negatives**
1. any
2. anything
3. any
4. any
5. anyone
6. any
7. anything
8. any
9. anybody
10. any

**Exercise 2   Using Negatives Correctly**
Sample sentences are given.
1. That day Rose couldn't do anything right.
2. We had no time left.
3. After dinner, there was nothing left of the pie.
4. Alex had never seen so many beautiful paintings before.
5. There are some things I won't do.
6. That night Bill had nowhere to go.
7. Haven't you ever been to Texas?
8. Nobody likes a dull party.
9. None of the children could guess the answer.
10. There has not been any sunshine today.

## 21.4   Double Negatives (Page 108)
**Practice 2**
**Exercise 1   Correcting Double Negatives**
1. That bicycle factory has made nothing for ten years.
   That bicycle factory hasn't made anything for ten years.
2. The railroad tracks that run past our yard lead

nowhere. The railroad tracks that run past our yard don't lead anywhere.
3. Eat nothing now, or you won't enjoy your dinner. Don't eat anything now, or you won't enjoy your dinner.
4. Lillian has no place to keep her model train set. Lillian hasn't any place to keep her model train set.
5. The Governor has shown nobody the speech he is delivering tonight. The Governor hasn't shown anybody the speech he is delivering tonight.
6. Lonnie has played no music with an orchestra. Lonnie hasn't played any music with an orchestra.
7. These sandals have no straps. These sandals don't have any straps.
8. There were no more seats on the bus after we got on. There weren't any more seats on the bus after we got on.
9. I can remember nothing about my dreams last night. I can't remember anything about my dreams last night.
10. Sheila would gave me none of her crackers. Sheila wouldn't give me any of her crackers.

## 21.4  Common Usage Problems (Page 109)
### Practice 1
**Exercise 1  Avoiding Some Common Usage Problems**
1. besides
2. accept
3. affect
4. is
5. from
6. except
7. that
8. effect
9. Besides
10. advise

**Exercise 2  Avoiding Other Common Usage Problems**
1. rather
2. further
3. whom
4. the place where
5. too
6. as
7. their
8. farther
9. rather
10. like

## 21.4  Common Usage Problems (Page 110)
### Practice 2
**Exercise 1  Avoiding Usage Problems**
1. advice
2. are
3. except
4. that
5. effect
6. accepted
7. affects
8. is
9. advises
10. that

**Exercise 2  Avoiding Usage Problems**
1. further
2. from
3. rather
4. in
5. beside
6. rather

7. from
8. Besides
9. farther
10. into

### Exercise 3  Avoiding Usage Problems
1. the place where
2. two
3. like
4. that
5. There
6. the time when
7. As
8. who
9. Too
10. they're

## 22.1  The Four Principal Parts of Verbs (Regular) (Page 111)
### Practice 1
**Exercise 1  Recognizing the Principal Parts of Regular Verbs**
1. past
2. present participle
3. present participle
4. present
5. past participle
6. past participle
7. past
8. past participle
9. present participle
10. past participle

**Exercise 2  Using the Principal Parts of Verbs**
1. closing
2. delivered
3. welcomed
4. reached
5. waiting
6. play
7. learned
8. demonstrated
9. refused
10. happened

## 22.1  The Four Principal Parts of Verbs (Regular) (Page 112)
### Practice 2
**Exercise 1  Recognizing the Principal Parts of Regular Verbs**
1. past
2. present participle
3. present participle
4. past participle
5. present
6. past participle
7. past
8. present participle
9. past participle
10. present participle

**Exercise 2  Using the Principal Parts of Regular Verbs**
1. sighed
2. asked
3. marched
4. complained
5. rolled
6. playing
7. noticed
8. polished
9. knocked

10. start

## 22.1 The Four Principal Parts of Verbs (Irregular) (Page 113)
### Practice 1
### Exercise 1 Completing the Principal Parts of Irregular Verbs
1. hold, (am) holding, held
2. ride, rode, (have) ridden
3. (am) setting, set, (have) set
4. swing, (am) swinging, (have) swung
5. (am) throwing, threw, (have) thrown
6. sink, (am) sinking, sank
7. break, broke, (have) broken
8. fight, fought, (have) fought
9. (am) shaking, shook, (have) shaken
10. catch, (am) catching, (have) caught

### Exercise 2 Using the Principal Parts of Irregular Verbs
1. sang
2. swam
3. known
4. gone
5. burst
6. blown
7. begun
8. brought
9. chosen
10. threw

## 22.1 The Four Principal Parts of Verbs (Irregular) (Page 114)
### Practice 2
### Exercise 1 Completing the Principal Parts of Irregular Verbs
1. teaching, taught, taught
2. cost, costing, cost
3. give, gave, given
4. wear, wearing, wore
5. catch, caught, caught
6. flying, flew, flown
7. burst, bursting, burst
8. go, going, gone
9. pay, paid, paid
10. shaking, shook, shaken
11. lose, losing, lost
12. lie, lying, lay
13. swear, swore, sworn
14. saying, said, said
15. find, finding, found
16. freeze, freezing, froze
17. get, getting, got or gotten
18. riding, rode, ridden
19. spring, sprang, sprung
20. put, putting, put
21. grow, grew, grown
22. sinking, sank, sunk
23. break, breaking, broke
24. fight, fighting, fought
25. lead, led, led

### Exercise 2 Supplying the Correct Principal Part of Irregular Verbs
1. laid
2. bought
3. drove
4. risen
5. fell

## 22.2 The Six Tenses of Verbs (Page 115)
### Practice 1
### Exercise 1 Identifying the Basic Forms of Verbs
1. present perfect
2. future
3. past
4. present perfect
5. present
6. past perfect
7. future perfect
8. past
9. present
10. future

### Exercise 2 Supplying the Correct Tense
1. stops
2. has been
3. had collected
4. swam
5. will ... eat
6. won
7. will pass
8. had hoped
9. will have finished
10. see

## 22.2 The Six Tenses of Verbs (Page 116)
### Practice 2
### Exercise 1 Identifying the Basic Forms of Verbs
1. past perfect
2. future
3. present
4. future perfect
5. present perfect
6. present
7. past
8. past perfect
9. future
10. present perfect

### Exercise 2 Supplying the Correct Tense
1. will replace
2. have started
3. bought
4. imagines
5. had wanted
6. will have guessed
7. has been
8. cost
9. makes
10. had seen

### Writing Application
### Using the Basic Form of the Six Tenses
Sample sentences are given.
1. I do the dishes every night. Carla did her homework. I will do the chores if you help me. We have done a great deal in the past year. After Liz had done her piano practicing, she went outside for a walk. By tomorrow Mike will have done a lot of gardening.
2. I speak to my mother on the telephone every day. She spoke to my aunt last week. I will speak to my friend overseas tomorrow. She has spoken to her family about coming home soon. By midnight, everyone had left the party. We will have spoken to all of our guests by the end of the wedding reception.

## 22.2 The Six Progressive Forms of Verbs (Page 117)

### Practice 1

### Exercise 1 Identifying the Tenses of Progressive Forms of Verbs

1. present perfect
2. past
3. past perfect
4. future
5. present
6. past perfect
7. future perfect
8. past
9. present perfect
10. future

### Exercise 2 Supplying the Correct Tense

1. is taking
2. will be visiting
3. had been expecting
4. is running
5. were giving
6. was winning
7. will have been working
8. has been struggling
9. is trying
10. had been studying

## 22.2 The Six Progressive Forms of Verbs (Page 118)

### Practice 2

### Exercise 1 Identifying the Progressive Forms of Verbs

1. present perfect
2. present
3. future
4. past perfect
5. past
6. present perfect
7. present
8. past perfect
9. future
10. present perfect
11. past
12. present
13. future perfect
14. future
15. present perfect
16. past
17. present
18. past perfect
19. future perfect
20. present perfect

### Exercise 2 Supplying the Correct Tense

1. has been painting
2. was cooking
3. will be designing
4. will have been publishing
5. am putting
6. was thinking
7. had been learning
8. will be starting
9. has been keeping
10. had been wanting

## 22.3 Glossary of Troublesome Verbs (Page 119)

### Practice 1

### Exercise 1 Avoiding Problems with Troublesome Verbs

1. drowned
2. rise
3. have
4. broken
5. did
6. laid
7. gone
8. Set
9. isn't
10. saw

### Exercise 2 Using Troublesome Verbs Correctly

Sample sentences are given.

1. Jane set down her packages.
2. Soon, the landlord will raise the rent.
3. Last Saturday Bob lay in bed until eleven o'clock.
4. Three sailors drowned in the ferocious storm.
5. The balloon burst in an instant.
6. Where have all the flowers gone?
7. That isn't funny.
8. Has anyone ever seen a unicorn?
9. Alison sat in her treehouse.
10. Harry has finally done his homework.

## 22.3 Glossary of Troublesome Verbs (Page 120)

### Practice 2

### Exercise 1 Avoiding Problems with Troublesome Verbs

1. did
2. drowned
3. burst
4. has gone
5. isn't
6. broken
7. went
8. drowned
9. aren't
10. have done

### Exercise 2 Avoiding Problems with Troublesome Verbs

1. laying
2. could have
3. saw
4. rise
5. sit
6. has seen
7. lay
8. raise
9. sets
10. have

### Exercise 3 Avoiding Problems with Troublesome Verbs

1. rise
2. have
3. drowned
4. did
5. broken
6. lay
7. Sit
8. isn't
9. went
10. had seen

**23 The Three Cases of Personal Pronouns (Page 121)**

**Practice 1**

**Exercise 1   Identifying Pronoun Case**

1. objective
2. nominative
3. possessive
4. nominative
5. possessive
6. possessive
7. nominative
8. objective
9. nominative
10. objective

**Exercise 2   Identifying Pronoun Case**

1. objective
2. nominative
3. objective
4. possessive
5. objective
6. nominative
7. objective
8. possessive
9. nominative
10. objective

**23 The Three Cases of Personal Pronouns (Page 122)**

**Practice 2**

**Exercise 1   Identifying Case**

1. possessive
2. nominative
3. objective
4. objective
5. nominative
6. objective
7. possessive
8. objective
9. nominative
10. objective
11. nominative
12. possessive
13. objective
14. objective
15. possessive

**Exercise 2   Identifying Case**

Jodie looked out at the members of her audience. They stared back at her. "Oh, no!" Jodie thought. "I have forgotten my lines!" As Jodie looked at her director, he pretended to be watering a plant. "Ah!" thought Jodie. Immediately, she walked to the table and took the plant off it, saying, "Let me give you some water."

Then Sam walked onto the stage, speaking his line. "If I had my way, we would get rid of that plant. Three of them have not done well. Their needs are not being met."

The director smiled from the sidelines. His play would be fine.

Nominative Case: They, I, he, she, I, we

Objective Case: her, it, me, you, them

Possessive Case: her, my, her, his, my, Their, His

**23 Cases of Personal Pronouns (Nominative, Objective) (Page 123)**

**Practice 1**

**Exercise 1   Identifying Pronouns in the Nominative Case**

1. he, S
2. she, PP
3. They, S
4. I, S
5. he, PP
6. she, S
7. he, PP
8. She, S
9. he, S
10. we, S

**Exercise 2   Identifying Pronouns in the Objective Case**

1. me, OP
2. him, DO
3. her, DO
4. them, DO
5. him, IO

**23 Cases of Personal Pronouns (Nominative, Objective) (Page 124)**

**Practice 2**

**Exercise 1   Using Personal Pronouns in the Nominative Case**

Sample pronouns are given.

1. I, subject
2. he, predicate pronoun
3. they, subject
4. we, predicate pronoun
5. they, subject
6. it, subject
7. she, predicate pronoun
8. it, subject
9. we, subject
10. I, predicate pronoun

**Exercise 2   Using Personal Pronouns in the Objective Case**

Sample pronouns are given.

1. them, object of preposition
2. us, indirect object
3. me, object of preposition
4. it, direct object
5. her, indirect object
6. him, direct object
7. me, object of preposition
8. us, object of preposition
9. them, indirect object
10. her, direct object

**23 Cases of Personal Pronouns (Possessive) (Page 125)**

**Practice 1**

**Exercise 1   Using Personal Pronouns in the Possessive Case**

1. mine
2. his
3. Yours
4. its
5. theirs
6. its
7. yours
8. their
9. Hers
10. ours

**Exercise 2   Using All Three Cases**

1.  I
2.  ours
3.  him
4.  theirs
5.  I
6.  him
7.  Yours
8.  them
9.  I
10. she

## 23 Cases of Personal Pronouns (Possessive) (Page 126)

**Practice 2**

**Exercise 1   Using Personal Pronouns in the Possessive Case**

1.  its
2.  his
3.  theirs
4.  ours
5.  hers
6.  yours
7.  It's
8.  his
9.  yours
10. its

**Exercise 2   Checking the Case of Personal Pronouns**

1.  I
2.  its
3.  correct
4.  me (*her* is correct)
5.  correct
6.  me
7.  It's
8.  correct
9.  theirs
10. I

## 24.1 Agreement Between Subjects and Verbs (Page 127)

**Practice 1**

**Exercise 1   Recognizing the Number of Nouns and Pronouns**

1.  P
2.  S
3.  P
4.  S
5.  S
6.  P
7.  S
8.  S
9.  P
10. P

**Exercise 2   Recognizing the Number of Verbs**

1.  swim, P
2.  is, S
3.  was, S
4.  is, S
5.  cost, P
6.  has been, S
7.  wants, S
8.  plays, S
9.  creep, P
10. think, P

## 24.1 Agreement Between Subjects and Verbs (Page 128)

**Practice 2**

**Exercise 1   Recognizing the Number of Nouns and Pronouns**

1.  plural
2.  singular
3.  plural
4.  plural
5.  singular
6.  plural
7.  plural
8.  singular
9.  singular
10. singular
11. singular
12. singular
13. singular
14. singular
15. singular
16. plural
17. singular
18. singular
19. singular
20. singular

**Exercise 2   Recognizing the Number of Verbs**

1.  says, singular
2.  are, plural
3.  was, singular
4.  waits, singular
5.  am, singular
6.  have, plural
7.  has been, singular
8.  are, plural
9.  is, singular
10. forgive, plural

## 24.1 Agreement Between Subjects and Verbs (Page 129)

**Practice 1**

**Exercise 1   Checking to See If Subjects and Verbs Agree**

1.  correct
2.  calls
3.  correct
4.  correct
5.  are
6.  look
7.  correct
8.  ride
9.  looks
10. is

**Exercise 2   Making Verbs Agree with Singular and Plural Subjects**

1.  opens, S
2.  disagree, P
3.  wins, S
4.  affects, S
5.  is, S
6.  was, S
7.  grow, P
8.  were, P
9.  are, P
10. is, S

## 24.1 Agreement Between Subjects and Verbs (Page 130)
### Practice 2
**Exercise 1    Making Verbs Agree with Singular and Plural Subjects**
1. has
2. grows
3. are
4. look
5. was
6. date
7. surrounds
8. indicate
9. are
10. seems
11. is
12. have
13. seem
14. approaches
15. is

**Exercise 2    Making Verbs Agree with Singular and Plural Subjects**
1. stain, plural subject
2. is, singular subject
3. make, plural subject
4. support, plural subject
5. needs, singular subject
6. brighten, plural subject
7. wants, singular subject
8. exceed, plural subject
9. resembles, singular subject
10. help, plural subject

## 24.1    Agreement with Compound Subjects (Page 131)
### Practice 1
**Exercise 1    Making Verbs Agree with Compound Subjects Joined by *or* or *nor***
1. was
2. were
3. is
4. are
5. cooks
6. make
7. taste
8. is
9. takes
10. has

**Exercise 2    Making Verbs Agree with Compound Subjects Joined by *and***
1. is
2. come
3. is
4. teach
5. write

## 24.1    Agreement with Compound Subjects (Page 132)
### Practice 2
**Exercise 1    Making Verbs Agree with Compound Subjects Joined by *or* or *nor***
1. drives
2. is
3. tastes
4. have been
5. go
6. capture
7. serve

8. wants
9. is
10. are

**Exercise 2    Making Verbs Agree with Compound Subjects Joined by *and***
1. were
2. is
3. were
4. is
5. were
6. live
7. was
8. stop
9. offers
10. are

**Exercise 3    Checking to See If Subjects and Verbs Agree**
1. have
2. was
3. comes
4. was
5. fits

## 24.1    Special Problems with Subject-Verb Agreement (Page 133)
### Practice 1
**Exercise 1    Checking Agreement in Sentences with Inverted Word Order**
1. are
2. has
3. lies
4. come
5. are
6. has
7. has
8. are
9. was
10. is
11. are
12. is
13. lies
14. has
15. were

**Exercise 2    Using Inverted Word Order in Sentences**
Sample sentences are given. Subjects are circled.

1. Here lies the buried (treasure) .

2. Where is (Lois) at this late hour?

3. Why were (you) so late?

4. There goes (Mary) along the road.

5. How many pears have the (Krugers) in their orchard?

## 24.1    Special Problems with Subject-Verb Agreement (Page 134)
### Practice 2
**Exercise 1    Checking Agreement in Sentences with Inverted Word Order**
Subjects are underlined.
1. has, she
2. has, Heather
3. are, reasons
4. are, fiddlers
5. has, Martin

## Exercise 2 Checking Agreement with Indefinite Pronouns
1. have
2. were
3. Do
4. were
5. has
6. laughs
7. has
8. represents
9. have
10. were

## Exercise 3 Checking Special Problems in Agreement
1. sticks
2. was
3. were
4. Haven't
5. has
6. are
7. wants
8. have
9. are
10. squeak

## 24.2 Agreement Between Pronouns and Antecedents (Page 135)
### Practice 1
### Exercise 1 Making Pronouns and Antecedents Agree
1. their
2. her
3. our
4. their
5. her
6. him
7. its
8. their
9. her
10. their

### Exercise 2 Making Pronouns and Indefinite Pronouns Agree
1. her
2. its
3. his
4. his
5. her

## 24.2 Agreement Between Pronouns and Antecedents (Page 136)
### Practice 2
### Exercise 1 Making Pronouns and Antecedents Agree
1. her
2. their
3. her
4. their
5. her
6. his
7. she
8. his
9. their
10. their

### Exercise 2 Avoiding Shifts in Person and Number
Pronouns and antecedents are underlined.
1. Julio now knows that he can't play in the school band without practicing.
2. Either Curtis or Tim will bring his surfboard today.
3. Each fish in the aquarium acted as if it could not be bothered by our attention.

4. All students should know that they have to register today.
5. The puppies rolled over and kicked their legs.

## 25.1 Comparison of Regular Adjectives and Adverbs (Page 137)
### Practice 1
### Exercise 1 Forming the Comparative and Superlative Degrees of One- and Two-Syllable Modifiers
1. colder, coldest
2. handsome, more handsome
3. fair, fairest
4. quickly, most quickly
5. more anxious, most anxious

### Exercise 2 Forming the Comparative and Superlative Degrees of Modifiers with More than Two Syllables
1. more comfortable, most comfortable
2. more ungrateful, most ungrateful
3. more thoroughly, most thoroughly
4. more happily, most happily
5. more carelessly, most carelessly

## 25.1 Comparison of Regular Adjectives and Adverbs (Page 138)
### Practice 2
### Exercise 1 Forming the Comparative and Superlative Degrees of One- and Two-Syllable Modifiers
1. more nervous, most nervous
2. more brightly, most brightly
3. more painful, most painful
4. more slowly, most slowly
5. quieter, quietest

### Exercise 2 Forming the Comparative and Superlative Degrees of Modifiers with More Than Two Syllables
1. more generous, most generous
2. more unattractive, most unattractive
3. more suddenly, most suddenly
4. more capable, most capable
5. more powerfully, most powerfully

### Writing Application
### Forming the Comparative and Superlative Degrees of Regular Modifiers
Sample sentences are given.
1. The children may choose their toys more wisely next time.
   The candidate spoke most wisely on that issue.
2. Next time we will get ready faster in order to catch the train.
   The winner was the racecar driver who was the fastest.
3. I think this office is colder than the hallway.
   The winter was the coldest she had remembered in years.
4. The vacation in Europe was more memorable than our previous two trips.
   His artwork was the most memorable of the entire class.
5. The dancer moved more gracefully than the others on stage.
   She ice-skated most gracefully of all the contestants.

## 25.1 Comparison of Irregular Adjectives and Adverbs (Page 139)
### Practice 1
### Exercise 1 Recognizing the Degree of Irregular Modifiers
1. comparative
2. superlative

3. positive
4. comparative
5. positive
6. superlative
7. positive
8. comparative
9. comparative
10. superlative

### Exercise 2 Using the Comparative and Superlative Forms of Irregular Modifiers
1. worst
2. better
3. farther
4. best
5. more
6. further
7. best
8. worse
9. most
10. most

## 25.1 Comparison of Irregular Adjectives and Adverbs (Page 140)
### Practice 2
### Exercise 1 Recognizing the Degree of Irregular Modifiers
1. comparative
2. positive
3. superlative
4. comparative
5. comparative
6. positive
7. superlative
8. superlative
9. positive
10. superlative

### Exercise 2 Using the Comparative and Superlative Degrees of Irregular Modifiers
1. more
2. worst
3. better
4. farthest
5. worse
6. more
7. best
8. more
9. worst
10. best

## 25.1 Using the Comparative and Superlative Degrees (Page 141)
### Practice 1
### Exercise 1 Using the Comparative and Superlative Degrees Correctly
1. most
2. oldest
3. safer
4. longest
5. more
6. best
7. longer
8. more
9. best
10. more

### Exercise 2 Correcting Inappropriate Comparisons
1. Which of the two jars contains more jelly beans?
2. Nate is the most consistent hitter of all the Bulldogs.
3. Of the two mountains, Mt. Everest is the higher.

4. Which is bigger, 5/16 or 1/4?
5. These cookies are even worse than the last batch.

## 25.1 Using the Comparative and Superlative Degrees (Page 142)
### Practice 2
### Exercise 1 Correcting Errors in Degree
1. The jester realized sooner than the rest of the court what the king meant.
2. Which of these two bushes has produced more roses?
3. correct
4. I couldn't judge whose work was best—Dean's, Helen's, or Chrisanne's.
5. Yesterday had to be the hottest day of the year.
6. Which one of your eyes is weaker?
7. Mr. Crespi grew fonder of that wild rabbit as the summer went on.
8. correct
9. If I had to choose between beets and sauerkraut, I would say that I dislike beets more.
10. The worst job Craig ever had to do involved counting bees in a hive.

### Writing Application
### Using the Comparative and Superlative Degrees
Sample sentences are given.
1. Mimi is sillier than her sister. Their brother is the silliest of the three.
2. My fleece jacket is warmer than my cotton pullover. My wool overcoat is the warmest of the three.
3. Tracy is more ambitious than the other law students. Her father, a lawyer, was the most ambitious of his graduating class.
4. The car in front stopped more suddenly than we expected. The ambulance, blaring its siren, arrived most suddenly of all the vehicles.
5. The crocheted blanket I received was more wonderful than the ones from the store. The handmade quilt was the most wonderful gift of all.
6. His manners are more pleasing now that he's started college. His sister's etiquette is the most pleasing of that of all the siblings.
7. One puppy behaved worse than the other, so they took him outside. The dog circling the tent without a leash was the worst behaved dog at the show.
8. On Sunday afternoons, Carol is lazier than usual. On vacation, she is the laziest.
9. My pair of cotton socks are softer than my wool socks. My cashmere socks are the softest of all the pairs.
10. This painting by Rembrandt is more colorful than that one by Brughel. The ones painted by Monet are the most colorful of all.

## 25.2 Glossary of Troublesome Adjectives and Adverbs (Page 143)
### Practice 1
### Exercise 1 Using Troublesome Adjectives and Adverbs Correctly
1. made only
2. bad
3. well
4. bad
5. fewer
6. fewer
7. good
8. badly
9. well

10. read just

## Exercise 2 Correcting Errors Caused by Troublesome Adjectives and Adverbs
1. correct
2. The boys felt bad about their practical joke.
3. Mr. Salvin assigned just the first ten problems, not all twenty-five.
4. The car has been running well since Dad had the tune-up.
5. Take this medicine only with meals.

## 25.2 Glossary of Troublesome Adjectives and Adverbs (Page 144)
### Practice 2
### Exercise 1 Correcting Errors Caused by Troublesome Adjectives and Adverbs
1. Tony reached the station just one minute before the train pulled out.
2. Chery looks very good with short hair.
3. I made only two dozen cookies for the party.
4. There is less snow on the ground this winter than last.
5. correct
6. You talk well, but you write better.
7. The bee sting I received yesterday looks bad.
8. correct
9. Cazzie needs just one more plant to make his botany project complete.
10. Add only a little water; otherwise, it will be impossible to mold the sand.

### Writing Application
### Using Troublesome Adjectives and Adverbs Correctly
Sample sentences are given.
1. We felt bad about the misunderstanding.
2. Paul reads very well for such a young child.
3. We have less strength than we did with James on our side.
4. Only three of the fifty applicants were accepted.
5. We have just five minutes before the teacher returns.

## 26.1 End Marks (Page 145)
### Practice 1
### Exercise 1 Using the Period
1. ending.
2. Mrs., Ave., sale.
3. R. N., week.
4. T. J. Mason.
5. Pvt., sergeant.
6. Prof. Bell.
7. St., parade.
8. S. J. Murphy.
9. leave.
10. Dr., Mr., R. L. Stevenson.

### Exercise 2 Using the Question Mark
1. invitation?
2. where?
3. be? when?
4. she?
5. arriving? airline?

## 26.1 End Marks (Page 146)
### Practice 2
### Exercise 1 Using the Period
1. Your appointment isX with Mrs. Rose Walters on Tuesday morning.
2. The letter was addressed to Sgt. Jesse JohnsonX of Houston, Texas.

3. Carla M. CarlsonX lives at 433 W. Fourth St.
4. Give the dog a bathX this afternoon.
5. This mail belongs to our next-door neighborX Mr. T. J. Albertson.
6. Get up right now and get readyX for school.
7. Everything that belonged to the old man was willed to his son, Mr. TomX Brady, Jr.
8. Listen carefully to what I amX about to tell you.
9. Mr. and Mrs. C. J. BelloX have invited us to a dinner party.
10. In about ten minutes, Dr. Nesbaum willX be able to see you.
11. The troops were led by Sgt. JohnX Timoney.
12. Go to the neighborsX and ask if we can borrow some butter.
13. Please give me a few minutes aloneX to prepare for the performance.
14. Don't make such a fuss.
15. The postcard is addressedX to a Mrs. Alicia Thomas.

### Exercise 2 Using the Period and Question Mark
1. Should I smooth the wet plaster with my hands?
2. Did you ask Donald Palmer, Jr., for his opinion?
3. Deliver this message to Mrs. Allen quickly.
4. Col. J. D. Packard, a friend of ours, is stationed in California.
5. Dr. Jefferson's new assistant is Lee Tomas, R. N.
6. Where is the movie playing? When?
7. I've asked you over and over to close the door behind you.
8. What time do we have to be at the airport?
9. Do you really want to go to that party? Why?
10. Is it true that you didn't finish the assignment? Why not?
11. What did Josh say that was so rude?
12. Do you think the price of digital camcorders will come down soon?
13. Did you really spend eighteen hours creating this toy? For what?
14. How often do you have to mow the lawn in the summer?
15. What gives you the right to make so much noise?

## 26.1 End Marks (Page 147)
### Practice 1
### Exercise 1 Using the Exclamation Mark
1. Hey! button!
2. was!
3. Phew! call!
4. Hooray! hit!
5. tastes!
6. Gosh! that!
7. once!
8. car!
9. Help! here!
10. is!

### Exercise 2 Using End Marks Correctly
1. (.)
2. (.)
3. (?)
4. (?)
5. Wow! (!)
6. (.)
7. (!)
8. (.)
9. (?)
10. (.)

## 26.1 End Marks (Page 148)
### Practice 2
### Exercise 1  Using the Exclamation Mark
1. Hooray! We finally won a game!
2. Don't light a match!
3. You're late again!
4. Oh! I have never been so furious at anyone in my life!
5. Say! That was an unexpected move!
6. Take your feet off the table now!
7. What an amazing act of courage that was!
8. Hey! I remember the answer now!
9. Wait for me!
10. Quick! Grab my hand!

### Writing Application
### Using End Marks Correctly in Sentences
Sample sentences are given.
1. Run for your life!
2. We had thought Mr. Barnes was a snob.
3. How do you fix this?
4. Don't tease the dog.
5. She had never seen snow before!
6. I prefer to take the train.
7. Ouch! That blouse still has a pin in it.
8. We have enough room for one more person. Care to come?
9. How much money is left? Ten dollars?
10. We must meet them in five minutes at J. B. Winberry's.

## 26.2  Commas in Compound Sentences (Page 149)
### Practice 1
### Exercise 1  Using Commas with Compound Sentences
1. directions, but
2. librarian, and
3. not needed
4. tired, for
5. cave, but
6. candies, but
7. not needed
8. languages, but
9. valuable, yet
10. not needed

### Exercise 2  Writing Compound Sentences
Samples are given.
1. The Browns have a terrific defense, but the Bombers' offense is stronger.
2. Replace the fuse right away, or the ice cream in the freezer will melt.
3. Jodi had better work harder, or the coach will throw her off the team.
4. We had eaten everything in the refrigerator, and we were still hungry.
5. Luis tried out for the lead in the class play, but Jed got the part.

## 26.2  Commas in Compound Sentences (Page 150)
### Practice 2
### Exercise 1  Using Commas with Compound Sentences
1. you, but
2. laundry, and
3. stunned, for
4. cabin, nor
5. frosting, and
6. flight, so
7. yourself, or
8. telephone, and
9. billfold, but
10. colder, yet
11. carefully, but
12. bridge, for
13. early, and
14. Saturday, or
15. rare, so

### Exercise 2  Using Commas
Val was almost ready to give up, but she finally✗ spotted a light in the distance. She had been lost✗ in the woods for hours, yet she had kept moving. The day had started out beautifully, and it had seemed like a good idea to go for a hike. Valerie was a person✗ who always tried to plan ahead. She had put some provisions in a backpack, for she wanted to be prepared for a hike of several hours. She had not counted on being out✗ for so long. Now she was hungry✗ and thirsty, since she used up her supplies hours ago. The distant light was a signal that all would be well, and Valerie hurried toward it.

## 26.2  Commas in a Series, Between Adjectives (Page 151)
### Practice 1
### Exercise 1  Using Commas with Items in a Series
1. apartment, down the stairs, and
2. meatloaf, hamburgers, or
3. flour, butter, and
4. Poinsettias, mistletoe, and
5. riding, brisk walking, and
6. go, what route we would take, and
7. cake, set the table, and
8. not needed
9. started, where the victims would be housed, and
10. liquids, extra rest, and

### Exercise 2  Using Commas Between Adjectives
1. not needed
2. large, devoted
3. tall, lanky
4. not needed
5. old, valuable

## 26.2  Commas in a Series, Between Adjectives (Page 152)
### Practice 2
### Exercise 1  Using Commas with Items in a Series
1. For exercise Robert lifted weights, rode a bicycle, and did push-ups.
2. Ann was scheduled to take English, algebra, earth science, Spanish, and gym.
3. Our small garden plot produced tomatoes, lettuce, radishes, and zucchini.
4. Sharon swept the sidewalk, raked the leaves, and painted the mailbox.
5. After the movie, I still didn't understand why the crime was committed, who did it, or whether the criminals were caught.
6. To get there you must walk past the large oak tree, over the grassy knoll, and along the gravel driveway.
7. To work here you must have a white uniform, comfortable shoes, a black apron, and a white cap.
8. Do you want to bring pretzels, salad, or soda to the picnic?
9. The best time to go fishing is before dawn, just at dawn, or several hours before dusk.
10. We had to decide whom we should invite, where we would have the reception, and what food we would serve.

## Exercise 2   Using Commas Between Adjectives
1. This quiet, obedient dog is a pleasure to have around.
2. not needed
3. Mowing the lawn on such a hazy, hot, humid day was no fun.
4. not needed
5. The shabby, frayed coat hung limply from the child's slender body.

## Writing Application

### Using Commas That Separate Basic Elements in Your Writing
Sample sentences are given.
1. The deer ran through the field, over the bridge, and into the thicket.
2. We found several old coins.
3. He ordered eggs, toast, and bacon for breakfast.
4. Some pesky squirrels scurried into the garage when she opened the door.
5. I have ten vacation days this year, but I am taking a class during five of the ten days.

## 26.2   Commas That Set Off Added Elements (Page 153)
### Practice 1
### Exercise 1   Using Commas After Introductory Material
1. frightened, the
2. boxes, Sue
3. carefully, we
4. enough, that
5. seats, we
6. No, I
7. directions, we
8. people, the
9. Frankly, we
10. Well, where

### Exercise 2 Using Commas with Parenthetical Expressions
1. Mrs. Wilson, I am happy to say, will
2. know, Sue, that
3. students, to be exact, received
4. first, however
5. Bart, president, in fact, is

## 26.2   Commas That Set Off Added Elements (Page 154)
### Practice 2
### Exercise 1   Using Commas with Introductory Material
1. Oh, how
2. afternoon, a
3. rainbow, they
4. Surprised, Oliver
5. Repaired, the bicycle
6. Goodness, no one
7. prize, a
8. year, I
9. nights, the
10. exam, she

### Exercise 2 Using Commas with Parenthetical Expressions
1. Wait, Ron and Hugh, until the elevator doors open.
2. We, nevertheless, appreciated your help during the campaign.
3. Travel in this helium-filled balloon is not without hazards, of course.
4. Write a one-page essay on the meaning of liberty, Lois.
5. Maxine did succeed, therefore, in raising her grade.

6. Don't feed peanuts to the giraffe, Elaine.
7. The truth, in fact, is just the opposite.
8. The praying mantis, on the other hand, kills many harmful insects.
9. Please, Vic, tell me which fork is used for salad.
10. This table, I think, should be placed near the door.

## 26.2   Commas That Set Off Nonessential Elements (Page 155)
### Practice 1
### Exercise 1   Recognizing Essential and Nonessential Expressions
1. N
2. E
3. N
4. N
5. E
6. E
7. E
8. N
9. N
10. E

### Exercise 2 Using Commas with Nonessential Expressions
1. *Sing Down the Moon*, which is about a Navaho girl, was written by Scott O'Dell.
3. Alana, whose father is an archaeologist, has traveled to Egypt.
4. Adam, a friend of mine from camp, will be visiting me next week.
8. The police, keeping well out of sight, followed the suspect for two miles.
9. The captain of the basketball team, who is also an A student, won a full scholarship.

## 26.2   Commas That Set Off Nonessential Elements (Page 156)
### Practice 2
### Exercise 1 Using Commas with Nonessential Expressions
1. E
2. brothers, who live next door
3. Edwards, my cousin, is
4. E
5. E
6. E
7. St. Vincent Millay, the well-known poet, wrote
8. E
9. Congress, influenced by John Muir, established
10. Monument, a redwood forest near San Francisco, was named

## Writing Application

### Using Commas to Set Off Added Elements
Sample sentences are given.
1. If it snows much more tonight, we won't have school tomorrow.
2. Tomorrow, I hope, will be a better day.
3. Jane, who lives by the lake, is going to Penn State this fall.
4. Hurry, David, or we won't make it to the movie in time.
5. My brother, a freshman in college, is coming home to visit me next week.

## 26.2 Special Uses of the Comma (Page 157)
### Practice 1
### Exercise 1 Using Commas with Dates and Geographical Names
1. Rome, Italy
2. Monday, September 28,
3. June 14, 2001,
4. (no commas needed)
5. Provincetown, Massachusetts

### Exercise 2 Using Commas in Other Situations
1. "The answer to the first question," said Phil, "is on page 1,237."
2. To date, record sales have raised $9,500,280 for charity.
3. Please mail this to Donna Harris, 328 Maple Street, Branford, Connecticut 06405.
4. Dear Cousin Betty, Your cousin, Harriet
5. "Do you think," Bert asked, "that you can come with us?"

## 26.2 Special Uses of the Comma (Page 158)
### Practice 2
### Exercise 1 Using Commas with Dates and Geographical Names
1. We will be visiting Annapolis, Maryland, on May 20.
2. On July 20, 1969, astronauts landed on the moon for the first time.
3. Anna expects her grandparents to arrive Friday, April 3.
4. After traveling to Bryce Canyon, Utah, Karen drove to Canyonlands National Park, Utah, where she took pictures of the sandstone formations.
5. On October 17, 1781, General Cornwallis surrendered in Yorktown, Virginia.

### Exercise 2 Using Commas in Other Situations
1. Beth answered dreamily, "What was the question?"
2. My dear Jason,
   Affectionately, Susan
3. She said, "Our new telephone number is (312) 555-0476."
4. "Coal is just one of many sources of energy," responded Chris.
5. This huge igloo is made of 3,500 blocks of ice.
6. He told them, "The serial number is 103 22 411."
7. Address the letter to Diane Freemont, 104 Fairview Drive, Richmond, Virginia 23227.
8. The teacher said, "You will find it on page 1,324."
9. "I am eager," said Nan, "to meet the new exchange student."
10. Mr. Frederick Clifford
    1490 Apple Orchard Street
    Covington, Kentucky 41011

### Writing Application
### Using Commas in Special Situations
Sample sentences are given.
1. I was born in Cleveland, Ohio.
2. Mom demanded, "Where have you been?"
3. The number on the account, 154 23 672, is no longer valid.
4. On July 4, 1776, the Declaration of Independence was delivered to the world.
5. His address is Franco Martin, 595 Second Avenue, New York, New York 10015

## 26.3 Semicolons (Page 159)
### Practice 1
### Exercise 1 Using Semicolons to Join Independent Clauses
1. evaporates; the
2. school; a
3. beautiful; no one
4. player; his
5. problem, she

### Exercise 2 Using Semicolons to Avoid Confusion
1. apartment (,)     homeroom (,)
2. cream (,)     soup (,)
3. Massachusetts (,)     Ohio (,)

## 26.3 Semicolons (Page 160)
### Practice 2
### Exercise 1 Using Semicolons to Join Independent Clauses
1. cow's milk; others
2. shopping; instead,
3. concave; the other
4. pond; their scales
5. schoolhouse; it was built

### Exercise 2 Using Semicolons to Avoid Confusion
1. We were served onion soup, topped with melted cheese; homemade rye bread, covered with butter; and fruit salad, made with six different kinds of fresh fruit.
2. The little girl was wearing a yellow raincoat, which was made of shiny vinyl; a matching hat, which was tied neatly under her chin; and red boots, which reached to her knees.
3. In less than a year, William had expanded the family to include a large woolly dog with a huge appetite; two skinny, stray cats with unfriendly dispositions; and a pair of cooing, fluttering pigeons.
4. The music was performed by Fred, who played the flute; Samantha, who played the clarinet; and Ella, who played the saxophone.
5. Richard, my cousin; Donna, the girl next door; and Liz, my best friend, went to the concert with me.

### Writing Application
### Using Semicolons in Your Own Writing
Sample sentences are given.
1. The museum was closed; therefore, we went shopping.
   Our car broke down near the gas station; fortunately, we were able to push it across the street and into their parking lot.
2. We invited Nancy, who is fourteen; Tom, who is sixteen; and Gloria, who is seventeen. The responsibilities of the job were to keep track of the orders, which were filed in a cabinet; to keep inventory; and to fill in for the cashier, who was often out of town.

## 26.3 Colons (Page 161)
### Practice 1
### Exercise 1 Using Colons to Introduce Lists of Items
1. follows: butter,
2. schools: basketball,
3. states: Florida,
4. Mexico: California,
5. items: sheets,

## Exercise 2  Using Colons in Special Situations
1. Warning: Keep
2. 7:10
3. Morgan:
4. Caution: Slippery
5. Madam:

## 26.3  Colons (Page 162)
### Practice 2
### Exercise 1  Using Colons to Introduce Lists of Items
1. products: paper plates,
2. rooms: three
3. study: Dickinson,
4. information: descriptions
5. savings: six
6. benefits: room
7. summer: June 30,
8. items: a picnic
9. following: rapid
10. countries: Japan

### Exercise 2  Using Colons in Special Situations
1. 6:30 P.M.
2. Caution: Falling rocks
3. Dear Mmes. Jordan and Farnsworth:
4. Gentlemen:
5. Warning: The Surgeon General has determined that cigarette smoking is dangerous to your health.

### Writing Application
### Using Colons in Your Own Writing
Sample sentences are given.
1. The show starts at 8:15 P.M.
2. Please bring three things: a sleeping bag, a flashlight, and a canteen of fresh water.
3. Our picnic lunch included sandwiches, potato chips, pickles, juice, and cupcakes.
4. Warning: Bridge freezes before road surface.

## 26.4  Quotation Marks with Direct Quotations (Page 163)
### Practice
### Exercise 1  Distinguishing Between Direct and Indirect Quotations
1. I
2. "We'll ... them," ...
3. I
4. "Is ... dromedary?" ...
5. "Try ... key," ...

### Exercise 2  Punctuating Direct Quotations
1. "Have ... yet?" the ... asked.
2. "No, I give up," said Alice. "What's the answer?"
3. "I ... idea," said ... Hatter.
4. "I ... time," said Alice, "than ... answers."
5. "If ... do," said the Hatter, "you ... it."

## 26.4  Quotation Marks with Direct Quotations (Page 164)
### Practice 2
### Exercise 1  Distinguishing Between Direct and Indirect Quotations
1. D
2. D
3. I
4. I
5. D
6. I
7. I
8. D
9. I

10. D

### Exercise 2  Using Direct Quotations with Introductory, Concluding, and Interrupting Expressions
1. "Why would you throw out these blue jeans?" asked Milly. "Don't you know they're an important part of my wardrobe?"
2. "I guess it's time," said Laverne, "to return to work."
3. "Here," laughed Lauren, "are the missing keys."
4. "Otters are among the most playful animals," Glenn explained.
5. "Stop!" the guard yelled. "This is private property!"
6. The secretary smiled icily and said, "You can't see her without an appointment."
7. "I can't decide whether to order the clams or the scallops," said Shirley. "Which is better?"
8. "A lion," Edna stated, "does not make a good pet."
9. Delphene moaned, "I can't walk another mile without stopping to rest."
10. "The pen I borrowed from you leaked all over my shirt," complained Arthur.

## 26.4  Quotation Marks with Other Punctuation (Page 165)
### Practice
### Exercise 1  Punctuating Direct Quotations
1. ... asked, ... right?"
2. ... Elena," Michelle said, "tell ...
3. ... sunset!" ...
4. "I agree," said ... case."
5. ... it!" ...
6. ... said, ... earned"?
7. ... now," ... anything?"
8. ... asked, "May ... you?"
9. ... page 3," ... said.
10. ... school," ...

### Exercise 2  Paragraphing Dialogue
1.  "Take , "I've , "You

## 26.4  Quotation Marks with Other Punctuation (Page 166)
### Practice 2
### Exercise 1  Using End Marks with Direct Quotations
1. The director told us, "Do not run near the pool."
2. Karen shrieked, "We won the game!"
3. Didn't you hear him say, "Tomorrow is a holiday"?
4. Mona thought, "Shouldn't a lifeguard be on duty?"
5. The small child cried, "I want that bear!"
6. Did the park attendant say, "Please place your rubbish in the containers"?
7. I was shocked to hear him say, "I won't answer you."
8. When did I last say, "That's a really tough job"?
9. Angrily, he shouted, "You don't know anything about it!"
10. Rosa asked, "Has the position been filled yet?"

### Exercise 2  Using Quotation Marks with Dialogue
"What," exclaimed Andrea, pointing at a strange-looking object lying on the sand, "is that?"

"Don't you know?" asked Marty. "That's an empty horseshoe crab shell."

"I've never seen anything like it," said Andrea. "Are horseshoe crabs good to eat?"

"No, they aren't," replied Marty. "Perhaps that's why they aren't an endangered species. In fact, these peculiar creatures have been in existence since the days of the dinosaurs."

## 26.4 Quotation Marks or Underlining (Page 167)
### Practice 1
### Exercise 1 Punctuating Different Types of Works
1. "Ave Maria"
2. "Fog"
3. Our Town
4. Silent Spring
5. "The Night the Bed Fell"
6. National History Magazine
7. "Somewhere Over the Rainbow," The Wizard of Oz
8. David
9. "The Raft Passage," The Adventures of Huckleberry Finn
10. Titanic

### Exercise 2 Choosing the Correct Form
1. "Richard Cory"
2. Julius Caesar
3. Atlantic
4. Collected Poems
5. "The Gift of the Magi"

## 26.4 Quotation Marks or Underlining (Page 168)
### Practice 2
### Exercise 1 Underlining Titles and Names
1. Science Weekly Magazine
2. Evangeline
3. Grease
4. The Dark at the Top of the Stairs
5. The Wonderful World of Nature
6. Viking I
7. An Episode of Sparrows
8. Half Moon
9. News World, Modern Life
10. Watson and the Shark

### Exercise 2 Using Quotation Marks with Titles
1. "Some Who Escaped," The Bermuda Triangle
2. "The Lee Boyhood Home," Colonial Homes
3. "School Days"
4. Peer Gynt Suite, "In the Hall of the Mountain King"
5. "Weekender Sloop," World of Sailing

### Writing Application
### Using Underlining and Quotation Marks
Sample sentences are given.
1. The song "Blue Skies" was written a long time ago.
2. The poem "Chicago" was written by Carl Sandburg.
3. "The Egyptian Civilization" is one of the chapters in the book A History of Ancient Civilizations.
4. The movie Dances With Wolves won an Academy Award in 1990.
5. The magazine Model Railroad Ideas is one of my favorites.

## 26.5 Hyphens (Page 169)
### Practice 1
### Exercise 1 Using Hyphens
1. two-thirds
2. brother-in-law
3. door-to-door
4. five-pound
5. all-time
6. forty-ninth
7. well-paved
8. city-states
9. Ninety-nine
10. Self-reliance

### Exercise 2 Hyphenating Words
1. England
2. enough
3. com/plete
4. hand/book
5. slipped
6. rhythm
7. re/ject
8. ath/lete
9. gra/cious
10. Shakespeare

## 26.5 Hyphens (Page 170)
### Practice 2
### Exercise 1 Using Hyphens with Numbers
1. thirty-three
2. correct
3. eighty-five
4. one-fifth, four-fifths
5. correct
6. two-thirds, one-third
7. correct
8. twenty-one
9. nine-tenths
10. Twenty-two

### Exercise 2 Using Hypens with Word Parts and Compound Words
1. pre-Columbian
2. mid-April
3. well-known
4. correct
5. senator-elect
6. self-improvement
7. all-important
8. daughter-in-law
9. four-year-olds
10. correct

### Exercise 3 Using Hyphens to Divide Words
1. dirty
2. fight
3. bet-
4. Spanish
5. ici-
6. well-
7. pay-
8. stretch
9. abol-
10. rest-

## 26.5 Apostrophes (Page 171)
### Practice 1
### Exercise 1 Writing Possessive Forms
1. a city's budget
2. the authors' royalties
3. the plants' roots
4. the mice's hole
5. the car's tires
6. the lovebirds' cage
7. the children's toys
8. strawberries' smell
9. the trees' foliage
10. women's suits

## Exercise 2   Using Apostrophes Correctly with Pronouns

1. ours
2. their
3. its
4. hers
5. someone else's

## 26.5   Apostrophes (Page 172)

### Practice 2

### Exercise 1   Using Apostrophes to Form Possessives of Nouns

1. boss's
2. piano's
3. stove's
4. butter's
5. wind's
6. Gus's
7. wheel's
8. bass's
9. chimney's
10. mouse's
11. mice's
12. homes'
13. authors'
14. women's
15. sweaters'
16. calves'
17. oaks'
18. cars'
19. children's
20. keys'

### Exercise 2   Using Apostrophes with Pronouns

Samples are given.
1. His, mine
2. Her
3. his, their
4. anyone's
5. Someone else's
6. its
7. everyone's, our
8. Everyone's
9. My, his
10. Hers, yours

## 26.5   Apostrophes (Page 173)

### Practice 1

### Exercise 1   Using Contractions Correctly

1. we're
2. It's
3. She'd
4. doesn't
5. he'll
6. don't
7. Mike's
8. We'd
9. I'll
10. won't

### Exercise 2   Using Apostrophes Correctly

1. won't
2. ?'s
3. Jim's
4. 7's
5. *if*'s
6. they'd
7. it's
8. who'll
9. wasn't
10. doesn't

## 26.5   Apostrophes (Page 174)

### Practice 2

### Exercise 1   Using Apostrophes with Contractions

1. Who'd/can't
2. wasn't/didn't
3. Who'll
4. Who's
5. Connie's/she'll
6. We'll/who'll
7. Where's
8. Weren't
9. didn't
10. couldn't/we'd

### Writing Application

### Using Apostrophes in Your Own Writing

Sample sentences are given.
1. The apartments' lawns look well maintained.
2. Perhaps they'll wait for us.
3. I accidentally took someone's pen.
4. The children's toys were scattered throughout the house.
5. The glass's weight is heavier than the cup's weight.
6. If you had come to visit yesterday, you'd have enjoyed meeting my cousin.
7. My niece is learning how to write her d' s.
8. Our neighbors took the cover off their pool.
9. The exchange in Morningside Heights is three 6's.
10. The actress's home is in Texas.

## 27   Capitals for Sentences and the Word *I* (Page 175)

### Practice 1

### Exercise 1   Using Capitals for Sentences and the Word *I*

1. Sometimes, I
2. Did
3. How, I
4. Please, I
5. We
6. How, I
7. Let, I
8. I
9. Several
10. When, I

### Exercise 2   Using Capitalized Words

Samples are given.
1. When
2. Which
3. John
4. I
5. Without
6. What
7. I
8. Seven
9. Every
10. I

## 27   Capitals for Sentences and the Word *I* (Page 176)

### Practice 2

### Exercise 1   Using Capitals to Begin Sentences

1. What
2. Sit
3. Would
4. Which, Right, Left
5. Show
6. If
7. Why, They

8. Today
9. My
10. Wow, These

### Exercise 2   Capitalizing the Word *I*
1. I began to wonder what I should do next.
2. The child smiling into the camera is I.
3. I think I am going to be a little late.
4. He said I would be the candidate.
5. After that experience, I'll never swim there again.

## 27   Capitals for Proper Nouns (Names, Places) (Page 177)
### Practice 1
### Exercise 1   Using Capitals for People's Names
1. Janice Lawson
2. Jason, Nancy, Ben
3. Joe, Elberta
4. Elaine, Paula
5. Frank's, Franklin Xavier Cambridge Jones
6. Scott O'Dell
7. Claire F. Rose
8. Alex's, J. C.
9. Linda Richmond
10. Frank Zappa, Moonunit, Dwiesel

### Exercise 2   Using Capitals for Geographical Names
1. Cleveland, Lake Erie
2. Yugoslavia, Belgrade
3. Yellow Sea, South Korea, China
4. Chicago, Cook County, Illinois
5. White Bear Lake, St. Paul, Minnesota
6. San Francisco, Oakland, San Francisco Bay
7. Allegheny, Monogahela rivers, Ohio River, Pittsburgh
8. Mohave Desert, California, Sierra Nevada Mountains
9. West Main Street, Canton, Ohio
10. Mount Rushmore, South Dakota

## 27   Capitals for Proper Nouns (Names, Places) (Page 178)
### Practice 2
### Exercise 1   Using Capitals for Names
1. Paul Zindel
2. Jamie, Pete
3. Anthony R. Hughes
4. Marcia, Jim
5. P. L. Martinez

### Exercise 2   Using Capitals for Geographical Names
1. Mount Rainier National Park
2. Grand Canyon
3. Canary Islands, Africa, Atlantic Ocean
4. Everglades
5. Tennessee
6. Australia, New Zealand
7. Matterhorn, Alps
8. Van Nuys, Orange County, California
9. Lake Winnipeg, Manitoba
10. White Sands Desert

## 27   Capitals for Proper Nouns (Page 179)
### Practice 1
### Exercise 1   Capitalizing Other Proper Nouns
1. University, Minnesota, September
2. Democrats, Ellicot Building
3. Purple Heart, World War
4. Pickle Players, Saturday, March
5. Bible, Torah, Koran
6. Parent-Teacher Association, October
7. Columbia, Tropical
8. French, Spanish
9. Rose Bowl Parade, New Year's Day
10. British, French, Indian War

### Exercise 2   Using Capitals for Proper Nouns
Samples are given.
1. the Boston Marathon
2. the Rolling Stones
3. Golden Crisps
4. United Enterprises
5. October
6. Ford
7. the Eiffel Tower
8. Mong
9. Christianity
10. Girl Scouts of America

## 27   Capitals for Proper Nouns (Page 180)
### Practice 2
### Exercise 1   Capitalizing Proper Nouns
1. Saturday, Century Building
2. Islam, Ramadan
3. British, Balfour Declaration, Middle East
4. Renaissance
5. Caldecott Medal
6. Portuguese, Spanish
7. University of Hawaii
8. Bill of Rights, Constitution, United States
9. Republicans, Democrats
10. Little League, Friday, May
11. Tennessee Valley Authority
12. General Automotive
13. Lincoln Memorial
14. Easter, Easter Parade
15. New Year's Eve, Staten Island Ferry
16. English, Battle of Waterloo
17. Supreme Court
18. Grainway's Rice Krispettes
19. Little Dipper, Polaris
20. Ben, Grant's Tomb

### Writing Application
### Using Capitals for Proper Nouns
Samples are given.
1. Who do you think will win the Academy Award for best actor this year?
2. I eat Sunbright Raisin Bran every morning.
3. The group always meets on the first Saturday in September.

## 27   Capitals for Proper Adjectives (Page 181)
### Practice 1
### Exercise 1   Forming Proper Adjectives
1. American clothes
2. Canadian geese
3. Egyptian pyramids
4. a Massachusetts senator
5. Blakely tea bags
6. Minnesota winters
7. Jewish traditions
8. Strategem cars
9. a Japanese camera
10. an English playwright

### Exercise 2   Using Capitals for Proper Adjectives
Samples are given.
1. Bright Star
2. Italian
3. Broadway

4. Flashbest
5. Polish
6. Allsport
7. American
8. Chinese
9. Dentoclean
10. French

## 27 Capitals for Proper Adjectives (Page 182)
### Practice 2
### Exercise 1  Using Capitals for Proper Adjectives
Samples are given.
1. Softmark
2. Swedish
3. Hansen
4. Italian
5. Sourdough
6. Bestspread
7. Outperform
8. Videosharp
9. Idaho
10. Photomark

### Writing Application
### Using Capitals for Proper Adjectives
Samples are given.

Checker cereal, Flavormate sauce, Italian bread, Swiss cheese, and Crown yogurt were all on sale at the grocery store in town.

## 27  Capitals for Titles of People (Page 183)
### Practice 1
### Exercise 1  Using Capitals for Social and Professional Titles
1. Senator
2. C
3. Father
4. Professor
5. C
6. Sir
7. Madame
8. C
9. Judge
10. Sister

### Exercise 2  Using Capitals for Family Titles
1. Uncle
2. C
3. Aunt
4. Mom
5. Papa

## 27  Capitals for Titles of People (Page 184)
### Practice 2
### Exercise 1  Using Capitals for Social and Professional Titles
1. Captain
2. Ambassador
3. Professor
4. Lieutenant
5. Sister
6. Colonel.
7. Attorney
8. Nurse
9. President
10. Governor

### Exercise 2  Using Capitals for Family Titles
1. Dad
2. uncle

3. correct
4. Uncle
5. mother
6. aunt
7. correct
8. Cousin
9. correct
10. Son

### Writing Application
### Using Capitals for Titles of People
Sample sentences are given.
1. Sergeant Miller has the troops stationed at Fort Henry.
2. Mom, could you help me zip this dress?
3. Mrs. Harrison is a museum benefactor.
4. Professor Jackson is chair of the History Department.
5. My sister's compact disk collection is quite extensive.

## 27  Capitals for Titles of Things (Page 185)
### Practice 1
### Exercise 1  Using Capitals for Titles of Works
1. *Popular Pets Magazine*
2. "A Day's Wait"
3. *Mr. Smith Goes to Washington*
4. *The Rise of Silas Lapham*
5. *Moonlight Sonata*
6. "The Wreck of the Hesperus"
7. "The Secret Life of Walter Mitty"
8. *Great Expectations*
9. "The Star-Spangled Banner"
10. *A Midsummer Night's Dream*

### Exercise 2  Using Capitals for Courses
1. Russian
2. C
3. Civics
4. chemistry
5. C

## 27  Capitals for Titles of Things (Page 186)
### Practice 2
### Exercise 1  Using Capitals for Written Works and Works of Art
1. *The Heart Is a Lonely Hunter*
2. *Fashion Illustrated*
3. "The Monkey's Paw"
4. *Joy in the Morning*
5. *Head of a Woman*
6. *The Gold of the Gods*
7. *The Man Who Came to Dinner*
8. "To a Field Mouse"
9. *Road and Car*
10. "To a Waterfowl"

### Exercise 2  Using Capitals for Courses
1. Civics I
2. physics
3. Russian
4. geometry
5. Spanish

### Writing Application
### Using Capitals for Titles of Things
Sample sentences are given.
1. Paul Laurence Dunbar's "We Wear the Mask" is an insightful poem.
2. French was a very challenging course.

3. It is fitting that one of Claude Monet's paintings, _Impression: Sunrise_, gave the movement its name.
4. I took geometry last year and really enjoyed it.
5. _Pride and Prejudice_ is one of my favorite books.

## 27 Capitals in Letters (Page 187)
### Practice 1
### Exercise 1   Using Capitals for Parts of Letters
1. My dear Miss Walker,
2. Affectionately,
3. Very truly yours,
4. My dear old Friend,
5. Dear Sir or Madame:
6. Your loving grandson,
7. With warmest regards,
8. Dear Sue and Amy,
9. Dear Uncle Al,
10. Your classmate,

### Exercise 2   Using Capitals in Letters
Samples are given.

> Jane Smith
> 45 Main Street
> Modena, NY 12567
> June 1, 2000

Dear Kate,

I hope that you and your family are doing well. I'd like to invite you to visit next month for a few days. I'm taking riding lessons at a local ranch, and I thought it would be fun to have you join me. Let me know.

> Sincerely,
> Jane

## 27 Capitals in Letters (Page 188)
### Practice 2
### Exercise 1   Using Capitals for Salutations and Closings in Letters
1. My dear Kevin,
2. Dearest friends,
3. Dear Gwen and Brenda,
4. Affectionately yours,
5. Yours truly,

### Writing Application
### Using Capitals in Letters
Sample letter is given.
Dear Stephanie,

Thank you for the wonderful candle and lamp set that you gave to David and me. The fragrance smells wonderful in our living room. It was very nice seeing you and Jon at Christmas and I wish you both a happy New Year.

> Love,
> Jane

## Diagraming Basic Sentence Parts (Subjects and Verbs)
(Page 189)
### Exercise 1   Diagraming Sentences
1.

2.

### Exercise 2   More Work with Diagraming
1.

2.

## Diagraming Basic Sentence Parts
(Page 190)
### Exercise 1   Diagraming Subjects and Verbs
1.
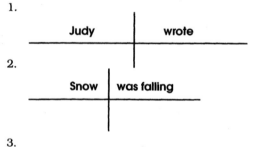
2.
3.

## Exercise 2 Diagraming Sentences with Modifiers and Conjunctions

1.

2.

3.

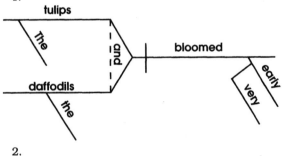

## Diagraming Basic Sentence Parts (Compound Subjects and Verbs) (Page 191)

### Exercise 1 Diagraming Compound Subjects and Verbs

1.

2.

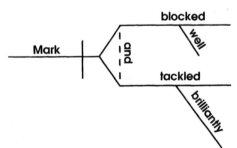

### Exercise 2 Diagraming Orders

1.

2.

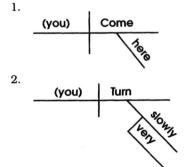

## Diagraming Basic Sentence Parts (Compound Subjects and Verbs) (Page 192)

### Exercise 1 Diagraming Compound Subjects and Compound Verbs

1.

2.

3.

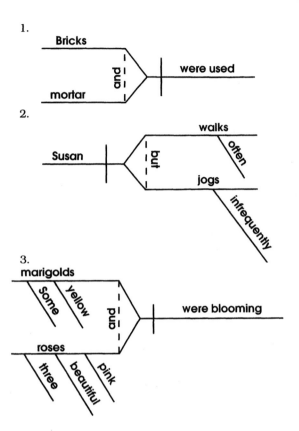

### Exercise 2 Diagraming Orders

1.

2.

3.

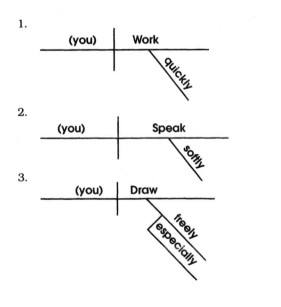

**Diagraming Basic Sentence Parts (Complements)**
**(Page 193)**

Exercise 1   Diagraming Direct Objects and Indirect Objects

1.

2.

Exercise 2   Diagraming Subject Complements

1.

2.

**Diagraming Basic Sentence Parts (Complements)**
**(Page 194)**

Exercise 1   Diagraming Direct Objects and Indirect Objects

1.

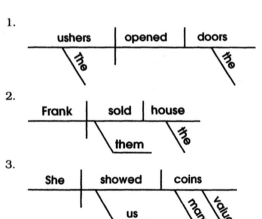

2.

3.

Exercise 2   Diagraming Subject Complements

1.

2.

3.

**Diagraming Prepositional Phrases and Appositives**
**(Page 195)**

Exercise 1   Diagraming Prepositional Phrases

1.

2.

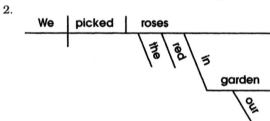

Exercise 2   Diagraming Appositive Phrases

1.

2.

## Diagraming Prepositional Phrases and Appositives (Page 196)

### Exercise 1  Diagraming Prepositional Phrases

1.

2.

3.
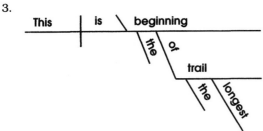

### Exercise 2  Diagraming Appositive Phrases

1.

2.

3.
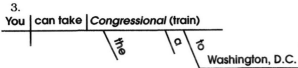

## Diagraming Clauses (Page 197)

### Exercise 1  Diagraming Compound Sentences

1.

2.
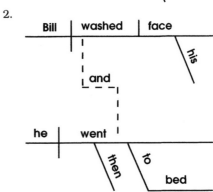

## Diagraming Clauses (Page 198)

### Exercise 1  Diagraming Complex Sentences

1.

2.
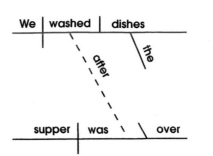

**Diagraming Clauses (Page 199)**

**Exercise 1    Diagraming Compound Sentences**

1.

2.

3.
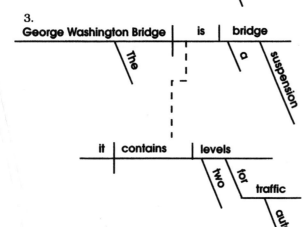

**Exercise 2    Diagraming Subordinate Clauses**

1.

2.

3.
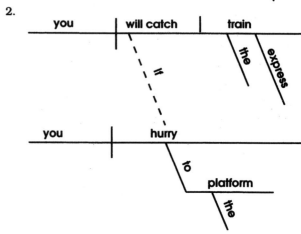